MODULAR MATHEMATICS

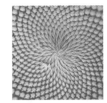

Intermediate GCSE for AQA

Brian Gaulter   Clive Simpson

The spirals in this sunflower follow a Fibonacci sequence.

You can find out about Fibonacci sequences on page 271.

OXFORD
UNIVERSITY PRESS

OXFORD

UNIVERSITY PRESS

Great Clarendon Street, Oxford OX2 6DP

Oxford University Press is a department of the University of Oxford.
It furthers the University's objective of excellence in research, scholarship,
and education by publishing worldwide in

Oxford New York
Auckland Bangkok Buenos Aires Cape Town Chennai
Dar es Salaam Delhi Hong Kong Istanbul Karachi Kolkata
Kuala Lumpur Madrid Melbourne Mexico City Mumbai Nairobi
São Paulo Shanghai Taipei Tokyo Toronto

Oxford is a registered trade mark of Oxford University Press
in the UK and in certain other countries

British Library Cataloguing in Publication Data

Data available

ISBN 0 19 914812 0

The authors would like to thank Paul Metcalf for his authoritative coursework guidance.

The publishers would like to thank AQA for their kind permission to reproduce past paper
questions. AQA accept no responsibility for the answers to the past paper questions which are
the sole responsibility of the publishers.

The photograph on the cover is reproduced courtesy of Stock Market Picture Library
The graphs on page 16 are reproduced courtesy of the Office of National Statistics
The photograph on page 234 is reproduced courtesy of Allsport
The photograph on page 267 is reproduced courtesy of Science Photo Library

Cartoons by Branwen Thomas

Typeset by TechSet Ltd., Gateshead, Tyne and Wear.
Printed and bound in Great Britain by Bell & Bain Ltd., Glasgow

About this book

This book is designed to help you get your best possible grade in the **AQA Specification B**, Intermediate modular examinations and coursework modules.

How to use this book

The book is arranged so that the content of each module is clear. You can use the tabs at the edge of the page to find the content you need.

The **content modules** – modules 1, 3 and 5 – are broken down into units of work that increase in difficulty.

Each unit starts with an overview of what you are going to learn and a list of what you should already know.

The **'Before you start'** section will help you to remember the key ideas and skills necessary for the exam. The **Check in** questions will help you see what you already know.

At the end of each unit there is a **summary** page.

The **'You should now know'** sections are useful as a quick revision guide and each **Check out** question points out important content that you should remember.

After the summary page you will find a **revision exercise** with past paper questions from AQA. This will help you to prepare for the style of questions you will see in the exam.

At the end of each module you also have two **Practice module tests** – one calculator and one non-calculator. These tests will help you prepare for the real thing.

The **coursework modules** – modules 2 and 4 – are located in a separate unit at the end of the book. The unit tells you what you have to do for your coursework. Each of the Tasks includes **Moderator comments** to help you get better marks.

The numerical **answers** are given at the end of the book. Use these to check you understand what you are doing.

Good luck in your exams!

Module 1 Contents

Module 2: Statistical Coursework

Module 3 Contents

D1 DATA HANDLING 1

Statistics is about handling information, or **data**.
You use statistics to collect facts and opinions.

This unit will show you how to:

● Use statistical terms
● Devise a hypothesis
● Conduct a survey
● Use a database

MODULE 1

1.1 Statistical terms

First you need to know some of the words most commonly used in statistics.

Data is information that you collect.

You collect data on a particular **variable**, for example height in cm.

Variables can change from one value to another.

Data can be
→ qualitative   (non-numerical)
→ quantitative   (numerical)

- **Qualitative** data is information that can be described in words.
  Examples are hair colour or pupils' names.

- **Quantitative** data is information that can be measured or counted.
  It is presented as a number, for example weights of babies or the number of people attending a hockey match.

Quantitative variables can be
→ continuous   (measurable)
→ discrete   (countable)

- **Continuous** variables can take any value within a given range.
  Examples are height, area or speed.

- **Discrete** variables can only take certain values.
  Examples are the number of pupils in a class, or clothes sizes.

You will learn more about variables in Unit AS1 when you study algebra.

Qualitative comes from the word quality; quantitative comes from the word quantity.

The height of a person is continuous, but the height of a person measured to the nearest centimetre is discrete.

Exercise 1A

In each question below, state whether the question will give qualitative or quantitative information. If the information is quantitative, state whether it will be discrete or continuous. You do not need to answer the questions.

1. What is your favourite song?

2. How many branches are on the tree?

3. What word would you use to best describe the last film you saw?

4. What is the colour of your front door?

5. In which month were you born?

6. How many days are there in this month?

7. Which party will you vote for in the next election?

8. What is your trouser size?

9. How much money have you in your pocket at this moment?

10. What is the area of the carpet?

11. What is your date of birth (in numbers)?

12. What is the height of the sunflower?

1.2 Hypotheses and types of data

Before you start collecting data you should have a clear idea what you are going to investigate. It often helps if you devise a **hypothesis**.

● A hypothesis is a general statement about an area of inquiry.

Examples of hypotheses are 'Smoking is linked to lung cancer' and 'Women live longer than men'.

Once the hypothesis has been made, data will need to be collected and analysed so that you can test whether the hypothesis is likely to be true or not.

Collecting data will need careful planning.

● You could gather evidence at first hand by conducting an experiment or survey, perhaps involving a questionnaire. These methods will give you **primary data**.

● If your hypothesis requires you to use data that has already been collected from a previous investigation or survey, then you will be obtaining **secondary data**.

Example

Suggest an appropriate method which could be used to test the following hypotheses.

(a) Women drivers have fewer accidents than men drivers.

(b) The most popular soap on terrestrial television is EastEnders.

(a) For 'the women drivers and fewer accidents' hypothesis you would have to use secondary data from insurance companies.

(b) A method for investigating the most popular soap would be to devise a suitable questionnaire and survey your local village or town.

When you have made your hypothesis and decided on the type of data you will collect, the following questions may help you to decide if your hypothesis is acceptable:

(i) Will I be able to test my hypothesis?

(ii) Will I be able to collect enough data?

(iii) What techniques will I use for displaying and analysing my data?

(iv) How will I know if I have proved or disproved my hypothesis?

If these questions raise problems, you may need to revise your hypothesis.

Exercise 1B

1. Suggest an appropriate method which could be used to test the following hypotheses.
   (a) Boys are better than girls at estimating distances.
   (b) Bournemouth has its least rainfall in the month of June.
   (c) Our town needs a hypermarket to offer shoppers a greater variety of choice.
   (d) The general public under-uses buses as a means of transport.

2. Devise a method to test the hypothesis:
   'There is more sport shown on BBC1 than on any other terrestrial TV channel.'

3. Devise a questionnaire to test the hypothesis:
   'School uniform should be abolished.'

You will learn more about questionnaires on page 5.

1.3 Surveys and questionnaires

Surveys

Surveys are used for obtaining and recording information about any chosen topic. A survey may be carried out either by **census** or by taking a **sample** from the population.

- In a census the entire population is used for the survey.
- In a sample survey only a proportion of the population is used.

The data that you collect in your survey can be either primary or secondary. The three main survey methods that you use to obtain primary data are:

(a) Asking questions face to face, for example giving a questionnaire to people in the street, consulting fellow pupils at school or members of your family.

(b) Observing situations and recording results, for example the colour of cars passing a particular road junction at a given time.

(c) Postal or telephone survey, where the responses to a questionnaire are recorded on a form.

These guidelines should be followed when conducting a survey:

- The survey should yield sufficient data. Usually between 20 and 50 responses would be the minimum acceptable for a conclusion to be made.

- There should be sufficient variety in the respondents to ensure a true picture of the population.

- Care should be taken to avoid **bias** when conducting a survey. Bias could occur, for example, if there is any form of deliberate selection of the people chosen to respond. Bias can distort results, and can make any conclusions drawn from the survey have little value.

Questionnaires

Questionnaires are commonly used to collect data, particularly on opinions.

When writing questions for a questionnaire, the questions must be carefully constructed and the following points must be remembered.

(a) The number of questions asked should be sufficient to gather all the information needed. However, the questionnaire should not be too lengthy.

(b) Make the questions easy to understand by using simple language.

In statistics, the word 'population' is used to mean all the items in a particular set.
Examples of populations include 'the entire set of people living in Birmingham' or 'the entire set of books in Tooting library'.

Frequently businesses need to conduct **market research** to decide how to improve their products and services.

MODULE 1

(c) The type of answer required should be clear. For example, the respondent may need to know whether the response is a 'yes/no' type, or a selection from a choice of possible answers.

(d) Avoid open-ended questions where possible. It is usually best to provide a choice of tick-box answers for people to select from.

(e) Do not ask leading questions, as the results from these responses will be invalid. An example of a leading question is 'Do you agree with the fact that spinach tastes nicer than broccoli?'

(f) Ask questions in a logical order.

(g) Avoid personal questions.

It is sensible to try a questionnaire out on a few people at first, in a **pilot survey**. This should enable you to find out if any of the questions need alteration.

Example

The following questions (a) and (b) were suggested as alternatives for a questionnaire. Criticise them, saying which you think is best, and suggest improvements.

(a) What is your age?

(b) Which is your age group? (Please tick the box)

Under 16 ☐
16–20 ☐
20–35 ☐
36–50 ☐
50–60 ☐

(a) This is a personal question, and older people may be reluctant to answer it truthfully.

(b) This is better than (a) as it is much less personal. However, a 20-year-old will have two possible responses, and anyone aged over 60 will have no responses.

An improvement would be to have a question like (b), but alter the categories to read:

Which is your age group? (Please tick the box)

Under 16 ☐
16–20 ☐
21–35 ☐
36–50 ☐
Over 50 ☐

Exercise 1C

1. The following questions were suggested for a questionnaire. Consider each question and give a reason for it being either a suitable or poor form of question to be asked.
    (a) What do you think of the improved library facilities?
    (b) Do you like chocolate?
    (c) How much money do you earn?
    (d) Meat is obtained through killing animals. Do you eat meat?
    (e) What is your date of birth?
    (f) Don't you agree that bus lanes are good for public transport?
    (g) Don't you think it's ridiculous to spend money on a project like the Millennium Dome or the new Wembley Stadium when people in Africa are starving?

2. Your school is planning to upgrade the library and learning resource centre. The following questions were put forward to be asked in a survey. Explain why each question is unsuitable in its present form and rewrite the question.
    (a) What is your age?
    (b) How often have you been to the library?
    (c) What did you read in the library?
    (d) How would you improve the library?

3. A survey of the school tuck shop is to be conducted. Suggest five questions which could be included with the choice of responses for each question.

4. The school council wanted to investigate the attitude of the pupils to the current school uniform. Suggest three questions which could be asked, with each question having up to five responses.

5. Ken and Jane are thinking of opening a newsagents shop in a shopping parade. Suggest four questions which could be asked to people living in the area which could enable Ken and Jane to decide whether the newsagent is likely to be successful.

1.4 Databases

Government departments routinely collect data on population, housing, transport and health. This data provides information for local councils to plan for people's needs. The vast amounts of data collected need to be entered into a computer database to enable analysis to be made quickly and efficiently.

Many different databases are used on a daily basis to check population data:

- A telephone directory is an example of a database that can be searched manually for information.
- Police have access to the national computer population database where names, addresses, dates of birth and other personal records for all UK citizens can be obtained.
- Many organisations, for example banks, gas, electricity and credit card companies, have access to a national population database which will give the names of all UK citizens who are registered as resident at a particular address.

Exercise 1D

1. Here is a database for a small second-hand car sales company.

Year	Registration letter	Make	Colour	Model	Mileage	Cost (£)
97	R	Ford	Red	Fiesta 1·25 LX	33 500	4695
97	P	Ford	Silver	Fiesta 1·25 Fusion	29 500	4695
97	P	Ford	Red	Fiesta 1·25 LX Auto	10 000	4995
97	R	Ford	Black	Fiesta 1·25 Flight	23 500	5896
97	R	Ford	Blue	Fiesta 1·8 Diesel	29 500	4995
97	P	Ford	White	Escort 1·4 Encore	30 500	3995
97	P	Ford	Red	Escort 1·8 Encore	28 500	4995
95	N	Ford	White	Escort 1·4 Encore	24 500	3485
97	R	Ford	Green	Escort 1·4 Encore	30 150	4995
96	N	Ford	Blue	Mondeo 2·0 LX	46 716	4495
96	N	Ford	Blue	Mondeo 2·5	67 129	4495
98	S	Ford	Blue	Mondeo 1·8 LX	39 500	6995
97	R	Ford	Green	Mondeo 1·8 Verona	29 500	7495
97	R	Ford	Blue	Mondeo 1·8 Verona	14 500	7495
00	W	Ford	Thistle	Fiesta 1·25 Ghia	2000	7995
00	X	Ford	Silver	Fiesta 1·25 Ghia	Delivery mileage	8495
00	W	Ford	Pepper red	Focus Zetec	2000	9999
00	X	Ford	Pacific blue	Puma 1·7 Coupe	Delivery mileage	12 495

(a) Jean likes white cars.
    Which cars are available and how much do they cost?

(b) Bill can afford £5000 and he wants to buy a car which
    has recorded less than 25 000 miles.
    From which cars can he choose?

(c) Brian can afford to spend up to £10 000 on a car but
    does not want to buy a car manufactured before 1999.
    Which cars can he choose from?

(d) Judith likes only Mondeo cars.
    From what colours of car can she choose?

(e) How many cars are available costing between £4500
    and £5000?

(f) Tony wants to buy a green car with the lowest mileage
    possible! Which car would he choose and what is the
    recorded mileage and price of this car?

2. Here is part of a database about students.

Student	Gender	Month of birth	Numeric day in the month	Day of birth
Aaron	M	February	17	Monday
Brenda	F	December	14	Wednesday
Colin	M	September	22	Friday
Debbie	F	June	1	Tuesday
Eric	M	March	3	Tuesday
Fiona	F	August	31	Friday
Gita	F	February	14	Wednesday
Helen	F	June	12	Friday
Ian	M	August	7	Monday
Jeremy	M	June	5	Wednesday
Kevin	M	December	27	Thursday

(a) How many students were born later than May in the
    year?

(b) How many male students were born in December?

(c) How many female students were born before the 16th
    of their month of birth?

3. The following database gives information about houses available for sale from an estate agent.

Town	Type of property	Number of bedrooms	Central heating	Cost
Dudley	Terrace	3	No	£34 950
Gornal	Flat	1	No	£15 000
Dudley	Detached	4	Yes	£107 950
Tipton	Terrace	3	Yes	£38 500
Dudley	Semi-detached	3	Yes	£48 000
Tipton	Detached	4	Yes	£76 500
Gornal	Semi-detached	3	No	£41 950
Dudley	Flat	2	Yes	£33 650
Gornal	Detached	5	Yes	£95 000
Dudley	Semi-detached	3	No	£45 000
Tipton	Detached	2	Yes	£32 000

(a) How many properties have 3 bedrooms?

(b) How many semi-detached houses cost more than £40 000?

(c) How many Dudley properties have 3 or more bedrooms, central heating and cost less than £50 000?

4. The following database gives information about 'Last Minute' holidays for 7 nights available in June 2001.

Country	Resort	Hotel rating (*'s)	Departure airport	Cost per adult (£)
Cyprus	Paphos	4	Birmingham	440
Rhodes	Rhodes Town	5	Luton	385
France	Cannes	4	Manchester	495
Crete	Rethymnon	3	Gatwick	219
Spain	Benidorm	3	Heathrow	199
Cyprus	Limassol	4	Manchester	289
Malta	Valetta	3	Manchester	430
Malta	Sliema	3	Gatwick	275
Spain	Nerja	4	Luton	195
Crete	Aghios Nikolaos	5	Luton	395
France	Nice	5	Luton	550
Crete	Rethymnon	2	Birmingham	175

(a) How many holidays at 4∗ hotels cost less than £350 per adult?

(b) I want to travel to France or Spain on holiday. What is the lowest cost of holiday available and at which resort?

(c) How many holidays costing between £300 and £400 are available at 5∗ hotels?

5. The database below contains information about a group of Year 8 pupils.

Pupil	Gender	Height (cm)	Hand span (cm)	Shoe size
Anne-Marie	F	165	18·5	38
Julian	M	183	29·5	48
Alex	M	147	16·8	36
Judith	F	158	17·5	38
Clive	M	182	21·0	48
George	M	177	20·5	48
Brian	M	195	24·8	52
Peter	M	163	18·0	44
Ann	F	131	18·3	40
Robin	M	175	20·0	46
Inder	F	168	19·5	42

(a) Which gender of student has the larger hand span?

(b) Which students have the same shoe size?

(c) How many students are shorter in height than Robin?

(d) What is the difference in height between the tallest and shortest pupils?

Summary

1. You know whether data is quantitative or qualitative.

2. You know the difference between discrete and continuous variables.

3. You know the meaning of a database.

4. You know the difference between a census and a sample.

5. You know how to carry out a survey.

6. You know how to construct a questionnaire.

7. You know what is meant by pilot survey, bias and hypothesis.

Check out D1

1. State whether the following are quantitative or qualitative data:
   (a) the number of cars in a traffic queue
   (b) the colour of the first car in a traffic queue
   (c) the number of books in a pupil's school bag
   (d) the weight of books in a school bag.

2. For those in question **1** which are quantitative data, is the variable continuous or discrete?

3. How would a bank check that you live at your address?

4. Why does the BBC not use a census to see how many people watched 'Neighbours' last week?

5. What is the minimum number of people needed in a survey to make an appropriate conclusion?

6. (a) State three rules that should be used when making a questionnaire.
   (b) You wish to investigate whether a person's income is related to the number of cigarettes they smoke. Write a short questionnaire (five or six questions) on this topic.

7. You wish to test the hypothesis that the time of day at which people visit a supermarket relates to their age.
   (a) Give three questions which you could ask to test this hypothesis.
   (b) How would you use a pilot survey to help you in your questionnaire?
   (c) How would you attempt to eliminate bias in the responses?

Revision exercise D1

1. A teacher asks all his class
'How many children are there in your family?'
Here are their replies.

Number of children in the family	Number of replies
1	17
2	12
3	5
4	2
5	0

(a) How many children are in the class?

(b) What is the most common number of children in the family for this class?

(c) Calculate the mean number of children per family in this class.
Give your answer to 1 decimal place.   [NEAB]

2. This statement is made on a television programme about health: 'Three in every eight pupils do not take any exercise outside school.'

(a) A school has 584 pupils.
According to the television programme, how many of these pupils do not take any exercise outside school?

(b) Clare says, 'I go to the gym twice a week after school.'
She decides to do a survey to investigate what exercise other pupils do outside school.
Write down two questions that she could ask.

(c) Matthew decides to do a survey in his school about the benefits of exercise.
He decides to ask the girls' netball team for their opinion.
Give two reasons why this is not a suitable sample to take.

MODULE 1

(d) This is part of Matthew's questionnaire.

Question   *Don't you agree that adults who were sportsmen when they were younger suffer more from injuries as they get older?*

Response   *Tick one box*

☐ *Yes*   ☐ *Usually*   ☐ *Sometimes*   ☐ *Occasionally*

(i)   Write down one criticism of Matthew's question.

(ii) Write down one criticism of Matthew's response section.   [NEAB]

3.   Jane does a survey about vehicles passing her school.
She wants to know about the types of vehicles and
their colours.

Design a suitable observation sheet to record this
information.
Fill in your observation sheet as if you had carried out
this survey.
You should invent suitable data for 25 vehicles.   [NEAB]

4.   Winston has designed a data collection sheet to record the
number of bottles that each person puts into a bottle bank.

Number of bottles	Tally	Frequency
0 to 2		
3 to 6		
6 to 8		

(a) Give three criticisms of the class intervals that Winston has
chosen.

Anna and Patrick watch people using the bottle bank.
Anna watches 60 people and calculates the mean to be 8·5
bottles per person.
Patrick watches 15 people and calculates the mean to be 9·2
bottles per person.

(b) Which of the two means would you expect to give the more reliable estimate of the mean number of bottles per person?
Give a reason for your answer.   [SEG]

5. A survey on clothes shopping included the following questions.

---

1 What is your total annual income?

2 How much do you spend per month on clothes?

£0–£20   £20–£40   £40–£60   £60–£80   £100 or more
☐   ☐   ☐   ☐   ☐

3 What are your hobbies?

(a) Why should question 1 not be asked?

(b) Write down one criticism for each of question 2 and question 3..   [SEG]

6. The table shows information about some cars.

Make	Colour	Mileage
Vauxhall	blue	8 606
Ford	white	12 214
Vauxhall	white	5 567
Rover	red	11 984
Rover	blue	9 085
Vauxhall	red	6 984
Ford	blue	8 763
Vauxhall	white	14 675

(a) What is the range in the mileage of these cars?

(b) Calculate the mean of the mileages.

(c) What is the modal make of car?.   [SEG]

D2 DATA HANDLING 2

Statistical diagrams make it easy to understand data.

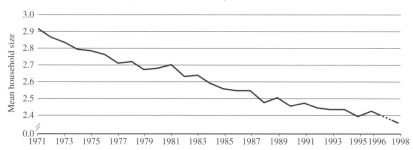

Mean household size: Great Britain, 1971-1998

This unit will show you how to:

- Use two-way tables and frequency tables
- Draw pictograms, bar charts and pie charts
- Draw line graphs and frequency polygons
- Draw stem-and-leaf diagrams

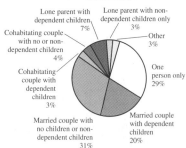

Households by the type of household: Great Britain, 1998

Households

Before you start:

You should know how to ...	Check in D2
1. Work with percentages For example, to find 12% of 60  $\frac{12}{100} \times 60 = 0.12 \times 60$ $= 7.2$	**1.** (a) Find 8% of 360. (b) Express 45 as a percentage of 360.
2. Simplify ratios For example, simplify 6 : 15 $\div 3 \left(\begin{array}{c} 6 : 15 \\ 2 : 5 \end{array} \right) \div 3$	**2.** Express the ratio 4 : 8 : 12 in its simplest form.

2.1 Two-way tables

A two-way table is a way of linking two pieces of information.

The rows show one piece of information and the columns show the other.

Example 1

The following two-way table describes the audience at a cinema.

	Children	**Adults**
Male	42	27
Female	69	96

Use the table to find
(a) how many children were at the cinema
(b) how many females were at the cinema.
(c) What was the total audience at the cinema?

(a) Children are represented in the first column:
$$42 + 69 = 111$$

(b) Females are represented in the second row:
$$69 + 96 = 165$$

(c) Add up all sections of the two-way table:
$$42 + 27 + 69 + 96 = 234$$

Example 2

A survey was conducted on how people travelled to a local supermarket.
195 people were asked and 47 of them were men.
139 people travelled by car and 21 travelled by bus.
Fill in the missing numbers represented by a, b, c and d.

(a) 139 travelled by car, so the missing number is
    $139 - 31 = 108$

(b) There are 47 men in the survey.
     So far there are $31 + 12 = 43$ in the table.
     So the missing number is 4

Method of travel

	Car	**Bus**	**Walk**
Men	31	b	12
Women	a	c	d

(c) Look at the bus column.
    4 was found for the top number.
    21 travelled by bus.
    $21 - 4 = 17$

(d) There are $195 - 47 = 148$ women.
     $148 - 108 - 17 = 23$

The completed table now becomes:

Method of travel

	Car	Bus	Walk
Men	31	4	12
Women	108	17	23

The figures in the table can now be added to check that the total is 195 people.

Exercise 2A

1. Kingswood School has an Activities Afternoon for Year 9 pupils. The pupils have two separate sessions and they must choose one activity for each session.
    The first session has Model-making or Cookery whilst the second session has Athletics or Tennis.
    The table shows the pupil choices.

	Athletics	**Tennis**
Model-making	49	21
Cookery	36	43

    Use the table to find how many pupils
    (a) chose Athletics
    (b) chose Tennis
    (c) there are in Year 9.

2. The table gives the examination level achieved by a number of Mathematics students at Year 9 (Key Stage 3) and then their GCSE grade in Year 11.

		GCSE Grade						
		F	**E**	**D**	**C**	**B**	**A**	**A***
Key Stage 3 Level	**4**	1	3	1				
	5		4	29	2			
	6			15	48	4		
	7				36	12	7	
	8						3	2

    (a) How many students achieved an A* grade?
    (b) How many students achieved a grade C or better in GCSE?

(c) At Key Stage 3, the average level is a 5 or a 6. How many students achieved an average Key Stage 3 result?

(d) What was the total number of students included for these results?

3. Pupils in Years 9, 10 and 11 took part in a sponsored walk. A total of 315 pupils took part and 138 were girls. Of these, 75 girls in Year 9 and 15 girls in Year 11 took part.

There was a total of 147 pupils in Year 9 and 111 pupils in Year 10 taking part.

(a) Copy the table and fill in the missing numbers of pupils.

	Year 9	Year 10	Year 11
Boys			
Girls			

(b) Use your table to write down the number of
   (i)   boys taking part for Year 9
   (ii) girls taking part for Year 10.

4. 450 television executives attended a conference. All those attending completed a questionnaire. The executives were asked whether they were from BBC, ITV, or an independent company. They were also asked how they travelled to the conference, using one of car, train or coach.

The total number of executives travelling by train was 82.

Out of the total of 83 executives who travelled by coach, 4 were from the BBC.

Out of 141 executives from ITV, 89 travelled by car and 36 by train.

Out of 196 executives from independent companies, 105 travelled by car.

Design a table to show this data and complete all the entries in your table.

(a) How many executives were from the BBC and travelled by car?

(b) How many executives attended from the BBC?

5. The table shows the amount of money earned by employees at a local factory, according to their age group. Each age group has the same number of employees.
Write down how many employees

		Age in years		
		Up to and including 20	21–45	Over 45
Wage per week	Up to £120	54	38	4
	£121–£350	18	27	–
	Over £350	3	–	42

(a) are in the age group 'up to and including 20'
(b) work at this factory
(c) are in the age group '21–45 years' and earn over £350
(d) are over 45 years old and earn between £121 and £350
(e) earn between £121 and £350
(f) are 45 or less and earn over £350.

2.2 Tally charts and frequency tables

Tally charts provide an effective format for recording original, or **raw**, data.

Suppose you asked 25 pupils in a class to choose their favourite sport from a list. The tally chart might look like this.

This means 2

Favourite sport	Tally	Frequency
Rugby	||	2
Swimming	ⅢⅠ ||	7
Soccer	ⅢⅠ ⅢⅠ ||	12
Tennis	|||	3
Orienteering			1

When the tally marks are complete, they are counted and the value is recorded in the column headed 'frequency'

This means 7

Tally charts allow you to show frequencies, or amounts.

Frequencies can be shown in a **frequency table** (like for favourite sport), in a diagram or just in a list.

However you display frequencies, it is known as a **frequency distribution**.

It is often helpful to combine the raw data into a more compact form.

The table records how many pupils in a form group buy a school dinner.

Number of pupils in a form group buying a school dinner	Frequency (or number in class)
0–4	1
5–9	3
10–14	5
15–19	13
20–24	14
25–29	4

This is an example of a **grouped frequency table**. The categories have been merged together into **classes**, or **intervals**.

Exercise 2B

1. The number of runs scored from each ball during the first 10 overs of a cricket match is listed below.

   0,0,0,1,2,3   4,0,1,1,2,0   0,0,0,1,3,4   0,1,3,4,1,0   0,0,1,1,0,1
   0,0,1,1,2,6   0,1,1,4,6,4   0,1,1,2,1,0   0,0,0,1,1,1   0,6,6,4,3,1

   Use a tally chart to obtain a frequency table for the data.

2. The following marks were obtained by pupils in a test.

90	16	22	35	68	19	42	28	19	83
61	42	60	18	26	58	82	42	77	59
57	63	43	7	35	71	19	18	62	50
47	68	75	67	58	69	43	37	35	48
59	63	51	43	62	12	19	72	81	34

   Use intervals 0–9, 10–19, 20–29, 30–39, 40–49, 50–59, 60–69, 70–79, 80–89, 90–99 to record the data in a frequency distribution using a tally chart.

   Hint:
   The first column should be headed 'number of runs'.

3. The heights (in centimetres) of 20 children are listed below.

127	111	119	136	125	120	158
117	145	147	148	128	142	151
149	138	127	146	113	129	

   Use intervals 110–119 cm, 120–129 cm, 130–139 cm, 140–149 cm, 150–159 cm to draw a tally chart and obtain the frequency table for the data.

4. The numbers of caravans parked on a holiday site in Cornwall was recorded over a four-week period in August. The numbers are given in the table.

	Mon	Tues	Wed	Thurs	Fri	Sat	Sun
Week 1	12	6	10	22	46	45	38
Week 2	17	7	15	24	41	48	29
Week 3	14	4	17	20	31	46	21
Week 4	15	8	29	32	35	21	41

Choose suitable intervals 0–9, 10–19, etc. to draw a tally chart and obtain the frequency table for the data.

5. Passengers getting onto a local bus during its journey were recorded in one of four categories: woman (W), man (M), boy (B) or girl (G). The results for the information collected are as follows.

M	W	W	W	B	G	M	G	G	B	W	M
M	W	M	W	B	M	W	W	W	W	M	W
B	G	W	M	B	W	W	M	W	M	B	G

Draw a tally chart to show this information and obtain the frequency distribution for the data.

6. During the first morning of a sale a shoe shop sold the following sizes of shoes.

$$7 \quad 2 \quad 2\tfrac{1}{2} \quad 6 \quad 6 \quad 7 \quad 7 \quad 8 \quad 10 \quad 10\tfrac{1}{2}$$
$$6\tfrac{1}{2} \quad 11 \quad 9 \quad 7\tfrac{1}{2} \quad 6 \quad 6\tfrac{1}{2} \quad 5\tfrac{1}{2} \quad 4 \quad 7 \quad 7$$
$$5\tfrac{1}{2} \quad 6 \quad 7 \quad 7\tfrac{1}{2} \quad 8 \quad 10\tfrac{1}{2} \quad 7 \quad 7 \quad 6 \quad 6\tfrac{1}{2}$$
$$7 \quad 8 \quad 8\tfrac{1}{2} \quad 7\tfrac{1}{2} \quad 6 \quad 5 \quad 5\tfrac{1}{2} \quad 5 \quad 4 \quad 6\tfrac{1}{2}$$
$$10 \quad 8 \quad 6 \quad 4\tfrac{1}{2} \quad 4 \quad 5 \quad 6 \quad 6 \quad 7 \quad 8\tfrac{1}{2}$$

Draw a tally chart to show this data and obtain the frequency distribution for the data.

2.3 Pictograms

Pictograms are diagrams in the form of pictures, and they are used to present information. Each picture or symbol is used to represent a number of items.

Example

The number of cans of drinks sold by a school tuck shop was recorded for one week.

Day	Number of cans sold
Monday	250
Tuesday	225
Wednesday	175
Thursday	300
Friday	250

Show this data by means of a pictogram.

Use one picture ◀ to represent 25 cans.

Then the pictogram would be:

Cans sold

Monday ◀ ◀ ◀ ◀ ◀ ◀ ◀ ◀ ◀ ◀

Tuesday ◀ ◀ ◀ ◀ ◀ ◀ ◀ ◀ ◀

Wednesday ◀ ◀ ◀ ◀ ◀ ◀ ◀

Thursday ◀ ◀ ◀ ◀ ◀ ◀ ◀ ◀ ◀ ◀ ◀ ◀

Friday ◀ ◀ ◀ ◀ ◀ ◀ ◀ ◀ ◀ ◀

Key: ◀ = 25 cans

- In a pictogram, it is essential

  (i) to use the same 'picture' in all the diagrams and

  (ii) to include a key.

Exercise 2C

1. The pictogram shows the number of sales of the South Coast Echo and Forest News newspapers by a newsagent during one week.

South Coast Echo

Forest News

Key: 📖 = 10 newspaper sales

Use the diagram to answer these questions.

(a) How many copies of the Forest News were sold during the week?

(b) Estimate how many copies of the South Coast Echo were sold.

2. The pictogram shows the result of a survey of Year 9 pupils to find which was the most popular TV programme.

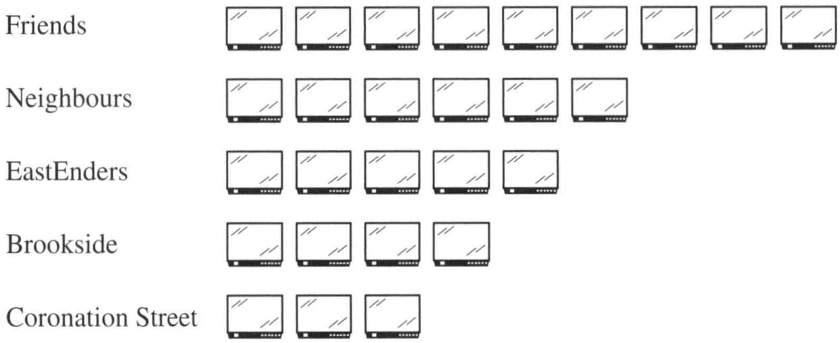

Friends

Neighbours

EastEnders

Brookside

Coronation Street

(a) Fifteen students chose Coronation Street. How many pupils chose Friends?

(b) How many students were included in the survey?

3. Draw a pictogram to illustrate the following data for the makes of a number of cars passing a junction.

| Vauxhall | 15 | Rover | 20 | Toyota | 5 |
| Peugeot | 12 | Ford | 28 | Citroen | 10 |

Hint:
Choose a car symbol to represent 5 cars. For Peugeot and Ford you will need to draw fractions of a symbol.

4. The pictogram shows the expenditure of a music company in advertising a concert.

Direct mail shots

Newspaper adverts

Posters

The company spent £80 on posters.
(a) How much was spent on direct mail shots?
(b) Each direct mail shot cost an average of 80p.
How many mail shots did they use?

5. Draw a pictogram to illustrate the following data, which was recorded when a Year 11 class was asked to state their most popular sport.

Football	15
Tennis	8
Hockey	2
Basketball	4
Cricket	2

2.4 Bar charts

Bar charts show information in a graphical form by the use of bars or columns.
The height or length of the column corresponds to the frequency.
Bar charts can be drawn either horizontally or vertically.

Example 1

The numbers of spectators attending Premier league football matches over one weekend in the 2000–2001 season were recorded. The bar chart shows this information.

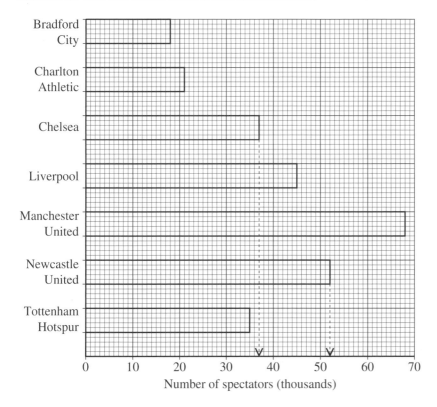

(a) Which football match had 37 000 spectators?

(b) How many spectators watched the Newcastle United match?

(a) Chelsea had 37 000 spectators.

(b) The arrow drawn from the Newcastle United bar shows that the crowd was approximately 52 000.

Sectional bar charts

If data has been subdivided into two or more parts, you can use a **sectional bar chart**.

> Sectional bar charts are also known as **component bar charts**.

Example 2

A survey was carried out to discover how the 800 pupils in a school travelled to school.

Method of transport	Boys	Girls
Bus	95	155
Car	52	98
Cycle	35	15
Train	32	18
Walk	185	115

Show the data by means of a sectional bar chart.

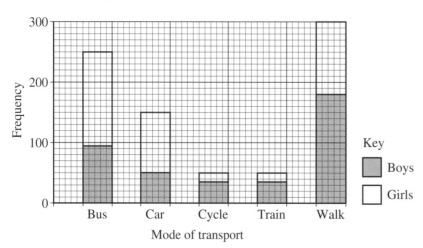

> This diagram shows the number of boys and girls in each category together with the totals.

Dual bar charts

When two different sets of information are given on the same topic, but the **total** is not meaningful, you can use a **dual bar chart**.

Example 3

The numbers of cars sold by four sales people working in a garage in January 2000 and January 2001 are given in the table.

Salesperson	January 2000	January 2001
Carol	11	13
Henry	8	9
Robert	17	14
Sam	6	11

Represent this data by means of a dual bar chart.

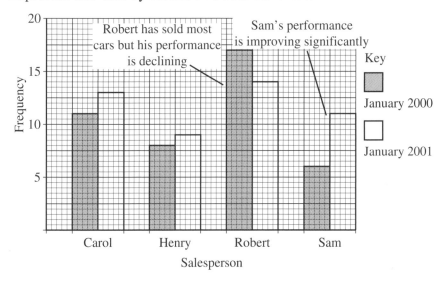

Exercise 2D

1. The bar chart shows the number of goals scored in football matches in a Sunday league.

   (a) What number of goals was scored most often in one of these football matches?

   (b) In how many matches were 4 goals scored?

   (c) In how many matches were less than 3 goals scored?

   (d) What was the total number of matches taking place in this Sunday league?

MODULE 1

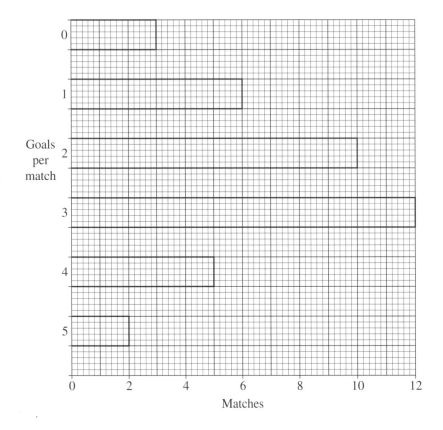

2. The bar chart shows the holiday destinations of a number of
   people entering an airport during a 30-minute survey.

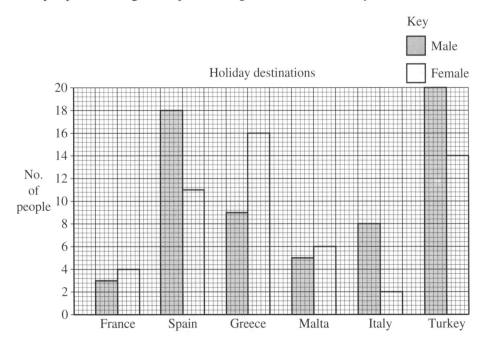

(a) Which holiday destination is the most popular for females?
(b) Which holiday destination is the least popular for males?
(c) How many males were questioned for the survey?
(d) What was the total number of people involved in the survey?
(e) Which is the most popular holiday destination from this survey?

3. On a walk through a wood, the following types of trees were seen:

Oak   65   Chestnut   49

Beech   23   Birch   21

Sycamore 42   Ash   15

Draw a suitable bar chart to illustrate this data.

4. Thirty people noted the television channel they were watching at 7.30 pm on two successive Saturday nights.

Channel	First Saturday	Second Saturday
BBC1	10	5
BBC2	3	1
ITV	11	14
Channel 4	2	2
Channel 5	1	4
Satellite	3	4

Draw a suitable bar chart to illustrate this data.

5. A group of 30 pupils were asked how often they had been swimming last month.
The data was recorded as shown in the table.

No. of times	Boys	Girls
0	5	2
1	6	4
2	1	4
3–5	1	5
Over 5	0	1

Represent this data by means of a bar chart.

2.5 Pie charts

Drawing pie charts

Pie charts are used commonly for displaying qualitative data. In a pie chart, a circular 'pie' is divided into sectors, and each sector is proportional to the size of the class it represents.

> To remind yourself what qualitative data means, look back at page 2.

Example

One evening, 120 people bought the following food from a take-away shop.

Type of take-away	Number of people
Fish and chips	58
Burger and chips	22
Pizza	31
Chinese	9
Total	120

Represent this data by means of a pie chart.

- First calculate the angle which represents each person.
  The complete pie chart is a circle, which contains 360°.
  Hence 120 people are represented by 360°.
  1 person is represented by 360° ÷ 120 = 3°.
  Thus the angle of the pie chart which represents 1 person is 3°.

- Then calculate the angles for each sector.
  There were 31 people buying pizza.
  Each person is represented by 3°.
  So the pizza sector is represented by $31 \times 3° = 93°$.

Similarly for the other categories:

Type of take-away	Angle in pie chart
Fish and chips	$58 \times 3° = 174°$
Burger and chips	$22 \times 3° = 66°$
Pizza	$31 \times 3° = 93°$
Chinese	$9 \times 3° = 27°$
Total	360°

- Now draw the pie chart.

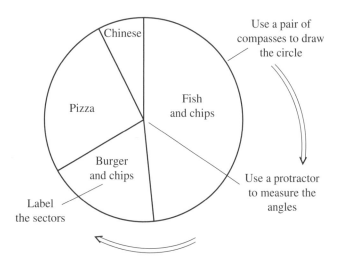

Exercise 2E

1. A box of 60 coloured pencils contains the following number of pencils of each colour.

Colour	Blue	Yellow	Red	Green	Black	Brown
No. of pencils	12	22	5	7	8	6

   (a) What angles in a pie chart would you use to represent each pencil colour?
   (b) Draw a pie chart to represent the data.

2. During December, 1800 new cars were sold in a town. 750 were sold by Ford, 800 by Vauxhall and 250 by Rover.
   (a) What angles in a pie chart would you use to represent each make of car?
   (b) Draw a pie chart to represent the data.

3. Marion spends her day as shown in the table.

Sleeping	8 hours
Eating	2 hours
Working	9 hours
Watching TV	2 hours
Driving	3 hours

   (a) Calculate the angle of each sector of a pie chart representing this data.
   (b) Draw the pie chart.

4. The numbers of pets kept by pupils in a Year 9 tutor group are shown in the table.

Type of pet	Dog	Cat	Goldfish	Hamster	Bird	Other	None
Number	15	16	10	5	4	1	3

(a) Calculate the angle of each sector of a pie chart representing this data.

(b) Draw the pie chart.

5. Bill earns £150 per week. He divides his money up as follows:

Rent   £35   Travel   £10   Clothes   £25
Food   £45   Savings   £20   Entertainment £15

Draw a pie chart to show how Bill divides up his earnings.

2.6 Interpreting pie charts

You should now know how to construct pie charts; you also need to know how to interpret them.

Example

This pie chart shows how Mark spent his time during one 24-hour period.

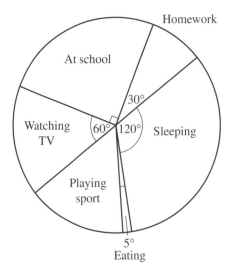

(a) How long did Mark spend sleeping?

(b) How many hours did Mark spend in total playing sport and watching TV?

(a) 120° represents the time Mark spent sleeping.

360° represents 24 hours,

so 1° represents $\frac{24}{360}$ hours,

∴ 120° represents $\frac{24}{360} \times 120$ hours.

Hence Mark spent 8 hours sleeping.

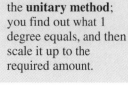

This is an example of the **unitary method**; you find out what 1 degree equals, and then scale it up to the required amount.

(b) First find the angle that represents playing sport:

The sum of the other sectors angles = 60° + 90° + 30° + 120° + 15° = 215°.

The angle representing playing sport is 360° − 215° = 45°.

∴ The total angle for playing sport and watching TV is 60° + 45° = 105°.

Now find the time taken for playing sport and watching TV:

1° represents $\frac{24}{360}$ hours.

Time spent playing sport and watching TV = $\frac{24}{360} \times 105$ hours.

∴ Mark spent 7 hours watching TV and playing sport.

Exercise 2F

1. The pie chart shows the results from asking forty men about the style of tie they would prefer to wear.
   (a) Measure the angles of each sector of the pie chart. Write down your angles for each style of tie preferred.
   (b) How many degrees in the pie chart represent the response from one man?
   (c) How many men prefer
      (i)   striped ties
      (ii) not to wear a tie at all?

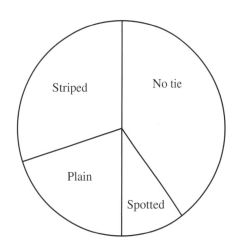

2. The pie chart shows the different activities taken by a Year 11 group during their sports afternoon. Netball was chosen by 50 pupils.
   (a) How many degrees are there in each sector of the pie chart? Write down your measurements, stating the angle for each activity.
   (b) How many students chose Dance?
   (c) How many students in total chose Hockey, Netball and Football?

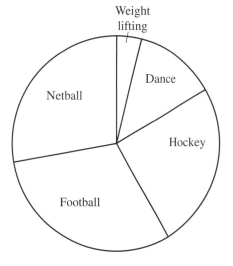

3. A class of 30 pupils drew a pie chart showing the number of pets they each have.
   (a) How many pupils have 4 pets?
   (b) Calculate the size of the angle marked x.
   (c) How many pets do these 30 students have in total?

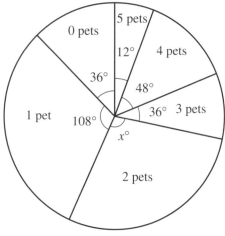

Not drawn to scale

4. In a survey on travel to school, 150 pupils travelled by car, bus or walked. 35 pupils walked to school.
   If 20 pupils travelled to school by bus and 95 pupils travelled by car, calculate the angles x and y.

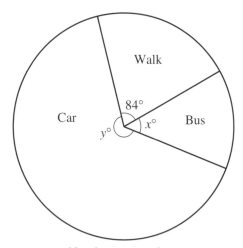

Not drawn to scale

5. A Year 7 group consisting of 240 pupils selected one activity each for their final week of the summer term. The choices were camping, fishing, computing, historical visits or sporting activities. The pie chart illustrates the choices made by all the pupils.
   The total number of pupils who chose sporting activities and fishing was exactly equal to the total number of pupils choosing camping, historical visits and computing.
   (a) Calculate the angles x and y.
   (b) How many pupils chose each individual activity?

2.7 Line graphs

You can often use a line graph to display continuous variables, such as length or time.

Example

The speed of a car was recorded every 5 seconds as it travelled between two sets of traffic lights.

Time (secs)	0	5	10	15	20	25	30	35	40	45	50	55	60
Speed (mph)	0	15·1	27·2	41·1	58·3	52·7	45·1	40·9	30·5	20·7	10·5	5·3	0

(a) Represent this data by means of a line graph.
(b) Use your graph to estimate
    (i)   the speed of the car after 22 seconds
    (ii) the time when the speed of the car was 29 mph.

(a) Take each pair of values in the table as coordinates:
    (0, 0), (5, 15·1), (10, 27·2), and so on.

Plot a graph on graph paper like this:

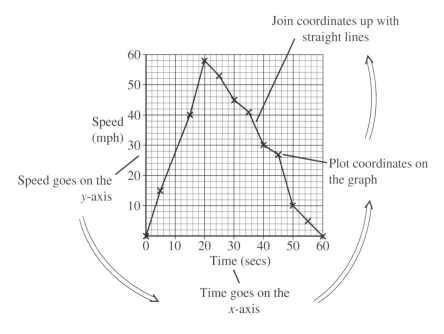

(b) (i) After 22 seconds the speed is roughly 55 mph.
   (ii) The speed is 29 mph after roughly 11 seconds.

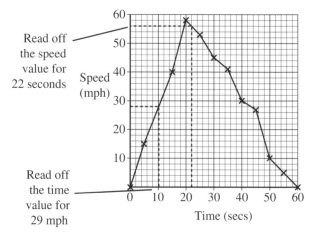

Read off the speed value for 22 seconds

Read off the time value for 29 mph

Speed (mph)

Time (secs)

Exercise 2G

1. A retailer of mobile phones recorded their sales figures at the end of each month for a nine-month period. The sales figures are given in the table.

	1999							2000	
Month	June	July	Aug	Sept	Oct	Nov	Dec	Jan	Feb
Phone sales	1200	1050	900	1120	1150	1230	1700	1240	970

   (a) Draw a line graph to illustrate the given data.
   (b) Consider the trend and comment on any fluctuations in the sales patterns, suggesting reasons why they may happen at those times.

2. A nurse records the temperature, hourly, for a patient admitted to a hospital ward. The graph shows the temperatures recorded.

   (a) The patient was given drugs on entry to the hospital ward. How long did it take before the drugs began to lower the temperature of the patient?
   (b) By how many degrees did the temperature fall and how long did it take before the temperature began to rise again?

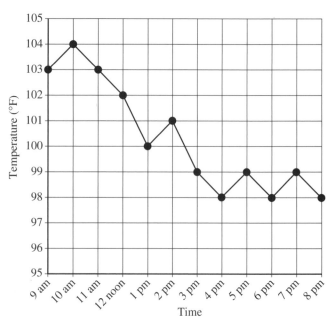

Temperature (°F)

Time

(c) The normal body temperature is 98·4 °F. How long did it take before the patient's temperature returned to normal?

(d) Is it possible to estimate the temperature at 1.30 pm? Justify your answer.

3. The table gives the monthly rainfall amounts for one year.

Month	Jan	Feb	Mar	Apr	May	Jun	Jul	Aug	Sep	Oct	Nov	Dec
Rainfall (cm)	8·2	9·4	4·6	4·4	3·3	2·4	2·2	0·8	3·9	5·7	9·9	12·4

(a) Draw a line graph to illustrate the monthly rainfall.

(b) Comment on any trends that you notice.

4. The daily takings for stamp sales for one week, at a village post office, are shown on the graph.

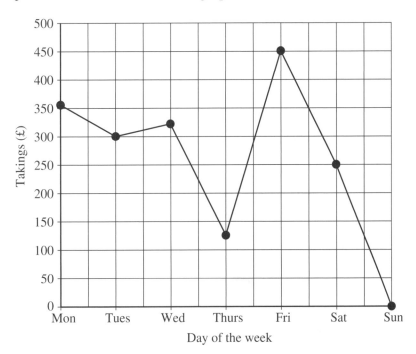

(a) On which day was the post office closed?

(b) On which day do you think the post office was only open in the morning?

(c) On which days were the stamp sales greater than those for Wednesday?

5. The number of vehicles using a motorway service area was recorded at the end of each hour during one day. The results are shown on the graph.

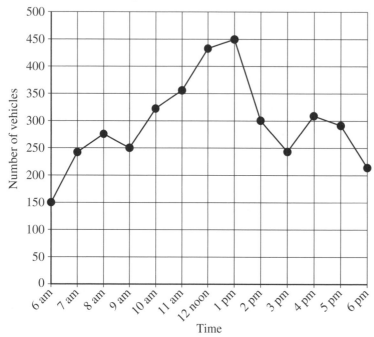

(a) What was the largest number of vehicles recorded using the service area and when did this occur?

(b) How many times were more than 300 vehicles recorded?

(c) Comment on the trend for the number of vehicles stopping at this service area.

(d) Is it possible to use this graph to estimate the number of vehicles at the service area at 10.30 am on this day? Justify your answer.

6. Robert records the maximum and minimum outdoor temperatures every day for two weeks over the Christmas holiday period. The table gives his recorded temperatures.

Day	First week							Second week						
	Tue	Wed	Thur	Fri	Sat	Sun	Mon	Tue	Wed	Thur	Fri	Sat	Sun	Mon
Max. temp. (°C)	14	18	13	14	8	10	15	19	18	12	11	10	7	9
Min. temp. (°C)	4	5	0	⁻1	⁻4	1	3	5	4	⁻1	⁻3	⁻6	⁻5	⁻1

(a) On the same axes, draw line graphs to illustrate both the maximum and minimum temperatures recorded over these two weeks.
(b) On which day did the greatest difference between the maximum and minimum temperatures occur?
How can you tell this by inspection of your graph?
(c) On which day was the difference between the maximum and minimum temperatures the least?

7. A water company needs to replace a supply pipe and has a work gang digging out the trench to re-lay this pipe. The length of trench dug out is recorded hourly from the 6 am start time, as shown in the table.

Time	6 am	7 am	8 am	9 am	10 am	11 am	12 noon	1 pm	2 pm	3 pm	4 pm	5 pm
Trench length (m)	0	3	7	11	16	18	24	24	28	33	37	45

(a) Draw a line graph to represent this data.
(b) Use your graph to estimate the length of the trench at
    (i) 8.30 am   (ii) 2.15 pm
(c) Explain fully what you think happened between 12 pm and 1 pm.

8. Jenny has a savings account with the school bank. The amount of money recorded in her account each week for the autumn term is given in the table.

Week	1	2	3	4	5	6	7	8	9	10	11	12	13	14	15	16
Account total (£)	20	25	32	36	45	62	32	39	45	50	56	68	73	44	20	20

(a) Draw a line graph to represent the data.
(b) Comment on any trends that you notice in how Jenny uses her savings account.
(c) Explain what happened between week 6 and week 7.

9. A supermarket sells petrol. The volume of unleaded petrol in the storage tanks is recorded hourly during opening hours on one day and is shown in the table.

Time	8 am	9 am	10 am	11 am	12 noon	1 pm	2 pm	3 pm	4 pm	5 pm	6 pm	7 pm
Volume (1000's litres)	3·2	2·5	1·9	9·3	8·9	8·6	8·2	8·1	7·9	7·5	5·4	4·5

(a) Draw a line graph to represent the data.
(b) What happened between 10 am and 11 am?
    Give a reason to explain your answer.
(c) Between which times was most petrol sold?
    Give a reason why you think this happened between these times.

2.8 Frequency polygons

A frequency polygon is a line graph which shows the shape of a grouped frequency distribution. It is constructed like a bar chart, but instead of drawing bars you plot points and join them up with straight lines.

● For grouped data the coordinates are plotted at the midpoint of each class interval.

Example 1

The speeds of 100 cars passing beneath a motorway bridge, after 3 pm on a weekday, were checked. The results were recorded in a table.

Represent this data by means of a frequency polygon.

Speed in mph (S)	$0 \leqslant S < 40$	$40 \leqslant S < 50$	$50 \leqslant S < 60$	$60 \leqslant S < 70$	$70 \leqslant S < 80$	$80 \leqslant S < 90$	$90 \leqslant S < 100$
Frequency	0	7	31	54	5	2	1

Plot coordinates using midpoints as shown   (20,0)   (45,7)   (55,31)   (65,54)   (75,5)   (85,2)   (95,1)

Plot the frequency polygon on graph paper.

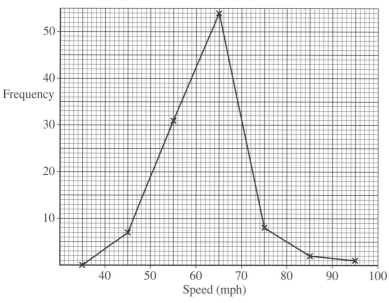

Example 2

Data was similarly collected for the first 100 cars passing the bridge after midnight on a weekday.

Speed in mph (S)	$0 \leqslant S < 60$	$60 \leqslant S < 70$	$70 \leqslant S < 80$	$80 \leqslant S < 90$	$90 \leqslant S < 100$	$100 \leqslant S < 110$
Frequency	0	43	38	12	3	4

(a) Draw the frequency polygon for this data on the same axes as the frequency polygon in Example 1.

(b) Compare the two distributions.

(a)

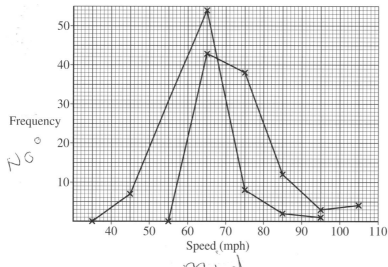

mid

(b) The second frequency polygon drawn is to the right of the first. The speed of cars after midnight was higher than the speed of the cars after 3 pm.

Exercise 2H

1. Fifty pupils were asked how many magazines they had bought last week. The responses are given in the table.

Number of magazines	Number of pupils
0	3
1	1
2	2
3	5
4	21
5	12
6	5
7	0
8	1

Show this data by means of a frequency polygon.

2. Over a period of three months, the number of people who ate in a restaurant in Benidorm was recorded on a daily basis.

Number of people	Number of days
0–10	4
11–20	11
21–30	33
31–40	31
41–50	17
51–60	2

Draw a frequency polygon to show this data.

3. The heights of sixty roses in a flower garden were measured in centimetres as:

> 25, 37, 11, 18, 29, 42, 38, 25, 26, 31, 17, 28, 35, 34, 37,
> 28, 12, 44, 38, 26, 25, 21, 31, 33, 29, 41, 32, 29, 32, 37,
> 21, 27, 35, 28, 12, 42, 38, 37, 12, 31, 25, 29, 36, 37, 28,
> 31, 41, 11, 27, 29, 17, 28, 35, 15, 37, 28, 26, 29, 38, 30.

Construct a frequency table using class intervals of 10–15, 16–20, 21–25, 26–30, 31–35, 36–40 and 41–45 centimetres.

Show the data as a frequency polygon.

4. The number of hours that two groups of people watched television in one week was recorded.

Number of hours (to the nearest hour)	Number of people in Group A	Number of people in Group B
0–4	3	4
5–9	7	5
10–14	21	14
15–19	11	15
20–24	5	11
25–29	2	1
30–34	1	0

Draw two frequency polygons to show this data, using the same axes and comment on your results.

5. The weights of two groups of people were recorded.

Weight (kg)	40–50	50–60	60–70	70–80	80–90	90–100
Group A (no. of people)	1	8	27	11	2	1
Group B (no. of people)	1	5	15	24	4	1

Draw the frequency polygons to show this data, using the same axes.
What can you deduce from these polygons?

6. Cara finds the number of letters per word in the first 100 words on page 6 of two newspapers. Cara's results are given in the table.

No. of letters	1	2	3	4	5	6	7	8	9	10	11	12
Paper A	1	1	8	15	20	24	18	7	0	3	2	1
Paper B	1	2	17	34	31	11	3	1	0	0	0	0

Draw the frequency polygons to show this data, using the same axes.
One of the papers is a tabloid, the other is a broadsheet. Which paper is which?

2.9 Stem-and-leaf diagrams

Stem-and-leaf diagrams are useful for ordering raw numerical data without losing any information.

Example

At the morning post collection, the numbers of letters in 15 post boxes were recorded as:

31, 49, 28, 33, 36, 41, 46, 36, 35, 27, 31, 35, 44, 25, 54.

Draw a stem-and-leaf diagram to show this data.

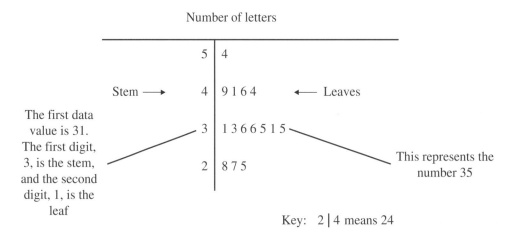

Number of letters

The first data value is 31. The first digit, 3, is the stem, and the second digit, 1, is the leaf

Stem →   5 | 4
         4 | 9 1 6 4   ← Leaves
         3 | 1 3 6 6 5 1 5   This represents the number 35
         2 | 8 7 5

Key: 2 | 4 means 24

As the numbers in the leaves are not in numerical order, this is an **unordered stem-and-leaf diagram**.

Redrawing it with the leaves in numerical order gives:

Number of letters

5	4
4	1 4 6 9
3	1 1 3 5 5 6 6
2	5 7 8

Key: 2 | 4 means 24

This is known as an **ordered stem-and-leaf diagram**.

● A stem-and-leaf diagram needs a heading and a key.

Exercise 2I

1. The numbers of passengers on a small 72-seater aeroplane in its 20 short flights on one day were recorded as:

> 33, 37, 41, 45, 61, 72, 68, 72, 65, 61,
> 65, 39, 41, 48, 53, 54, 57, 49, 41, 31.

Draw a stem-and-leaf diagram to show this data.

2. The numbers of supporters of a football club who travelled on Byron's coaches to away matches were:

> 84, 76, 92, 41, 62, 71, 59, 63, 70, 81,
> 74, 65, 67, 58, 49, 63, 71, 49, 54, 61.

Draw a stem-and-leaf diagram to show this data.

3. The numbers of tourists travelling on a pleasure boat in the Solent on 14 days in August were:

> 71, 49, 82, 61, 91, 85, 89, 74, 92, 75, 64, 48, 52, 57.

Draw a stem-and-leaf diagram to show this data.

4. The weights of packets, in kg, received by a small company were recorded as:

> 2·1, 4·8, 7·1, 5·2, 2·7, 3·5, 3·6, 4·1, 5·3, 4·7,
> 3·8, 2·7, 2·8, 4·7, 3·9, 6·2, 5·3, 6·8, 4·8.

Using a key 4 | 3 to mean 4·3, draw a stem-and-leaf diagram to show this data.

5. Alan tested a machine to check that it delivered the correct weight of sweets. He took a sample of 25 packets and weighed them.
The weights in grams of each packet are:

239, 255, 249, 239, 237, 240, 248,
240, 245, 244, 245, 238, 232, 237,
251, 241, 246, 235, 250, 236, 234,
237, 245, 247, 241

(a) Using a key 23|9 to mean 239, draw a stem-and-leaf diagram to show this data.

(b) The machine is set to weigh sweets to an average weight of 240 grams and is allowed to vary between 235 and 245 grams. What conclusion should Alan make from his test on this weighing machine?

2.10 Back-to-back stem-and-leaf diagrams

You can compare two similar sets of data using a **back-to-back stem-and-leaf diagram**.

Example

The ages in years of holidaymakers in two small hotels were:

Hotel Du Parc: 37, 28, 41, 71, 62, 47, 54, 49,
63, 41, 38, 75, 51, 49, 47, 65,
58, 57, 51, 68, 72, 35, 51, 46,
52, 57, 64, 65

Hotel Le Soleil: 52, 49, 75, 35, 36, 49, 25, 29,
31, 37, 28, 39, 62, 41, 25, 28,
32, 71, 36, 39, 29, 41, 31, 32,
35, 41, 59, 48, 72, 27, 41, 37,
25

(a) Show this information in a back-to-back stem-and-leaf diagram.

(b) Compare the two age distributions.

(a) Hotel du Parc is shown on the left in order **away** from the stem

Hotel Le Soleil is shown on the right of the stem

Ages of holidaymakers

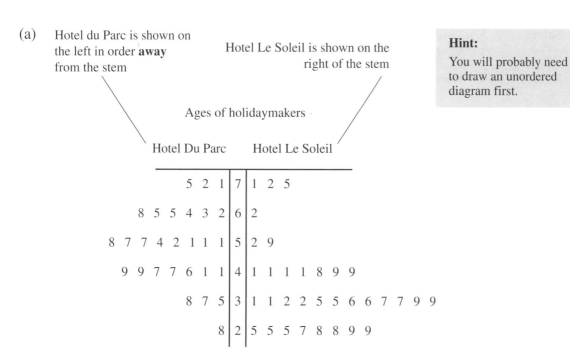

Hotel Du Parc   Hotel Le Soleil

```
          5  2  1 | 7 | 1  2  5
    8  5  5  4  3  2 | 6 | 2
 8  7  7  4  2  1  1  1 | 5 | 2  9
    9  9  7  7  6  1  1 | 4 | 1  1  1  1  8  9  9
          8  7  5 | 3 | 1  1  2  2  5  5  6  6  7  7  9  9
             8 | 2 | 5  5  5  7  8  8  9  9
```

Key: 2 | 4 means 24

(b) From this diagram you can see at a glance that the guests at the Hotel Le Soleil tend to be younger than those at the Hotel Du Parc.

Exercise 2J

1. The sales of a bottle of coke in two small convenience stores were recorded over a ten-day period.

   For 'Open All Hours' the sales were
   7, 19, 15, 22, 14, 16, 17, 19, 21, 9.

   For 'Pricetrim' the sales were
   17, 11, 15, 23, 14, 18, 19, 9, 21, 8.

   Show this data by means of a back-to-back stem-and-leaf diagram.

2. The numbers of cars passing a counter on a road in the New Forest per half-hour period from 8 am until 8 pm on a particular Monday and Saturday in June were:

   Monday: 44, 39, 31, 21, 19, 17, 25, 15, 29, 27, 24, 15,
              13, 17, 19, 28, 34, 32, 29, 34, 33, 21, 15, 11

Saturday: 3, 4, 11, 31, 42, 47, 51, 49, 56, 51, 67, 71, 49,
53, 51, 69, 51, 42, 41, 39, 28, 31, 29, 25

Draw a back-to-back stem-and-leaf diagram to show this data.

3. The numbers of passengers in an aeroplane in the Caribbean on
15 short flights on a Wednesday and a Sunday were recorded:

Wednesday: 8, 12, 15, 21, 17, 19, 23, 31, 31, 28, 15, 11, 16, 9, 6

Sunday: 19, 28, 27, 29, 28, 30, 30, 31, 29, 24, 21, 25, 17, 15, 12

(a) Draw a back-to-back stem-and-leaf diagram to show this data.
(b) What conclusions can you draw from this diagram?

4. During October the numbers of hours of sunshine recorded
each day in two resorts, one in Portugal and the other in the
South of England, were:

Portugal: 8·1, 7·9, 6·7, 5·4, 4·9, 5·2, 4·1, 3·1, 1·9, 6·9,
9·2, 8·7, 8·5, 9·2, 8·7, 7·4, 5·2, 4·1, 1·1, 4·2,
1·5, 7·2, 8·4, 7·9, 8·3, 9·2, 9·1, 8·9, 8·8, 7·1, 8·2

England: 5·8, 4·7, 3·3, 3·2, 3·7, 3·8, 3·9, 0·1, 0·2, 0·1,
1·1, 2·3, 3·7, 3·5, 3·6, 3·3, 4·1, 8·1, 7·1, 3·9,
4·5, 4·7, 3·9, 4·8, 2·1, 1·7, 1·5, 1·9, 4·9, 2·8, 2·9

(a) Using a key 4 | 3 to mean 4·3, draw a back-to-back
stem-and-leaf diagram to show this data.
(b) What conclusion can you draw from the diagram?

5. The numbers of male and female customers in 'Le Bistro'
restaurant were recorded for a three-week period:

Male: 21, 15, 17, 19, 35, 42, 51, 34, 47, 25, 31, 25,
17, 21, 29, 38, 52, 47, 8, 38, 28

Female: 24, 17, 19, 31, 21, 12, 8, 25, 19, 34, 15, 21,
11, 32, 24, 17, 12, 21, 38, 17, 31

(a) Draw a back-to-back stem-and-leaf diagram to show
this data.
(b) Use your evidence from (a) to compare the male and
female numbers using this restaurant.

Summary

You can use a two-way table.

2. You can complete a tally chart.

3. You can draw a pictogram.

4. You can draw a bar chart.

5. You recognise the difference between dual bar charts and sectional bar charts.

6. You can draw a pie chart.

Check out D2

1. In one year group, the number of pupils with cats and dogs was recorded.

	No. of pupils with cats	**No. of pupils with dogs**
Girls	17	8
Boys	5	19

How many boys had dogs?

2. The numbers of people waiting at twenty bus stops were:

6, 9, 4, 7, 8, 9, 7, 8, 4, 6, 3, 6, 4, 8, 6, 6, 4, 3, 4, 5.

Record this data in a tally chart.

3. The numbers of sweets eaten by six friends were:

John 25, Sharon 15, Ahmed 20, Chloe 30, Emma 25 and Andy 10.

Record this data as a pictogram.

4. Record the data shown in the tally chart in question **2** in a bar chart.

5. At 7 pm one evening all thirty pupils in a tutor group recorded which TV channel they were watching.

	BBC1	**BBC2**	**ITV**	**Ch 4**	**Other**
Boys	4	1	6	3	4
Girls	5	2	3	1	1

Record this data by means of a sectional bar chart.

6. Record in a pie chart the data shown in the tally chart in question **2**.

7. You can interpret pictograms, bar charts and pie charts.

7. (a) The pie chart shows the number of houses of different types on a housing estate.

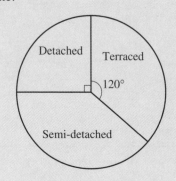

(i) What type of house is most common?

(ii) There are 180 houses on the estate. How many are detached?

(b) The pictogram shows the method by which a class arrive at school.

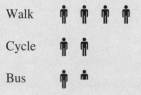

Key: 🧍 represents 4 pupils

Show this information by means of a bar chart.

8. You can draw a line graph.

8. The monthly rainfall in a town was recorded over 10 months. In centimetres this was:

Jan	Feb	Mar	Apr	May
11·2	8·4	7·8	5·7	2·9

June	July	Aug	Sep	Oct
3·1	1·1	0·8	4·7	11·2

Represent the data on a line graph.

9. You can draw a frequency polygon.

9. The number of letters which a postman delivered to 300 homes were recorded.

Number of letters	Number of homes
0	17
1	41
2	67
3	76
4	45
5	31
6	15
7	7
8	1

Draw the frequency polygon for this data.

10. You can draw a stem-and-leaf diagram.

10. The weights of fish (in pounds) caught in a lake in one day were:

7·4, 8·2, 4·3, 5·4, 6·7, 7·2, 7·5, 8·1, 8·9, 6·7, 4·7, 3·8.

Using a key 3 | 4 to represent 3·4, show this data on a stem-and-leaf diagram.

Revision exercise D2

1. The pie chart shows information about the loaves of sliced bread sold by a supermarket one day.

(a) The supermarket sold 150 medium sliced loaves.
How many thick sliced loaves were sold?

The supermarket sells both sliced bread and unsliced bread.

(b) Three quarters of the loaves of bread sold that day were sliced.
How many loaves of bread were sold altogether that day?   [SEG]

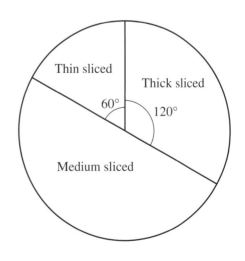

2. The pie chart shows information from a survey about the holiday destinations of a number of people.

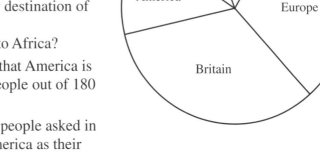

(a) (i) Which holiday destination is the mode?

(ii) America is the holiday destination of 24 people.
How many people go to Africa?

In another survey it was found that America is the holiday destination of 21 people out of 180 people asked.

(b) What percentage of all the people asked in these two surveys gave America as their holiday destination?   [SEG]

3. One Saturday a newsagent sells the following:

National daily newspapers   510
Echo   360
Magazines and comics   210

(a) Draw a clearly labelled pie chart to represent these sales.

The frequency polygon shows the sales of national daily newspapers.

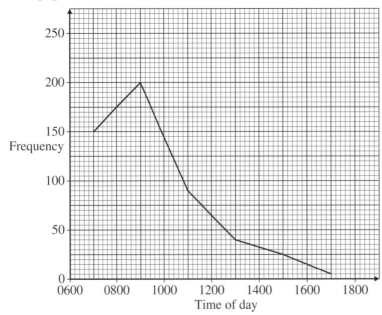

(b) (i) How many of these papers were sold between
1000 and 1400?

The table shows the sales of the Echo.

Time of day	0600–	0800–	1000–	1200–	1400–	1600–1800
Frequency	0	0	0	20	125	215

   (ii) On a copy of the diagram on page 52 draw a frequency
polygon to show the sales of the Echo.

   (iii) Compare and comment on the sales of these two
types of paper.   [SEG]

4. The two-way table shows the number of visits made by
students to dentists and to doctors.

			Number of visits made to the doctor			
			0	**1**	**2**	**3**
Number of visits made to the dentist		**0**	24	10	2	1
		1	8	5	3	1
		2	10	7	0	0
		3	5	3	1	0

(a) How many students did not visit the doctor?
(b) How many students visited the dentist exactly 3 times?
(c) How many students made more visits to the doctor than
they made to the dentist?   [SEG]

5. (a) The table shows the fuels used for heating in all the
houses in a large town.

Fuel	Number of houses (in 1000's)
Solid fuel	8
Electricity	42
Gas	70
Total	120

Draw a clearly labelled pie chart to represent this information.

(b) This pie chart shows the fuels used for heating in all the houses in a small village.

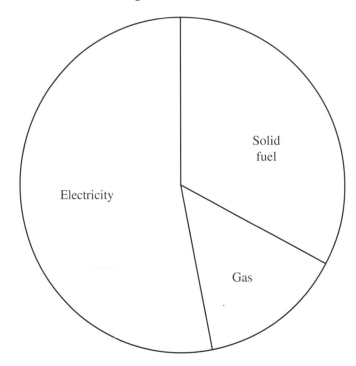

(i) What fraction of these houses use gas?

(ii) Solid fuel is used in 24 houses.
How many houses are in the village?

(c) Use the information from these two pie charts to say which fuel is most likely to be the mode.
Give a reason for your answer.   [SEG]

D3 DATA HANDLING 3

If you want to describe a typical data value, you can use averages.

We are the party for the average person on the street

This unit will show you how to:

- Find the mean, median and mode of a distribution
- Decide which is the most appropriate average to use
- Calculate moving averages

Before you start:

You should know how to...	Check in D3
1. Perform arithmetic without a calculator	**1.** Without using a calculator, find (a) $37 + 213 + 72$ (b) 17×8 (c) 18×5.5 (d) $\frac{276}{6}$ (e) $\frac{19.67}{7}$
2. Put numbers in order	**2.** Place these numbers in ascending order. $15, 8, 1, 21, 19, 11, 12$

3.1 The arithmetic mean

The **arithmetic mean** of a set of data is defined as the sum of the values divided by the number of values.

- $\text{Mean} = \dfrac{\text{Sum of values}}{\text{Number of values}}$

> The arithmetic mean is often just called the mean.

Example

The numbers of people waiting at five bus stops are:

6, 10, 12, 3, 4

What is the mean number of people waiting?

First find the total number of people: $6 + 10 + 12 + 3 + 4 = 35$

Divide by the number of bus stops: $\frac{35}{5} = 7$

The mean number of people waiting at a bus stop is 7.

You can write the mean as a **formula**:

> There is more about formulae on page 234.

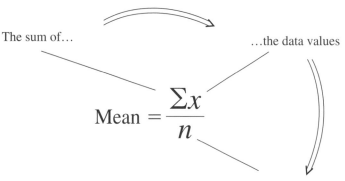

The sum of… …the data values

$$\text{Mean} = \frac{\Sigma x}{n}$$

…divided by the number of values

> Σ is a Greek letter pronounced 'sigma'. In mathematics it means 'the sum of'.

Exercise 3A

1. A train travels from Wolverhampton to Birmingham. The time taken by the train is recorded in minutes for 12 journeys, and these times were:

    28, 29, 32, 27, 31, 43, 27, 27, 31, 30, 24, 38 $\leftarrow + AT = 367$

    Find the mean time taken. $= 30.5$

2. A local insurance firm sends the following numbers of letters out daily over a 3-week period:

    88, 96, 122, 101, 49, 183, 72, 68, 105, 67, 142, 69, 77, $= 1426$
    84, 103

    Find the mean number of letters sent out per day. ~ 95.0

3. A rugby team scored the following numbers of points in their first 14 matches:

> 42, 12, 19, 37, 25, 21, 72, 61, 4, 32, 27, 47, 33, 16

Calculate the mean number of points scored per match.

4. The number of cars parked in a multi-storey car park was recorded hourly over an eight-hour period. The figures were:

> 354, 291, 272, 153, 351, 350, 295, 62

Calculate the mean number of cars parked each hour.

5. The heights of a group of students were measured. Those heights, in centimetres, are:

> 159, 173, 160, 185, 160, 181

(a) Calculate the mean height of these students.
(b) Two more students with heights 157 cm and 169 cm joined the group.
   Calculate the new mean height of all these students.

6. Five charity boxes contain the following amounts of money:

> £42·50, £63·15, £71·90, £23·84, £112·11

(a) Calculate the mean amount of money in these boxes.
(b) The money from a sixth box is then added, giving a mean for all six boxes of £59·77. How much money was in the sixth box?

7. Five men athletes have an average time of 10·15 seconds for running 100 metres. Four women athletes have an average time of 11·25 seconds for running 100 metres. What is the average time taken by these nine athletes for running 100 metres?

8. John was given his science module test marks for the year. So far he has gained marks of:

> 17, 19, 12, 12, 7, 14 and 12

What mark must he achieve in his eighth test if he needs to gain an overall average mark of 14 to pass?

MODULE 1

3.2 The mode

● The **mode** of a discrete distribution is the value that occurs most frequently.

Example 1

The numbers of people waiting at six different bus stops were:

     8, 7, 5, 7, 6, 9

Find the modal number of people.

7 appears most frequently.

The mode is 7.

● For a grouped distribution, the **modal class** is the class which occurs most frequently.

Example 2

At a post office the weights of 20 small packets were recorded.

Weight (grams) W	Frequency
$50 \leqslant W < 100$	1
$100 \leqslant W < 150$	5
$150 \leqslant W < 200$	11
$200 \leqslant W < 250$	2
$250 \leqslant W < 300$	1

Remember:

$50 \leqslant W \leqslant 100$ means a weight lying in between 50 and 100 grams.

Find the modal class.

The class with the largest frequency is 150–200 grams.

The modal class is 150–200 grams.

Exercise 3B

1. Find the mode of
   (a) 7, 6, 5, 10, 6, 8, 6, 3, 9
   (b) 15, 21, 25, 21, 17, 21, 15, 19, 15, 15

2. Ten policemen were measured and their heights, in metres, were:

       1·80, 1·83, 1·81, 1·80, 1·85, 1·83, 1·80, 1·81, 1·84, 1·80

   What is the modal height?

3. The lengths of telephone calls from a mobile phone were recorded.

Call length (seconds)	Frequency
60 and below	5
61–90	7
91–120	9
121–150	14
151–180	68
181–240	38
241–300	72
Over 300	20

What is the modal class?

4. A group of twenty pupils compare their eye colour. The colours are:

> green, blue, brown, brown, blue, blue, green, brown, blue, green, blue, brown, blue, green, blue, green, brown, blue, green, brown.

What is the modal colour?

5. Fifty students ran 400 metres, and their times were recorded as follows.

Time (seconds)	Frequency
70–	4
80–	12
90–	11
100–	18
110–	5

What is the modal class?

3.3 The median

- The **median** of a set of numbers is the middle number in order of size.

Example 1

Find the median of the following numbers:

6, 15, 12, 11, 8, 16, 21, 9, 13

6, 8, 9, 11, 12, 13, 15, 16, 21

Rearrange the numbers in order, starting with the smallest:

6, 8, 9, 11, 12, 13, 15, 16, 21

The middle number is 12

The median is 12.

In the previous example there were 9 data values. When there is an even number of values, you get two 'middle' numbers.

12. 16 .

Example 2

Find the median of the following numbers:

6, 15, 12, 11, 8, 16, 21, 9, 13, 18   6, 8, 9, 11, 12, (13) 15, 16, 18, 21

Rearrange these numbers in order:

6, 8, 9, 11, 12, 13, 15, 16, 18, 21

The two 'middle' numbers are 12 and 13.

The median lies half way between the two middle numbers.

The median is $12\frac{1}{2}$.

With 9 values the median is the 5th value.

With 10 values the median is the $5\frac{1}{2}$th value.

> **Hint:**
> You can find the halfway value by adding the two numbers together and dividing by 2:
> $\frac{12 + 13}{2} = 12\frac{1}{2}$

> **Hint:**
> Count the numbers in the previous two examples to check that this is true.

- Generally, to find the median of a set of numbers
  (i)   **add up** how many numbers you are given
  (ii) **add 1** to this total
  (iii) **divide this total by 2** to find the position of the median number.

For example, if there are 41 numbers:

- add 1: $41 + 1 = 42$
- divide by 2: $42 \div 2 = 21$

> **Note:**
> This does not mean that the median is 21.

The median is the 21st number when all 41 numbers are written in order.

Exercise 3C

1. Find the median for each of these sets of data.
   (a) 1, 8, 4, 6, 7, 5, 3, 5, 4
   (b) 15, 21, 17, 14, 16, 19, 22
   (c) 21, 25, 287, 17, 11, 19
   (d) 18, 25, 16, 12, 11, 16
   (e) 25, 121, 79, 82, 84, 77, 95, 15, 111, 78
   (f) 3·7, 3·0, 2·9, 2·8, 3·1, 3·0, 2·7, 3·2, 2·9, 3·7

2. An eight-sided dice was rolled 16 times and the scores were:

6, 5, 4, 3, 7, 1, 1, 2, 4, 8, 3, 2, 3, 6, 5, 4

What was the median score?

3. Write down
(a) seven different numbers with a median of 14
(b) nine different numbers with a median of $8\frac{1}{2}$.

4. (a) These marks were obtained in a test: 2, 3, 8, 7, 5.
What should the next mark be to give a median of 6?

(b) If these marks were obtained: 4, 3, 6, 8, 7, 2, 4, 6, what should the next mark be to give a median of 5?

5. Bookings made at a local youth hostel during a two-month period are shown in the table.

Number of bookings	24	25	26	27	28	29	30	31
Frequency	4	12	17	22	36	5	2	1

What was the median number of bookings made at the youth hostel?

3.4 Use of the mean, mode and median

When deciding which of the three averages to use, you should consider what the average is being used for.

- Use the arithmetic mean to compare totals.
  If the mean weight of luggage on a European flight is 19 kg per passenger, you can easily find the total weight of luggage when you know the number of passengers.

- Use the mode to find the most common value.
  A shopkeeper selling shoes should always have the mode in stock as that is the size most likely to sell.

- Use the median when you want to ignore extreme values.
  To find the typical time taken by a Year 10 girl to run 100 metres, you may not wish to consider the very fastest or very slowest runners as neither of these would be representative. The median would be chosen because it is unaffected by values at either end.

Exercise 3D

1. In a small firm each of the seven employees earns £120 per week. The manager pays herself £800 per week.

    (a) What is the modal wage for the firm?

    (b) What is the median wage for the firm?

    (c) What is the mean wage for the firm?

    (d) Which of these averages gives a fair reflection for the wages earned by people from the firm?

2. Find the mode, mean and median for the number of letters in

    (a) the days of the week

    (b) the months of the year.

3. Witnesses to an accident are asked to estimate the speed of a car.

    Their estimates are

    50 mph, 45 mph, 52 mph, 80 mph, 49 mph.

    Which average would you use to estimate the speed of the car?

4. Six students are asked how much per hour they are paid for their part-time jobs.

    The replies were

    £4, £3·60, £4·20, £4·80, £12, £470.

    Which average is most appropriate to give the typical pay of the students?

5. The numbers of copies of 'The Daily Journal' sold in one shop on successive Mondays were

    72, 81, 47, 58, 61, 70.

    Which average is the most appropriate to use for the newsagent to estimate the total sale on Mondays of 'The Daily Journal' over the year?

3.5 The mean of a frequency distribution

Example 1

A particular football team kept a record of the number of goals they scored in each match last season.

Number of goals	Number of matches	Matches × goals
0	10	$10 \times 0 = 0$
1	7	$7 \times 1 = 7$
2	6	$6 \times 2 = 12$
3	3	$3 \times 3 = 9$
4	1	$1 \times 4 = 4$
5	2	$2 \times 5 = 10$
6	1	$1 \times 6 = 6$

The team has scored two goals in six matches

The total number of goals scored in these matches is 12

Find the mean number of goals per match.

Add up the last column to find the **total number of goals**:

$$0 + 7 + 12 + 9 + 4 + 10 + 6 = 48$$

Add up the second column to find the **total number of matches**:

$$10 + 7 + 6 + 3 + 1 + 2 + 1 = 30$$

Divide the total number of goals by the total number of matches:

$$\frac{48}{30} = 1 \cdot 6$$

The mean number of goals scored per match is 1·6.

You can use a formula to work out the mean of a frequency distribution.

Remember:
Σ means 'the sum of'.

- Mean $= \dfrac{\Sigma fx}{\Sigma f}$

x is the variable (in the example x is the number of goals).
f is the frequency (in the example f is the number of matches).

In the example you could lay out your working in a table like this.

x	f	fx
0	10	0
6	1	6
	$\Sigma f = 30$	$\Sigma fx = 48$

Mean $= \dfrac{48}{30} = 1\cdot6$

- If the data is grouped, use the **mid-interval** of each class as your x value.

Note:
You cannot actually score $1\cdot6$ goals in football. The mean is not always a real data value.

Example 2

Twenty letters were weighed and their weights were recorded.

Weight (grams) W	Number of letters
$0 \leqslant W < 20$	5
$20 \leqslant W < 40$	7
$40 \leqslant W < 60$	4
$60 \leqslant W < 80$	3
$80 \leqslant W < 100$	1

Estimate the mean weight of a letter.

You will need to extend the table to make two extra columns.

10 is half way between 0 and 20

Weight (grams) W	No. of letters f	Mid-interval x	fx
$0 \leqslant W < 20$	5	10	50
$20 \leqslant W < 40$	7	30	210
$40 \leqslant W < 60$	4	50	200
$60 \leqslant W < 80$	3	70	210
$80 \leqslant W < 100$	1	90	90
Totals	20		760

This is Σf

This is Σfx

Note: This is only an estimate. The data in the table does not give you the exact weight of any of the letters.

Mean weight is $\dfrac{\Sigma fx}{\Sigma f} = \dfrac{760}{20} = 38$ grams.

Exercise 3E

1. A group of 40 pupils were asked by their form teacher how many magazines they had read during the last two weeks. The results are recorded in the table.

Number of magazines read	0	1	2	3	4	5	6	7
Number of pupils	4	4	5	7	10	5	4	1

Calculate the mean number of magazines read per pupil.

2. A group of 40 mathematics students took a mental arithmetic test and the marks are given in the table.

Mark	0–2	3–5	6–8	9–11	12–14	15–17	18–20
Number of students	1	2	3	5	6	9	14

Calculate an estimate for the mean mark for these students.

3. The heights of 50 women were as given in the table.

Height (cm)	150–154	155–159	160–164	165–169	170–174
Number of women	6	11	17	11	5

Calculate an estimate for the mean height of the women.

4. A car survey recorded the ages of 150 cars. The results are listed in the table.

Age (A) in years	$0 \leqslant A < 2$	$2 \leqslant A < 4$	$4 \leqslant A < 6$	$6 \leqslant A < 8$	$8 \leqslant A < 10$	$10 \leqslant A < 12$	$12 \leqslant A < 20$
Number of cars	38	42	25	21	11	9	4

Calculate an estimate for the mean age of the cars in this survey.

5. A ferry across a lake can take up to 45 vehicles. On one particular trip the vehicles' weights were as in the table.

Weight of vehicle (W) in tonnes	$0 \leqslant W < 2$	$2 \leqslant W < 4$	$4 \leqslant W < 6$	$6 \leqslant W < 8$
Number of vehicles	24	13	6	2

Calculate an estimate for the mean weight of a vehicle on this ferry trip.

6. The length of each rally (number of hits of the ball) in the men's Wimbledon tennis final was recorded and is given in the table.

Length of rally	1	2	3	4	5	6	7	8	9	10
Frequency	17	32	65	61	32	15	14	8	5	2

Calculate the mean number of hits per rally.

7. A group of 20 people set off on a sponsored walk. Their times for the first mile, rounded to the nearest minute, are listed in the table.

Time taken (minutes)	1–11	12–23	24–35	36–47	48–59
Number of people	0	9	8	2	1

Calculate an estimate for the mean length of time taken to walk the first mile.

3.6 Moving averages

Sometimes data is presented in a definite order, or series. For example, data that show changes over time are called **time series**. There are often hidden patterns in data series that cannot be seen easily in the original data.

● A **moving average** is the average of consecutive items in a series of data.

Example

Cara's absences due to illness in each term (Autumn, Spring and Summer) in Years 7, 8 and 9 are as shown in the table.

	Year 7			Year 8			Year 9		
Term	Au	Sp	Su	Au	Sp	Su	Au	Sp	Su
Absences due to illness	18	11	7	15	9	8	12	9	6

(a) Calculate the three-point moving averages for this data.
(b) Draw line graphs showing (i) the original data, and (ii) the three-point moving averages.
(c) Comment on any trends you see in the graph.

Note:
A **three-point** moving average is the average of three items of data, in this case three terms.
A **four-point** moving average would be the average of four items, and so on.

(a) Redraw the table in columns.

Year group	Term	Absence due to illness	Three-point moving average
Year 7	Au	18	
	Sp	11	12
	Su	7	11
Year 8	Au	15	$10\frac{1}{3}$
	Sp	9	$10\frac{2}{3}$
	Su	8	$9\frac{2}{3}$
Year 9	Au	12	$9\frac{2}{3}$
	Sp	9	9
	Su	6	

Add up 18, 11 and 7 and then divide the total by 3 to get a mean of 12

This is the mean of 15, 9 and 8

(b) To plot a line graph:
  ● Draw axes with time along the *x*-axis.
  ● Plot the original data with crosses (as shown in the diagram).
  ● Plot the moving averages with a ⊙ (as shown in the diagram).

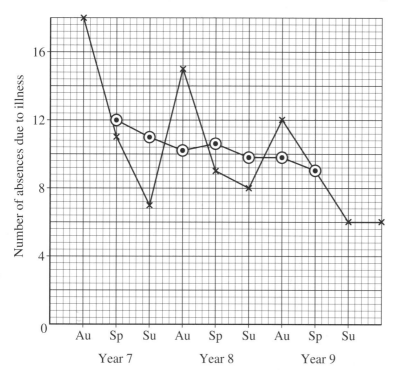

(c) The trend shows a reduction in absences due to illness.

Exercise 3F

1. Sharon opens her club on Thursday, Friday and Saturday evenings. The attendances over four weeks were as given in the table.

Week 1			Week 2			Week 3			Week 4		
Thurs	Fri	Sat	Thurs	Fri	Sat	Thurs	Fri	Sat	Thurs	Fri	Sat
71	182	215	79	149	235	81	161	240	84	172	247

   Sharon uses a three-point moving average to show this data.
   (a) Why does Sharon use a **three**-point moving average?
   (b) Plot the given data and the moving averages.
   (c) What trend does the moving average show?

2. A shop is closed on Sunday and Monday every week. Its sales, rounded to the nearest £250 over a three-week period are given in the table.

Week 1					Week 2					Week 3				
Tue	Wed	Thur	Fri	Sat	Tue	Wed	Thur	Fri	Sat	Tue	Wed	Thur	Fri	Sat
250	500	1000	3000	5000	500	500	1500	2500	3500	500	500	2000	3000	4500

   (a) What moving average should be used to show this data?
   (b) Plot the given data and the appropriate moving averages.
   (c) What trend is shown by your graph?

3. The quarterly gas bills for one family over a three-year period are given in the table.

Year	1998				1999				2000			
Month	Mar	Jun	Sep	Dec	Mar	Jun	Sep	Dec	Mar	Jun	Sep	Dec
Cost of gas (£)	192	64	72	110	166	66	74	100	210	66	80	90

   (a) Draw a graph for the data.
   (b) Calculate the four-quarterly moving average for the data.
   (c) Plot the moving averages on the same graph as the original data, joining up the points with a dotted line.
   (d) What is the trend in payments over this period?
   (e) Do you notice any seasonal variations in the charges?

4. The table shows the profits (in millions of pounds, £M) of a
   firm over a 10-year period.

Year	1989	1990	1991	1992	1993	1994	1995	1996	1997	1998
Profit (£M)	17	15	16	16	14·5	13·5	17	14·5	15	17

   (a) Use the information to find a three-yearly moving
       average for this data.
   (b) Draw a line graph to show the original profit data for
       the years 1989 to 1998.
   (c) Plot the three-yearly moving average on the same
       graph and join this up with a dotted line.
   (d) What does the moving average line tell you about the
       firm's profits?

5. A local employment agency records the number of
   vacancies available at the beginning of every month for one
   year.

Month	Jan	Feb	Mar	Apr	May	Jun	Jul	Aug	Sep	Oct	Nov	Dec
Vacancies	322	333	363	379	381	396	421	395	382	376	372	370

   (a) Draw a graph for the data.
   (b) Use the data to find the three-monthly moving average
       for the number of vacancies at the employment agency.
   (c) Plot the moving averages on the same graph as the
       original data, joining up the points with a dotted line.
   (d) What does the moving average tell you about the
       employment prospects for the unemployed attending
       this agency?

6. A charity shop notes how much is donated each week in
   gift boxes over an 18-week period.

Week	1	2	3	4	5	6	7	8	9	10	11	12	13	14	15	16	17	18
Donation (£)	88	90	82	85	79	80	82	78	82	79	85	74	82	75	76	84	73	79

   (a) Draw a graph for the data.
   (b) Calculate a six-weekly moving average for the amount
       of the donations.

MODULE 1

(c) Plot the moving averages on the same graph as the original data, joining up the points with a dotted line.

(d) Describe the trend in donations. Would you agree with the statement that 'The charity donations are being reduced by too many other charity shops competing for the same funds'?

7. A community disco records numbers attending for the first 15 weeks after opening.

Week	1	2	3	4	5	6	7	8	9	10	11	12	13	14	15
Number attending	42	38	57	46	32	47	53	37	51	27	67	43	51	38	49

(a) Draw a graph for the data.
(b) Calculate the five-weekly moving average for the data.
(c) Plot the moving averages on the same graph as the original data, joining up the points with a dotted line.
(d) What is the attendance trend at the disco?

Summary

1. You can find the arithmetic mean.

2. You can find the median.

3. You can find the mode and modal class.

4. You can decide which is the most appropriate average to use for the circumstances.

Check out D3

1. Find the mean of 17, 21, 31, 18, 24, 29.

2. Find the median of
   (a) 17, 19, 11, 21, 18, 30, 31
   (b) 21, 28, 24, 25, 29, 19

3. Find the mode of 17, 11, 9, 8, 11, 9, 12, 15, 9, 10.

4. A union negotiator is trying to justify a pay claim. Which 'average' of the workers' pay should be used?

5. You can find the mean of a frequency distribution.

5. (a) The number of books in 60 pupils' bags were recorded.

Number of books	Number of pupils
0	0
1	7
2	15
3	34
4	3
5	1

Find the mean number of books in a pupil's bag.

(b) The numbers of people in 50 train carriages were recorded.

Number of people in carriage	Number of carriages
0–10	4
11–20	16
21–30	23
31–40	6
41–50	1

Find the mean number of people in a carriage.

6. You can decide which is the most appropriate moving average to use and you can calculate it.

6. A farmers' market is open on Tuesday, Saturday and Sunday each week.
The sales, in £, of one stall over a period of four weeks are given in the table.

Week 1	Tuesday	21
	Saturday	97
	Sunday	67
Week 2	Tuesday	25
	Saturday	89
	Sunday	74
Week 3	Tuesday	27
	Saturday	93
	Sunday	75
Week 4	Tuesday	26
	Saturday	104
	Sunday	81

(a) What moving average should be used?
(b) Calculate the first five of these moving averages and plot them on a graph.

Revision exercise D3

1. The graph shows the weekly pocket money of 100 children aged 10 years.

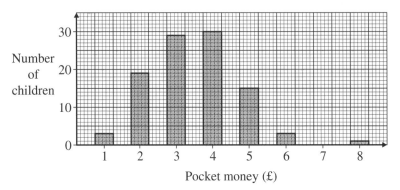

Pocket money (£)

(a) (i) What is the median amount of pocket money?
   (ii) Calculate the mean amount of pocket money.

The table shows the weekly pocket money of 100 students aged 16 years.

Pocket money (£)	0–	5–	10–	15–	20–25
Number of students	19	18	21	19	23

(b) Do the 10-year-olds or the 16-year-olds have the larger range in pocket money?
   Give a reason for your answer. [SEG]

2. Some women walked one mile.
   The time taken by each was recorded.
   The results are as follows.

Time t minutes	$12 \leqslant t < 16$	$16 \leqslant t < 20$	$20 \leqslant t < 24$	$24 \leqslant t < 28$	$28 \leqslant t < 32$
Number of women	1	9	43	22	5

(a) (i) What is the modal class for the time taken?
   (ii) Calculate an estimate of the mean time taken.

One mile is approximately 1·6 km.

(b) Use the data to calculate an estimate of the mean time taken by these women to walk one kilometre. [SEG]

3. A survey was made of the amount of money spent at a
supermarket by 100 shoppers on a Monday. The table shows
the results.

Amount spent M (£)	Number of shoppers
$0 \leqslant M < 20$	42
$20 \leqslant M < 40$	37
$40 \leqslant M < 60$	18
$60 \leqslant M < 80$	3

(a) Calculate an estimate of the mean amount of money
spent by these shoppers.

The frequency polygon shows the amount of money spent
by 100 shoppers at the supermarket on a Saturday.

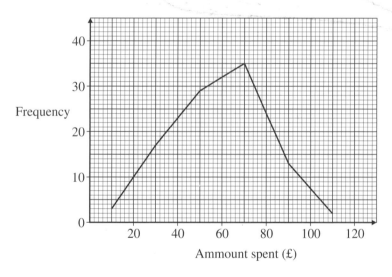

(b) On a copy of the diagram draw a frequency polygon
for the amount of money spent by the shoppers on
Monday.

(c) Compare and comment on the amount of money spent
by shoppers on these two days.   [SEG]

4. The maximum load for a lift is 1200 kg.

   The table shows the distribution of the weights of 22 people waiting for the lift.

Weight (w kg)	Frequency
$30 \leqslant w < 50$	8
$50 \leqslant w < 70$	10
$70 \leqslant w < 90$	4

   Will the lift be overloaded if all of these people get in?

   You must show working to support your answer.   [SEG]

5. David is playing cricket.

   The table shows the number of runs he has scored off each ball so far.

Number of runs	0	1	2	3	4	5	6
Number of balls	3	8	4	3	5	0	2

   (a) (i) What is the median number of runs per ball?
       (ii) Calculate the mean number of runs per ball.

   Off the next five balls, David scores the following runs:

       4, 4, 5, 3 and 6.

   (b) (i) Calculate the new median.
       (ii) Calculate the new mean.

   (c) Give a reason why the mean is used, rather than the median, to give the average number of runs scored per ball.   [SEG]

D4 DATA HANDLING 4

Measures of **dispersion** describe how data is spread out.

This unit will show you how to:

- Find the range of a distribution
- Draw cumulative frequency graphs
- Find the quartiles of a distribution
- Draw box-and-whisker diagrams
- Describe the skewness of a distribution

Before you start:

You should know how to ...	Check in D4
1. Find the median	**1.** Find the median of:
For example, find the median of the set of numbers:	11, 23, 34, 28, 15, 17, 26
19, 4, 8, 5, 9, 7, 12	
Rearrange in ascending order:	
4, 5, 7, 8, 9, 12, 19	
the median is 8	

4.1 The range

The **range** is the simplest measure of spread.

● The range is the difference between the largest and smallest data values.

Example

The runs scored by two cricketers in their last 11 innings are given in the table.

Batsman A	31	34	28	29	30	37	30	27	29	25	30
Batsman B	33	1	27	121	20	27	29	20	23	11	18

Find
(a) the mean score for both batsmen
(b) the range for both batsmen.
(c) Compare the performance of the two batsmen.

(a) For batsman A, the total is 330.

The mean for batsman B is $\dfrac{330}{11} = 30$.

For batsman B, the total is 330.

The mean for batsman B is $\dfrac{330}{11} = 30$.

(b) The range for batsman A is $37 - 25 = 12$.
The range for batsman B is $121 - 1 = 120$.

(c) The two batsmen have the same mean score, but the range indicates that batsman A is much more consistent.

Check:
You should check these totals for yourself.

Exercise 4A

1. The numbers of goals scored by a football team in the last ten matches were:

1, 5, 2, 0, 0, 3, 1, 1, 6, 1

Find (a) the mean number of goals scored
(b) the range in the number of goals scored.

2. The cost of a CD in 8 shops is:

£11·25, £12·99, £14·99, £16·99, £15, £14·50, £11·99, £15·99

Find (a) the mean cost of the CD
(b) the range in the price of the CD.

3. In September twelve friends in a school add up the number of parties which they have attended during the summer holiday. The results were:

14, 6, 8, 25, 16, 12, 8, 10, 11, 17, 15, 16

Find (a) the mean number of parties attended
     (b) the range in the number of parties attended.

4. In Year 10 examinations, Emma gained the following results:

Subject	Result (percentage)
Mathematics	68
English	41
French	32
Science	74
Geography	82
Technology	70
History	45
ICT	39

Find (a) the mean number of markes Emma achieved in the examinations
     (b) the range in Emma's marks.

5. The amounts which nine students say that they spent on their mothers' birthday presents are:

£15, £9, £3, £18, £22, £9.99, £11, £14, £30.

Find (a) the mean price of the presents
     (b) the range in the price of the presents the students bought.

4.2 Cumulative frequency

You can measure the spread of a frequency distribution using **cumulative frequency**.

- Cumulative frequency is the total frequency up to a given data value.
- For continuous data, cumulative frequency is the total frequency up to a given class boundary.

Hint:
You can think of cumulative frequency as a running total.

The heights of 96 girls in Year 11 were recorded.

Height in cms (h)	Frequency (number of girls)	Cumulative frequency
$120 \leqslant h < 130$	1	1
$130 \leqslant h < 140$	5	$1 + 5 = 6$
$140 \leqslant h < 150$	18	$1 + 5 + 18 = 24$
$150 \leqslant h < 160$	31	55
$160 \leqslant h < 170$	24	79
$170 \leqslant h < 180$	13	92
$180 \leqslant h < 190$	4	96

There are 55 girls with a height of less than 160 cm

The total frequency should be the same as the last cumulative frequency

Total = 96

You can illustrate cumulative frequency with a graph.

To draw a cumulative frequency graph you plot cumulative frequencies against the corresponding upper class boundaries.

- A **cumulative frequency curve** connects all the points with a smooth curve.
- A **cumulative frequency polygon** connects all the points with straight lines.

Example

(a) Draw a cumulative frequency curve using the data above for the heights of 96 girls in Year 11.

(b) Use your curve to estimate the percentage of students with a height exceeding 165 cm.

(a)

Height in cms (h)	Cumulative frequency	
$120 \leqslant h < 130$	1	(130, 1)
$130 \leqslant h < 140$	6	(140, 6)
$140 \leqslant h < 150$	24	(150, 24)
$150 \leqslant h < 160$	55	(160, 55)
$160 \leqslant h < 170$	79	(170, 79)
$170 \leqslant h < 180$	92	(180, 92)
$180 \leqslant h < 190$	96	(190, 96)

The first coordinate will be (130, 1)

Now draw a grid on graph paper, and plot the coordinates:

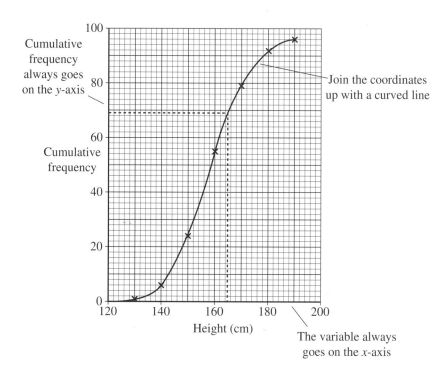

Cumulative frequency always goes on the *y*-axis

Join the coordinates up with a curved line

Cumulative frequency

Height (cm)

The variable always goes on the *x*-axis

Cumulative frequency curves often have this distinctive *S* shape.

(b) From the graph, there are roughly 69 students under 165 cm tall.

$96 - 69 = 27$ ⟶   There are roughly 27 students **over** 165 cm tall.

$\dfrac{27}{96} \times 100 = 28.1\%$ ⟶ The percentage of students over 165 cm tall is about 28%.

Exercise 4B

1. The nurse at a doctor's surgery measured the heights of 100 men. The measurements are recorded in the table.

Height (cm)	168–170	171–173	174–176	177–179	180–182	183–185	186–188	189–191
Number of men	4	10	14	26	22	14	7	3

(a) Calculate the cumulative frequencies for the distribution and draw a cumulative frequency curve.

(b) Use your graph to estimate the number of men who were taller than 178·5 cm.

> **Hint:**
> The upper class boundaries are 170·5, 173·5 etc.

2. The speeds of 250 vehicles travelling past a particular place on a dual carriageway were recorded. The results are shown in the table.

Speed (mph)	26–30	31–35	36–40	41–45	46–50	51–55	56–60
Number of cars	8	21	41	65	71	38	6

(a) Calculate the cumulative frequencies for the distribution and draw the cumulative frequency curve.

(b) Estimate the percentage of cars travelling at speeds greater than 48 mph.

3. 200 light bulbs were tested for performance. The length of time that each bulb worked normally was recorded.

Lifetime (L) hours	Number of bulbs (frequency)
$L < 1000$	6
$1000 \leqslant L < 1100$	10
$1100 \leqslant L < 1200$	18
$1200 \leqslant L < 1300$	46
$1300 \leqslant L < 1400$	66
$1400 \leqslant L < 1500$	36
$1500 \leqslant L < 1600$	14
$1600 \leqslant L < 1700$	2
$1700 \leqslant L < 1800$	2

> This type of testing is called destructive testing.

(a) Draw a cumulative frequency curve for the data.
A different set of 200 light bulbs were tested to destruction and these results are shown in the table.

Lifetime (L) hours	Number of bulbs (frequency)
$L < 1000$	2
$1000 \leqslant L < 1100$	2
$1100 \leqslant L < 1200$	4
$1200 \leqslant L < 1300$	8
$1300 \leqslant L < 1400$	16
$1400 \leqslant L < 1500$	26
$1500 \leqslant L < 1600$	36
$1600 \leqslant L < 1700$	36
$1700 \leqslant L < 1800$	42
$1800 \leqslant L < 1900$	20
$1900 \leqslant L < 2000$	8

(b) Draw a cumulative frequency curve for the second group of bulbs using the same axes as the first graph.

4. The table shows the marks gained by 500 students taking an end-of-module test.

Mark	Number of students
10 or less	15
11–20	10
21–30	15
31–40	35
41–50	95
51–60	180
61–70	105
71–80	30
81–90	10
91–100	5

(a) Draw a cumulative frequency polygon for this data.
(b) Estimate the pass mark if 60% of the students passed the examination.

5. The table shows the number of cars that crossed a bridge each hour.

Time, t	Number of cars
$1000 \leqslant t < 1100$	15
$1100 \leqslant t < 1200$	20
$1200 \leqslant t < 1300$	25
$1300 \leqslant t < 1400$	15
$1400 \leqslant t < 1500$	10
$1500 \leqslant t < 1600$	10
$1600 \leqslant t < 1700$	5

(a) How many cars crossed the bridge in total?

(b) Draw a cumulative frequency graph for these data.

4.3 Median and quartiles

Median

You can use a cumulative frequency graph to find the **median**.

Note:

For large grouped data sets, the median is the $\frac{n}{2}$-th value.

Example 1

Find the median height for the data of the 96 pupils on page 78. $n = 96$, so the median is the height of the 48th pupil.

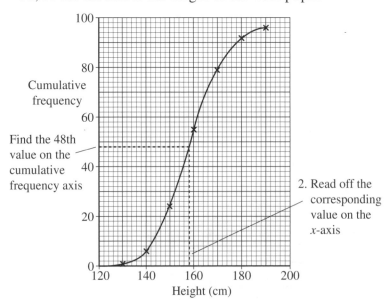

Find the 48th value on the cumulative frequency axis

2. Read off the corresponding value on the x-axis

Note:

This can only be an estimate because you were not given the raw data.

An estimate for the median is 158 cm.

Quartiles

Quartiles divide a set of data into four quarters.

minimum   lower quartile   median   upper quartile   maximum
data value   data value

- The **lower quartile** is the value that is a quarter of the way along a distribution.
- The **upper quartile** is the value that is three-quarters of the way along a distribution.

Example 2

For the data in the example on page 78, use the cumulative frequency graph to estimate the upper and lower quartiles.

$$n = 96$$

The lower quartile is the $\dfrac{96}{4}$ th value, that is the 24th value.

The upper quartile is the $3 \times \dfrac{96}{4}$ th value, that is the 72nd value.

Now use the graph.

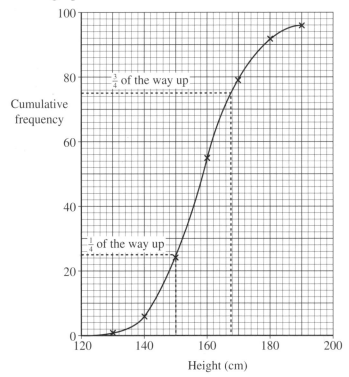

An estimate of the lower quartile is 150 cm.
An estimate of the upper quartile is 167 cm.

● The **interquartile range** is the difference between the upper and lower quartiles.

The interquartile range is a measure of dispersion which shows the range of the central 50% of a distribution.

Example 3

For the data on page 78:
(a) Find the interquartile range.
(b) What does the interquartile range tell you in this context?

(a) Interquartile range = upper quartile − lower quartile
$$= 167 - 150$$
$$= 17 \, \text{cm}$$

(b) The interquartile range shows that the middle 50% of the heights measured are within a range of 17 cm.

Exercise 4C

1. Use the graph that you drew in Exercise 4B question 1 to find
    (a) the median
    (b) the upper and lower quartiles
    (c) the interquartile range.

2. Use the graph that you drew in Exercise 4B question 2 to find
    (a) the median
    (b) the upper and lower quartiies
    (c) the interquartile range.

3. (a) Use the graph that you drew in Exercise 4B question 3 to find the median, quartiles and interquartile range for both sets of bulbs.
    (b) Use your findings to compare the two different types of light bulb.

4. (a) Use the graph that you drew in Exercise 4B question 4 to find the median and the interquartile range of the marks.
    (b) A mark of 75 or more is awarded a distinction. What percentage of the students gained a distinction?

5. (a) Using your cumulative frequency graph from Exercise 4B question 5, estimate the time when half the total number of cars have crossed the bridge.
    (b) Use your graph to estimate how many cars crossed the bridge before 1550.

4.4 Box-and-whisker diagrams

A box-and-whisker diagram, sometimes known as **box plot**, shows

   (i)   the median
  (ii) the upper and lower quartiles
 (iii) the maximum and minimum values of a distribution.

For the distribution in the example on page 78

the median is	158
the upper quartile is	167
the lower quartile is	150
the maximum value is	190
the minimum value is	120.

The box plot would look like this.

The 'box' contains
the quartiles

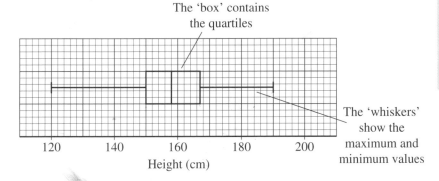

The 'whiskers'
show the
maximum and
minimum values

Height (cm)

You can use a box plot to describe the shape, or **skewness** of a distribution.

● If the median is to the left of the centre of the box, the distribution is **positively skewed**.
● If the median is to the right of the centre of the box, the distribution is **negatively skewed**.

Example

The heights of sixty trees in a plantation are measured.
A box plot is drawn from the data collected.

Find (a) the median

    (b) the interquartile range

    (c) the range of the heights in metres.

    (d) Describe the skewness of the distribution.

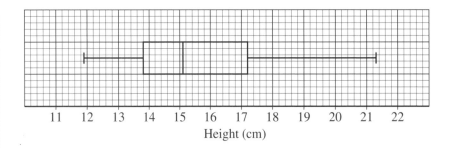

From the diagram:

(a) the median is   15·1 m

(b) the upper quartile is   17·2 m

       the lower quartile is   13·8 m

       the interquartile range is 17·2 − 13·8 m

                                                    = 3·4 m

(c) the maximum height is   21·3 m

       the minimum height is   11·9 m

       the range is   21·3 − 11·9 m

                                                    = 9·4 m

(d) The distribution of heights is positively skewed.

Exercise 4D

1–4 Draw a box-and-whisker diagram for the data given for
each of questions 1–4 in Exercise 4B.

5. The speeds in miles per hour of 32 cars on a motorway
     were recorded.
     The speeds were:

         68, 69, 74, 81, 61, 70, 65, 91, 58, 71, 68,
         74, 82, 83, 55, 97, 82, 71, 68, 67, 75, 65,
         61, 78, 71, 61, 62, 69, 51, 92, 41, 54

     (a) Draw a box-and-whisker diagram to show this data.
     (b) Describe the skewness of the distribution of speeds.

6. The numbers of passengers in a 72-seater aeroplane was
     noted on each of its 20 flights in one day.
     The numbers were:

         48, 54, 72, 21, 37, 45, 72, 41, 59, 63, 54, 59, 68, 72, 70,
         64, 41, 32, 24, 31

     (a) Draw a box-and-whisker diagram to show this data.
     (b) Describe the skewness of this distribution.

Summary

1. You can find the range of a distribution.

2. You can draw a cumulative frequency curve or polygon.

3. You can draw a box-and-whisker diagram.

4. You can interpret a box-and-whisker diagram.

Check out D4

1. Find the range of these scores:

3, 1, 72, 15, 11, 21, 17, 10

2. The numbers of dinners served by one waiter in a restaurant over 70 evenings were recorded.

Number of dinners	Numbers of nights
0–5	2
6–10	18
11–15	31
16–20	14
21–25	4
26–30	1

Draw the cumulative frequency curve for this data.

Find

(a) the median number of dinners the waiter served

(b) the upper quartile of the number served

(c) the lower quartile of the number served

(d) the interquartile range of the number served.

3. Draw a box plot of the data in question **2**.

4. For a month, the number of people travelling on a bus was recorded when it arrived at a village at a particular time.

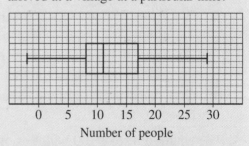

Number of people

(a) State the median, range and interquartile range of the number of people on the bus.

(b) Describe the skewness of this distribution.

Revision exercise D4

1. The frequency diagram shows the distribution of shoe sizes for a class of 40 pupils.

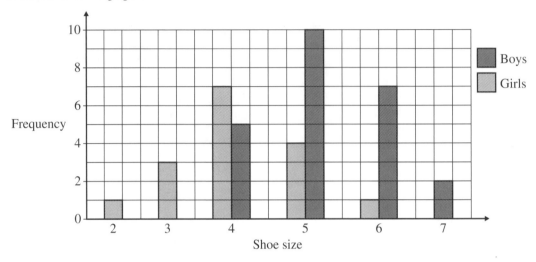

(a) What is the ratio of boys to girls in the class? Give your answer in its simplest form.

(b) What percentage of the class have shoe size 6?

(c) By working out the range and mode for the boys and for the girls, compare and comment on the shoe sizes for boys and girls.   [SEG]

2. (a) The lateness of 12 trains is recorded. The results, in minutes, are shown.

     1 1 2 2 3 3 3 5 7 7 9 15

(i) What is the range in lateness for these trains?

(ii) What is the mean lateness for these trains?

The lateness of 12 buses is also recorded. The range in lateness for these buses is 7 minutes and the mean lateness is 12 minutes.

(b) Give one difference in the lateness for these trains and buses.   [SEG]

3. The length of life of 100 batteries of a certain make was recorded. The table shows the results.

Length of life (hours)	<10	<15	<20	<25	<30	<35	<40
Cumulative frequency	0	2	9	50	86	96	100

(a) Draw a cumulative frequency graph to illustrate these data.
(b) How many batteries had a life of more than 32 hours?
(c) Use your graph to estimate:
   (i) the median
   (ii) the interquartile range.
(d) Another make of battery has a median length of life of 25 hours
   and an interquartile range of 7 hours.
   Is this make of battery likely to be more reliable than the first?
   Give a reason for your answer.   [SEG]

4. A cumulative frequency graph of the distribution of the weights
of 100 baking potatoes is shown.

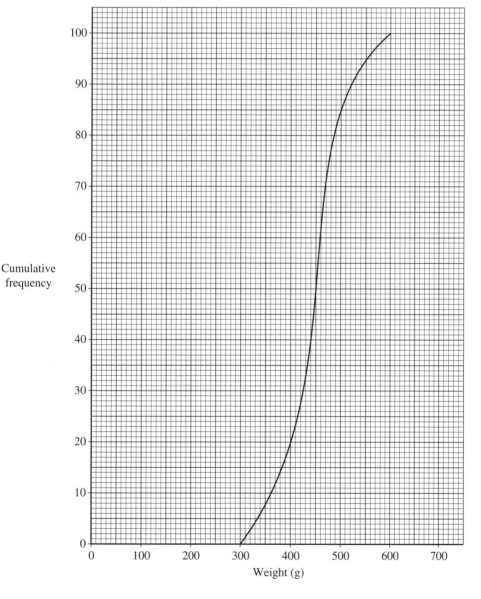

A cumulative frequency distribution of the weights of 100 economy potatoes is given below.

Weight (g)	Cumulative frequency
$0 \leqslant g < 50$	0
$0 \leqslant g < 100$	8
$0 \leqslant g < 200$	37
$0 \leqslant g < 300$	72
$0 \leqslant g < 400$	89
$0 \leqslant g < 500$	100

(a) On a copy of the diagram draw a cumulative frequency curve for economy potatoes.

(b) By comparing the interquartile ranges, comment on the spread of weights of economy and baking potatoes. You must show all your working.   [SEG]

5. The graph shows the number of burglaries in a town between 1985 and 1988.

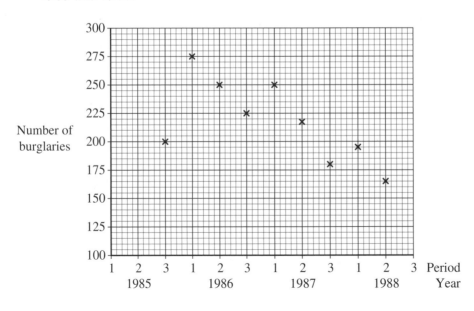

(a) Calculate the 3-point moving averages for the data.

Year	4 monthly period	Number of burglaries
1985	3	200
1986	1	276
	2	250
	3	225
1987	1	250
	2	218
	3	180
1988	1	195
	2	164

(b) Plot the moving averages on a copy of the graph. [SEG]

D5 DATA HANDLING 5

The measure of the link between two variables is called **correlation**.

This unit will show you how to:

- Draw a scatter graph
- Describe correlation
- Draw a line of best fit

Before you start:

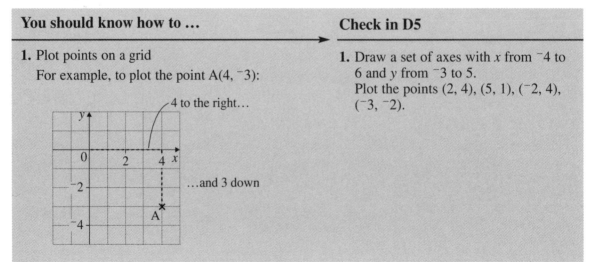

You should know how to ...	Check in D5
1. Plot points on a grid For example, to plot the point A(4, ⁻3):	**1.** Draw a set of axes with x from ⁻4 to 6 and y from ⁻3 to 5. Plot the points (2, 4), (5, 1), (⁻2, 4), (⁻3, ⁻2).

5.1 Scatter graphs

You can illustrate the link between two variables by using a scatter graph.

Example

Barry wants to buy a used Vauxhall Corsa.

He finds the prices of 10 cars.

Draw a scatter graph of the data.

Price of car (£)	3250	1500	220	2400	710	1400	620	2800	1700	1250
Age (years)	2	5	10	4	8	6	9	3	5	7

(2, 3250)...   ...(8, 710)...

Write each pair of values as coordinates with age as *x* and price as *y*

Draw a grid with age along the *x*-axis and price along the *y*-axis

Plot the points; for example, (2, 3250) comes here

Exercise 5A

1. A sample of Year 10 students had their height and weight measured in a survey. The results are given in the table.

Student	A	B	C	D	E	F	G	H
Height (cm)	150	164	157	159	170	176	174	162
Weight (kg)	50	61·5	55·9	56·1	63·8	71·2	68·3	58·4

   Draw a scatter graph for the data.
   Use a scale of 2 cm to represent 5 cm of height on the horizontal axis and a scale of 2 cm to represent 5 kg on the vertical axis.

2. A group of 13 students took examinations in both History and Religious Studies. Their results are recorded in the table.

History (%)	46	56	83	50	89	52	74	84	86	39	48	56	44
Religious studies (%)	55	47	67	70	75	40	83	71	77	53	61	55	51

   Show this information on a scatter graph.
   Use a scale of 1 cm to represent 5 marks on each axis.
   Use the horizontal axis to represent History and the vertical axis to represent Religious Studies.

3. Eight pear trees were measured and the results recorded in the table.

Height (metres)	2·6	2·3	3·2	3·9	4·35	4	4·9	4·85
Circumference (cm)	7	8	13·5	19·5	22	25·5	28·5	31·5

   Draw a scatter graph for the data. Choose your own scale for both axes.

4. A consumer magazine tested a number of different sized cars to find out how far each one would travel on a gallon of petrol. The results are given in the table.

Engine size (litres)	0·8	2·0	1·6	1·0	2·6	1·3	1·8	2·5
Distance travelled (miles)	60	36	45	55	24	51	39	26

Draw a scatter graph for the data. Decide on your own scale.

5. For a trip to Denmark, ten students bought kroner at a particular bank. The table below records the data.

Number of kroner	Cost in pounds
500	38·71
750	56·57
370	28·00
200	17·29
150	13·71
400	31·57
525	40·50
900	67·29
700	53·00
300	24·43

Draw a scatter diagram to show the number of kroner bought and the cost, in pounds.

5.2 Correlation

The scatter graph in the example on page 93 shows a definite link between the two variables:

As age increases, price decreases.

The variables 'age' and 'price' are **correlated**.

However the points do not lie on an exact straight line.

You can say that there is **low correlation** between the variables 'age of car' and 'price'.

This scatter graph shows the number of US dollars you would obtain when exchanging an amount in pounds sterling.

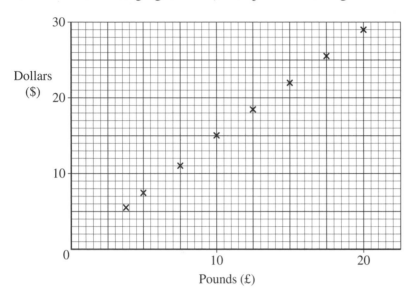

In this graph the points lie in an exact straight line.
The variables 'amount of dollars' and 'amount of pounds' are **perfectly correlated**.
- The closer the points are to a straight line, the higher the degree of correlation.

There are different types of correlation, as illustrated by these scatter graphs.

This graph shows the relationship between height and weight for a sample of children.

One variable increases as the other increases.

This is an example of **positive correlation**.

This graph shows the relationship between age and time taken to run 100 m for a sample of children.

One variable decreases as the other increases.

This is an example of **negative correlation**.

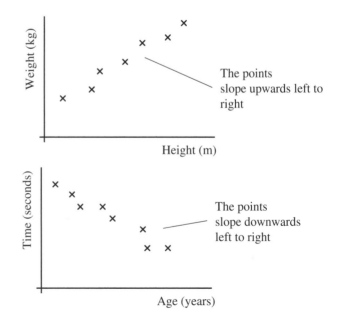

This graph shows the relationship between height of pupils and the distance they travel to school.

There is no pattern linking the variables.

This is an example of **zero correlation**.

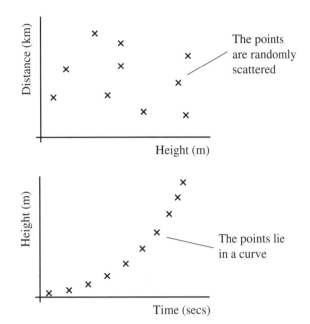

This graph shows the relationship between the height of a stone above ground and the time it takes to fall.

There is a clear relationship between the two variables but it is **non-linear**.

- If two variables are linked so that one **increases** as the other **increases**, the variables are **positively** correlated.

- If two variables are linked so that one **decreases** as the other **increases**, the variables are **negatively** correlated.

Exercise 5B

1–5 For questions 1 to 5 of Exercise 5A, describe the correlation shown by the scatter diagrams that you drew. Use words such as high, low, zero, positive, negative and correlation.

5.3 Line of best fit

If a scatter graph shows correlation, then you can draw a **line of best fit**.

- A line of best fit is the line that passes as close as possible to the points on a scatter graph.

You can use a line of best fit to estimate values.

Example

For the scatter graph of age and price of car on page 93

(a) draw a line of best fit.
(b) Use your line to estimate the likely value of a car that is 5 years old.

(c) Can you estimate the likely value of a car that is 32 years old?
Explain your answer.

(a)

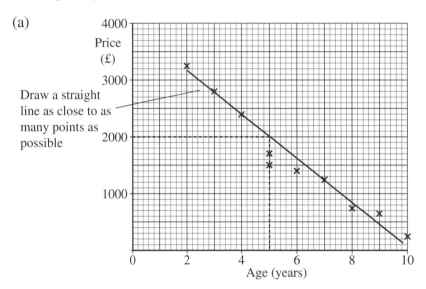

Draw a straight line as close to as many points as possible

Hint:
It helps if you use a transparent ruler.

(b) To estimate the required value from the graph:
- Read along the *x*-axis to the 5-years-old mark.
- Read up until you hit the line of best fit.
- Read along until you hit the price axis.

The likely value of a 5-year-old car is £2000.

Note:
If you extended the graph to include 32 years, the corresponding price would be negative. This means that they would pay you to take the car away!

(c) The data illustrated by the graph gives no values greater than 10 years old. If you used this graph to estimate the value of a car that is 32 years old, the answer would be highly unreliable.

Exercise 5C

1. The diameter and circumference of different sized circular objects were measured.

Diameter (cm)	2·5	4·9	7·6	12·8	14·2	16·1
Circumference (cm)	7·6	15·8	24·5	39·9	44·5	50·6

Draw a scatter graph to show this data and draw the line of best fit.
Use your graph to estimate
(a) the circumference of a circle with diameter 6·4 cm
(b) the diameter of a circle with a circumference of 46·5 cm.

2. The marks of 12 students in a mathematics examination consisting of two papers are given in the table.

Paper 1	30	33	39	42	42	46	50	58	60	60	69	76
Paper 2	41	42	47	48	50	52	54	60	60	62	67	73

Draw a scatter graph to show this data and draw a line of best fit.

Due to illness, two students failed to sit one of the papers.

(i) One student scored a mark of 53 on Paper 1 but missed Paper 2 out.

(ii) Another student scored a mark of 65 on Paper 2 having missed taking Paper 1.

Use your graph to estimate what each of these students might have scored on the paper they failed to sit.

3. The average house price in six districts of a large town is given in the table. (Each price is given to the nearest £1000.)

Detached house (£ thousands)	92	96	103	117	130	135
Semi-detached house (£ thousands)	53	55	60	68	77	81

Draw a scatter graph to show this data and draw a line of best fit.

Use your graph to estimate

(a) the value of a detached property in a district where the semi-detached price is £63 000

(b) the value of a semi-detached property in a district where the value of a detached property is £124 000.

(c) In a rather exclusive district of the same town the average value of a detached property is £350 000. Can you use the graph to estimate the value of a semi-detached property in this district? Explain your answer.

4. Over a seven-day period, the number of ice-creams sold by Chloe on a beach was recorded together with the maximum daily temperature.

Day of the week	Number of ice-creams sold	Maximum temp (°C)
Monday	87	32
Tuesday	68	28
Wednesday	51	24
Thursday	54	25
Friday	83	31
Saturday	76	29
Sunday	91	33

(a) Draw a scatter diagram to show the data.

(b) Draw a line of best fit.

(c) Use your line of best fit to estimate the number of ice-creams sold on the next Monday when the temperature was 27 °C.

5. The scatter diagram shows the heights of sixteen Year 9 boys and their fathers.

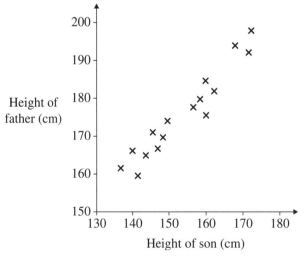

(a) What does the scatter diagram tell you about the relationship between the heights of these boys and their fathers?

(b) Draw a line of best fit on the diagram.

(c) Bill, another Year 9 boy, is 155 cm tall.
Use the diagram to estimate the height of Bill's father.
Explain clearly how you obtained your answer.

Summary

1. You can draw a scatter graph.

2. You can draw the line of best fit and deduce likely data from it.

3. You can decide whether data shows high, low, positive, negative or zero correlation.

Check out D5

1. The maximum temperature, in °C, and the hours of sunshine were recorded on one day in eight towns in Southern England. Draw a scatter graph of the data.

Town	Maximum temp (°C)	Hours of sunshine
A	20	3·4
B	23	4·7
C	24	5·4
D	21	4·3
E	26	6·5
F	27	7·2
G	21	4·1
H	24	4·9

2. (a) Draw the line of best fit for the scatter graph of question **1**.

(b) Another town, J, has 6·8 hours of sunshine that day. What would you expect the maximum temperature to be in town J?

3. Describe the correlation shown in the graphs below.

(a)

(b)

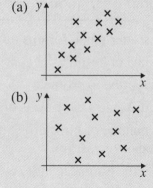

Revision exercise D5

1. The table shows the ages and weights of chickens.

Age (days)	10	20	40	50	70	80	100
Weight (g)	100	300	1000	1300	2000	2000	2400

(a) Use this information to draw a scatter graph.

(b) Draw a line of best fit on the diagram.

(c) (i) Use the line of best fit to estimate the weight of a chicken aged 140 days.

    (ii) Give a reason why your answer may not be very reliable. [SEG]

2. The table gives information about the age and mileage of a number of cars.
The mileages are given to the nearest thousand miles.

Age (years)	1	3	5	3	5	4	7	$4\frac{1}{2}$
Mileage (nearest 1000)	9 000	26 000	46 000	27 000	41 000	39 000	60 000	40 000

(a) Use this information to draw a scatter graph.

(b) What type of correlation is there between the age and mileage of cars?

(c) By drawing a line of best fit estimate the age of a car with a mileage of 54 000. [SEG]

3. The table gives information about the petrol used for car journeys.

Petrol (litres)	3	5	6	8	4	11	10	9	2
Distance (km)	28	50	70	110	50	110	120	130	24

(a) Draw a scatter graph for this information.

(b) Draw a line of best fit.

(c) Use your graph to estimate

    (i) the distance a car travels on 7 litres of petrol

    (ii) the number of litres of petrol used by a car travelling a distance of 150 km.

(d) Which of the estimates in (c) is likely to be more reliable? Give a reason for your answer. [SEG]

D6 DATA HANDLING 6

Probability is a measure of how likely a particular outcome is to occur.

This unit will show you how to:

- Use relative frequency
- Calculate with equally likely outcomes
- Calculate with independent events
- Calculate with mutually exclusive outcomes
- Draw a tree diagram
- Use expected frequency

Before you start:

You should know how to …	Check in D6
1. Complete a tally chart	**1.** The number of of cold drinks which 15 friends drank on one summer day were: 3, 4, 1, 6, 6, 4, 7, 2, 4, 3, 2, 6, 4, 6, 4. Record this data in a tally chart.
2. Calculate with fractions For example, $\frac{2}{5} + \frac{1}{3}$ $\times 3 \left(\right) \times 5$ $= \frac{6}{15} + \frac{5}{15}$ $= \frac{11}{15}$	**2.** Find the value of (a) $\frac{1}{6} + \frac{1}{3}$ (b) $\frac{1}{3} \times \frac{1}{4}$ (c) $\frac{2}{5} \times \frac{3}{8}$

MODULE 1

6.1 Probability scale

Uncertain situations are often described using **probability**. An **event** is a situation that can have a number of possible results.

These possible results are called **outcomes**, and each outcome will occur with a given probability.

Probabilities can take any value between 0 and 1. They should be expressed either as fractions, decimals or percentages.

This **probability scale** shows a range of probabilities expressed as fractions.

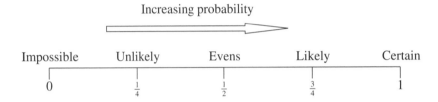

Example

Mark the probabilities of these outcomes on a probability scale.

(a) One day every year is 26 hours long.

(b) England has won the football World Cup at least once.

(c) A playing card picked from a complete well-shuffled pack is a Diamond.

(d) You will score a five if you roll an ordinary dice.

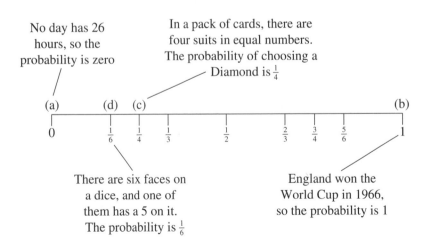

Exercise 6A

1. Use the words impossible, very unlikely, unlikely, evens, likely, very likely and certain to describe each of these events.

   (a) It will rain next Monday.

   (b) You will be involved in a road accident within the next month.

   (c) The next baby to be born in the maternity ward will be male.

   (d) Snow will fall in England on Christmas Day.

   (e) The colour of a banana skin is bright red.

   (f) The next time you roll an ordinary dice it will land on 2.

2. Draw a probability scale and mark where the probability of each of the following events should be placed.

   (a) Someone in your family will win the National Lottery grand prize.

   (b) It will be dark tonight.

   (c) The next time you toss a coin it will land on heads.

   (d) Your pet cat will live for ever.

   (e) You will watch television today.

   (f) You will use a calculator this week.

3. In her purse, Alice has one each of the four coins, £1, 20p, 10p and 5p.
   She picks out a coin at random.
   What is the probability that Alice picks the 20p coin?

4. A pack of cards contains 12 Hearts, 12 Diamonds, 12 Spades and 12 Clubs.
   Henry picks out a card at random.
   What is the probability of picking a red card?

5. The probability of a train being late is $\frac{3}{4}$.
   What is the probability of the train not being late?

6.2 Experimental probability

You can estimate unknown probabilities by performing an **experiment**.

Example 1

Toss two coins simultaneously and record the result. Repeat the experiment 100 times and record your results in a tally chart.

Use your results to estimate the probability of obtaining two heads when two coins are tossed.

Faces shown	Tally	Frequency
Tail and Tail	ЖЖ ЖЖ ЖЖ ЖЖ I	21
Tail and Head	ЖЖ ЖЖ ЖЖ ЖЖ ЖЖ ЖЖ ЖЖ ЖЖ ЖЖ III	48
Head and Head	ЖЖ ЖЖ ЖЖ ЖЖ ЖЖ ЖЖ I	31

From the tally chart, 31 results out of 100 give two heads.

Probability of obtaining two heads $= \dfrac{31}{100} = 0.31$.

The estimated probability of obtaining two heads is 0·31.

In the example, the experiment was repeated a large number of times to ensure accuracy in estimating the probability. Each repetition is called a **trial**.

● You can use a formula to estimate probabilities from an experiment:

$$\text{Estimated probability} = \frac{\text{Number of successful trials}}{\text{Total number of trials}}$$

This estimated probability is also called **relative frequency**.

Relative frequency can be used to test whether a game of chance is fair. For example, tossing a coin a large number of times can test whether it is biased.

Example 2

A dice is suspected of being biased. It was rolled 400 times and after every 25 rolls the number of ones obtained was recorded. The results were:

4, 5, 5, 2, 3, 2, 8, 4, 3, 3, 4, 7, 2, 3, 5, 5

The relative frequency of ones was calculated, and the table gives the results.

Remember:
Bias means a tendency towards a particular outcome or view. There is more about bias on page 5.

MODULE 1

Number of trials	Number of successful outcomes	Relative frequency
25	4	$\frac{4}{25} = 0{\cdot}16$
50	9	$\frac{9}{50} = 0{\cdot}18$
75	14	$\frac{14}{75} = 0{\cdot}187$
100	16	$\frac{16}{100} = 0{\cdot}16$
125	19	$\frac{19}{125} = 0{\cdot}152$
150	21	$\frac{21}{150} = 0{\cdot}14$
175	29	$\frac{29}{175} = 0{\cdot}166$
200	33	$\frac{33}{200} = 0{\cdot}165$
225	36	$\frac{36}{225} = 0{\cdot}16$
250	39	$\frac{39}{250} = 0{\cdot}156$
275	43	$\frac{43}{275} = 0{\cdot}156$
300	50	$\frac{50}{300} = 0{\cdot}167$
325	52	$\frac{52}{325} = 0{\cdot}16$
350	55	$\frac{55}{350} = 0{\cdot}157$
375	60	$\frac{60}{375} = 0{\cdot}16$
400	65	$\frac{65}{400} = 0{\cdot}163$

These results are shown on the graph.

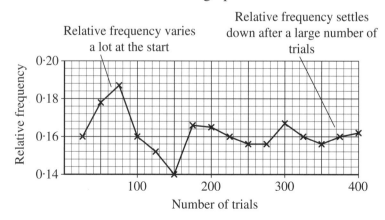

Relative frequency varies a lot at the start

Relative frequency settles down after a large number of trials

The graph shows that the relative frequency of rolling a 1 settles down to around 0·16.

If the dice was fair, you would expect a probability of
$\frac{1}{6} = 0.166\,667$.

The relative frequency is very close to the expected probability,
so it is reasonable to assume that the dice is fair.

Exercise 6B

To complete the following exercise you will need a dice and a
pack of playing cards.

1. Roll a dice 10 times and record the number of threes rolled.
   Repeat the experiment 6 times and record your results in a
   tally chart as follows.

Number of trials	Tally	Frequency	Relative frequency
10			
20			
30			
40			
50			
60			

   (a) Draw a graph of relative frequency against number of trials.
   (b) Use your results to estimate the probability of rolling a 3.
   (c) Is your dice fair or biased?

2. You will need a normal pack of 52 playing cards.
   In this experiment you will draw a card at random from the
   pack, and then replace it randomly in the pack.
   You will repeat this 100 times.
   (a) Make a prediction for the frequency of each of these four
       events: Ace, picture card, even number, odd number.
   (b) Copy the tally chart and record the results as you carry
       out the experiment.

Card drawn	Tally	Frequency
Ace		
Picture		
Even number		
Odd number		

(c) How close to your predicted frequency were the actual results from the experiment?
(d) Use your results from the experiment to estimate the probability that the result will be
  (i) an Ace
  (ii) a picture card
  (iii) an even-numbered card
  (iv) an odd-numbered card.
(e) Which event, from your results, is least likely to happen?
(f) Which event, from your results, is most likely to happen?

3. Laura and Alex play noughts and crosses games. Laura keeps a note of her results. Out of the first 10 games Laura wins 7. Out of the first 40 games Laura wins 24 games. Use these results to estimate the probability that Laura will win her next game of noughts and crosses with Alex.

4. A playing card is drawn from a pack and the result recorded. The card is then replaced in the pack and the pack reshuffled. After many trials the relative frequency of drawing a Spade is found to be 0·35. Do you think this pack is fair? Give a reason for your answer.

5. A spinner has an equal chance of giving any one of the digits from 1 to 8. Five pupils were asked to test the spinner before it was used at a Summer Fayre.

Each pupil spun the spinner a number of times and recorded the number of sevens they obtained. The results are given in the table.

	Number of spins	**Number of sevens**	**Relative frequency**
Mary	10	4	0.2
Jayne	100	9	0.09
Mike	250	45	0.18
Bill	450	59	0.131
Dominic	1000	117	0.117

One person incorrectly recorded their results for the spinner. Which person do you think recorded their results incorrectly? Give a reason for your answer.

6. A coloured bead is taken at random out of a bag. The colour of the bead is recorded and the bead is then replaced in the bag. This experiment is repeated 400 times. The number of blue beads taken from the bag after every 100 trials is recorded in the table.

Number of trials	Number of blue beads taken
100	38
200	82
300	121
400	158

(a) Calculate the relative frequency after each 100 trials.
(b) Use your calculations to estimate the probability of drawing a blue bead from the bag.

6.3 Equally likely outcomes

There are two types of probability: **experimental** (explained in the previous section) and **theoretical**.
Theoretical probabilities are based on an **assumption**, often that all possible outcomes are equally likely.

Theoretical probability saves you having to roll dice hundreds of times!

● If all outcomes are equally likely:

$$\text{Probability of a particular outcome} = \frac{\text{Number of times the outcome can occur}}{\text{Total number of possible outcomes}}$$

Example

A survey on favourite TV soap operas is carried out amongst a class of pupils.

The table shows the numbers of boys and girls who prefer watching EastEnders, Friends or Neighbours, or none of these.

	Boys	Girls
EastEnders	5	4
Friends	1	7
Neighbours	2	3
None of these	8	0

A pupil is drawn at random from this class.

(a) What is the probability that the pupil is a girl?
(b) What is the probability that a boy is chosen who prefers Friends?
(c) What is the probability that the pupil prefers Neighbours?
(d) What is the probability that the pupil chosen prefers Friends or Neighbours?

> **Note:**
> The assumption is that all pupils are equally likely to be chosen.

There are 16 boys and 14 girls in this class.

A pupil is chosen at random so there are $(16 + 14) = 30$ equally likely outcomes.

> **Note:**
> You can use P( ) to stand for probability. The outcome goes inside the brackets.

(a) $\text{P(choosing a girl)} = \dfrac{14}{30} = \dfrac{7}{15}$

(b) There is one boy who prefers Friends.

$\therefore \text{P(choosing a boy who prefers Friends)} = \dfrac{1}{30}$

(c) Neighbours is preferred by $(2 + 3) = 5$ pupils.

$\therefore \text{P(pupil prefers Neighbours)} = \dfrac{5}{30} = \dfrac{1}{6}$

(d)   Friends or Neighbours are preferred by $(1 + 7 + 2 + 3) = 13$ pupils.

$\therefore \text{P(pupil prefers either Friends or Neighbours)} = \dfrac{13}{30}$

Exercise 6C

1. A card is chosen at random from a full pack of playing cards, with no Jokers. What is the probability that the chosen card is
   (a) a red card
   (b) a spade
   (c) the seven of hearts
   (d) not a Diamond?

2. A normal dice is rolled. What is the probability of obtaining
   (a) a five
   (b) an even number
   (c) a number greater than four
   (d) a number less than five?

3. The letters of the word PERCENTAGE are written on separate cards. The cards are then shuffled and dealt face down onto a table. A card is selected at random. What is the probability that the card selected is

(a) the letter R   (b) the letter E   (c) a vowel?

4. In a Christmas raffle, 2500 tickets are sold. Gabriella buys 20, Craig buys 100, Peta buys 60 and Rashid buys 75.
There is one winning ticket.
Writing your answers in their simplest form, what is the probability that

(a) Gabriella wins

(b) Craig wins

(c) Peta wins

(d) Rashid wins?

5. A 'Pick and Mix' bag of sweets contains 7 toffees, 3 spearmints, 6 fruit gums, 4 hazelnut whirls and 8 mini chocolate bars. One sweet is chosen at random from the bag. What is the probability that the sweet will be

(a) a spearmint

(b) a hazelnut whirl

(c) a mini chocolate bar

(d) a fruit gum or a toffee

(e) not a toffee?

6. The table shows the lunchtime eating preferences of a class of 30 pupils.

	Boys	**Girls**
Eat school dinner	9	10
Eat sandwiches	5	6

A pupil from the class is chosen at random.
What is the probability that the pupil

(a) is a boy

(b) is a girl who eats school dinner

(c) does not eat sandwiches?

A girl from the class is chosen at random.

(d) What is the probability that she eats sandwiches?

MODULE 1

7. A bag contains 6 red counters, 9 blue counters and 5 yellow counters. A counter is taken from the bag at random.
   What is the probability that the counter is
   (a) yellow
   (b) not blue
   (c) red or blue
   (d) red, blue or yellow
   (e) purple?

8. A cash bag contains two 50p coins, five 20p coins, four 10p coins, six 5p coins, one 2p coin and two 1p coins. One coin is selected at random.
   What is the probability that the coin chosen will be
   (a) a 20p coin
   (b) a coin less than the 20p coin in value
   (c) a silver coin?

9. A bag contains 20 red balls, 20 white balls and 20 black balls. Six red balls, seven white balls and eleven black balls are taken out of the bag and not replaced. What is the probability that the next ball randomly chosen from the bag will be red?

10. Twenty discs numbered from 1 to 20 are placed in a bag and one disc is drawn out at random.
    What is the probability that the disc drawn out is
    (a) a number that divides by 5
    (b) a square number
    (c) a number smaller than 16
    (d) a prime number?

6.4 Compound events

When two or more events occur together, you can call it a **compound event**. To find probabilities associated with compound events you need to list all possible outcomes, perhaps in a table or a **sample space diagram**.

Example

A 20p coin is tossed and a normal dice is rolled at the same time.

(a) List all the possible outcomes in a sample space diagram.
(b) Find the probability of obtaining a tail and an odd number.

(a) The possible outcomes can be written in a sample space diagram.

Dice outcome

		1	2	3	4	5	6
Coin outcome	**H**	H1	H2	H3	H4	H5	H6
	T	T1	T2	T3	T4	T5	T6

H = Head and T = Tail

Note:

A sample space diagram is just a table that shows all combinations of two events.

(b) There are three outcomes that give a tail and an odd number: T1, T3 and T5.

There are 12 outcomes altogether.

Probability of a tail and an odd number $= \frac{3}{12} = \frac{1}{4}$

Exercise 6D

1. One day of the week is chosen at random.
   (a) List all the possible outcomes.
   (b) How many of the outcomes begin with the letter T?

2. Five friends, Anna, Bill, Clive, David and Eileen, each write their name on a card and the five cards are placed in a hat. Two cards are chosen at random. List all the possible choices.

3. The menu in a restaurant has two choices of starter, three main courses and two choices of dessert, as shown.

```
                    MENU

    Starters
            Soup              (A)
            Melon             (B)

    Main Courses
            Gammon            (C)
            Fish and Chips    (D)
            Lasagne           (E)

    Desserts
            Apple Pie         (F)
            Ice Cream         (G)
```

List all of the different combinations that could be chosen from this menu.

4. Four girls, Fiona, Geeta, Heidi and Irene, enter the 800 metres race on Sports Day.
   (a) List all the different ways in which the race could finish.
   (b) In how many of these different ways does Heidi finish in front of Fiona?

5. A blue dice and a green dice, each numbered from 1 to 6, are rolled together.
   (a) Draw a sample space diagram to show all the possible outcomes.
   (b) How many of these results give a total of 8 when the scores on the two dice are added together?

6. Three coins, 20p, 20p and 50p, are tossed together. List all the different ways in which these coins could land.

7. A blue spinner and a red spinner are spun together.
   (a) List all the possible outcomes.
   (b) In how many ways is it possible to obtain a total of 5 when the scores on the two spinners are added together?

 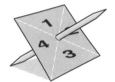

8. Four coins are tossed together. List all the different possible outcomes.
   (a) How many different outcomes are possible?
   (b) How many of these outcomes contain exactly two heads and two tails?

9. A game uses both a spinner and a dice at the same time. A win results when the number on the spinner is greater than or equal to the number showing on the dice.
   (a) Draw a sample space diagram to show all the possible outcomes.
   (b) In how many ways can a win happen?

10. Inter-form group competitions are organised by the PE department at a school. All eight forms must play each other once during the next seven weeks. Matches take place every Monday lunchtime and four games have to be played at the same time. The matches on week 1 could be

    Form A v Form B
    Form C v Form D
    Form E v Form F
    Form G v Form H

Work out a possible match schedule for the remaining six weeks so that all teams will have played each other.

Check carefully that each form team has played each other team once only.

11. Brian and Marion are travelling to France on holiday. They can travel from their home to the English coast by car, coach or train.

They are able to cross the English channel using the ferry, channel tunnel, catamaran or helicopter.
   (a) Draw a sample space diagram to show all the different possible ways to travel from their home to France.
   (b) How many different travel possibilities are available to Brian and Marion?

6.5 Mutually exclusive outcomes

Mutually exclusive outcomes *cannot* occur at the same time.

When a teacher takes the class register, each student can either be recorded as present or absent. It is not possible to be absent and present at the same time.

'Present' and 'absent' are mutually exclusive outcomes.

Probability rules for mutually exclusive outcomes
- When two outcomes, A and B, are mutually exclusive:
  P(A or B) = P(A) + P(B)

- The probabilities of all mutually exclusive outcomes add up to 1.

- For **any** outcome A:
  P(A does not occur) = 1 − P(A)

This is known as the **addition law** in probability.
It is sometimes called the OR rule.

Example
A dice is rolled. What is the probability of rolling
(a) a three
(b) not a three
(c) an even number
(d) not an even number?

(a) There are six equally likely outcomes when rolling a dice:
1, 2, 3, 4, 5 and 6.

$$P(3) = \tfrac{1}{6}$$

(b) $P(\text{not a } 3) = 1 - P(3)$
$$= 1 - \tfrac{1}{6}$$
$$= \tfrac{5}{6}$$

(c) There are three even numbers on a dice: 2, 4 and 6.

$$P(\text{even number}) = \tfrac{3}{6}$$
$$= \tfrac{1}{2}$$

(d) $P(\text{not an even number}) = 1 - P(\text{even number})$
$$= 1 - \tfrac{1}{2}$$
$$= \tfrac{1}{2}$$

Exercise 6E

1. State whether or not each of the following pairs of events are mutually exclusive.

(a) Eating a hot school dinner; eating sandwiches for dinner.

(b) Watching TV; going to the cinema.

(c) Sitting next to a left-handed person; sitting next to a person with brown eyes.

(d) Being a supporter of Manchester United; being a supporter of Everton.

(e) Getting an even number with a dice; getting an odd number with a dice.

(f) The weather is warm today; the weather is windy today.

2. When a five-sided spinner is spun, what is the probability of getting

(a) a three

(b) not a three

(c) an even number

(d) not an even number?

3. Natasha can go home from school by car, by bus or on foot. The probability that she will go home by car is 0·5 and on foot is 0·1.

What is the probability that she will go home by bus?

4. Eleven counters numbered 2 to 12 are put into a bag. One counter is selected at random from the bag.
   What is the probability of getting a counter with
   (a) a number 7
   (b) an even number
   (c) not an even number
   (d) a square number
   (e) a multiple of 4
   (f) a prime number?

5. In a raffle, 1500 tickets are sold. Brian buys 20 tickets.
   (a) What is his chance of winning the raffle?
   (b) Jenny buys tickets for the same raffle. She knows that her chance of winning the raffle is 0·005.
       What is the probability of her not winning?

6. A survey found that 9 out of 100 women measured were taller than 1·70 metres. A woman is picked at random from this group of women. What is the probability that she is not taller than 1·70 metres?

7. Live birth statistics show that the probability of a woman giving birth to a girl is 0·494.
   What is the probability of the birth being a boy?

8. At a school sports day, it is estimated that the probability that Mohammed will win his race is 25%. What is the probability that Mohammed will not win his race?

9. The Ace of Hearts is removed from a normal pack of playing cards. One card is selected from the remaining cards. What is the probability of
   (a) choosing an Ace
   (b) not choosing an Ace
   (c) choosing a Heart?

10. A bag contains a large number of balls, each coloured blue, green, red or white. The probabilities of selecting each colour are given in the table.

Colour	Blue	Green	Red	White
Probability	0·15		0·4	0·35

What is the probability of choosing a ball that is
(a) green   (b) not red?

6.6 Independent events

● Two events are **independent** if the outcome of one event is unaffected by the outcome of the other.

For example, when two coins are tossed together the outcome of a 'head' on the first coin does not affect the possible outcome on the second coin. These two events are independent.

● When two events, A and B, are independent you can calculate the probability that both A and B happen by using the **multiplication law**:

$$P(A \text{ and } B) = P(A) \times P(B)$$

Note:
The multiplication law is also called the AND rule.

Example 1

A fair coin is tossed and a fair 5-sided spinner spun. Find the probability that a tail and a 4 will be obtained.
Both events (tossing the coin and spinning the spinner) are independent.

$$P(\text{Tail}) = \tfrac{1}{2}, \quad P(4) = \tfrac{1}{5}$$

Using the multiplication law for independent events:

$$P(\text{Tail and } 4) = P(\text{Tail}) \times P(4)$$
$$= \tfrac{1}{2} \times \tfrac{1}{5}$$
$$= \tfrac{1}{10}$$

Note:
You could also work this out by using a sample space diagram.

Example 2

A dice is rolled and a card is drawn from a normal pack of 52 playing cards. What is the probability that a 5 and a Diamond will be obtained?
These events are independent so use the multiplication law.

$$P(5) = \tfrac{1}{6}, \quad P(\text{Diamond}) = \tfrac{13}{52} = \tfrac{1}{4}$$

$$P(5 \text{ and Diamond}) = P(5) \times P(\text{Diamond})$$
$$= \tfrac{1}{6} \times \tfrac{1}{4}$$
$$= \tfrac{1}{24}$$

Exercise 6F

1. Two fair dice are rolled. What is the probability of obtaining a 4 on each of the dice?

2. A card is drawn from a normal pack of 52 playing cards and a dice is rolled. What is the probability of obtaining
   (a) an ace and a 5 on the dice
   (b) a black card and an even number on the dice
   (c) a picture card and a prime number on the dice?

3. The letters of the word STATISTICS are written on individual cards and placed in a box. One card is selected from the box, the letter noted and then replaced in the box. A second card is then selected from the box.

   What is the probability of obtaining
   (a) the letter 'C' twice
   (b) the letter 'S' twice
   (c) a consonant twice
   (d) a vowel twice?

4. Kingswinford Ladies netball team have a probability of $\frac{2}{5}$ that they will lose any match. What is the probability that they will lose the next two netball matches they play?

5. A bag contains 4 red beads, 5 blue beads and 6 black beads. One bead is taken out of the bag and not replaced. A second bead is then taken from the bag. What is the probability that
   (a) two red beads are chosen
   (b) two blue beads are chosen
   (c) a red bead and a black bead are chosen?

6. James and Gemma toss a coin to find out who does the washing up after tea during the week (Monday to Friday). James does the washing up if it is heads, and Gemma does it if the coin lands tails.

   What is the probability that Gemma does the washing up every day for one week?

7. A coin is biased so that a tail result occurs with a probability of $\frac{2}{5}$. The same coin is tossed four times.
   What is the probability of obtaining
   (a) a tail on the first two tosses
   (b) a head result for each of the first three tosses
   (c) a head, a tail, a head and a tail in that order?

8. Two dice are rolled and the scores recorded. Calculate the probability that
    (a) the sum of the dice scores will be 9
    (b) the difference between the dice scores will be 2
    (c) the scores on each dice will be the same.

9. A spinner in the shape of a regular octagon has the numbers 1, 2, 3, 4, 5, 6, 7 and 8 written on it.
   The spinner is spun twice and the numbers landed on are added together.
   Calculate the probability that the total score will be

    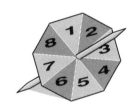

    (a) 3
    (b) 7
    (c) an odd number
    (d) at least 9.

6.7 Tree diagrams

You can use a **tree diagram** to find probabilities associated with compound events. Sometimes this can be better than a sample space diagram, particularly when a situation involves more than two events.

If you toss two fair coins together, you could illustrate all possible outcomes with a sample space diagram.

		Second coin	
		H	**T**
First coin	**H**	HH	HT
	T	TH	TT

H = heads, T = tails

However, this diagram does not give you the probabilities for each outcome.

A tree diagram for this situation would look like this.

First coin   **Second coin**

$\frac{1}{2}$ ———— Head

Head

$\frac{1}{2}$ ———— Tail

$\frac{1}{2}$

$\frac{1}{2}$ ———— Head

Tail

$\frac{1}{2}$ ———— Tail

> Probabilities are written on the branches; outcomes are written at the ends of the branches.

You can also list the outcomes on the diagram, together with the probability for each outcome.

First coin	**Second coin**	**Outcome**	**Probability**
	Head	(Head, Head)	$\frac{1}{2} \times \frac{1}{2} = \frac{1}{4}$
Head			
	Tail	(Head, Tail)	$\frac{1}{2} \times \frac{1}{2} = \frac{1}{4}$
	Head	(Tail, Head)	$\frac{1}{2} \times \frac{1}{2} = \frac{1}{4}$
Tail			
	Tail	(Tail, Tail)	$\frac{1}{2} \times \frac{1}{2} = \frac{1}{4}$

Example

Two fair coins are tossed simultaneously. Use a tree diagram to find the probability of obtaining

(a) two heads
(b) one head and one tail.

(a) Probability of tossing two heads:

$$P(\text{Head and Head}) = P(\text{Head}) \times P(\text{Head})$$
$$= \frac{1}{2} \times \frac{1}{2}$$
$$= \frac{1}{4}$$

Hint:
There are two paths:

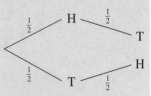

Remember:
And means $\times$
Or means $+$

(b) Probability of tossing one head and one tail:

P(one head and one tail) = P(Head **and** Tail) **or** P(Tail **and** Head)

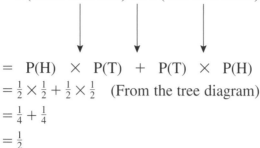

$$= \text{P(H)} \times \text{P(T)} + \text{P(T)} \times \text{P(H)}$$
$$= \tfrac{1}{2} \times \tfrac{1}{2} + \tfrac{1}{2} \times \tfrac{1}{2} \quad \text{(From the tree diagram)}$$
$$= \tfrac{1}{4} + \tfrac{1}{4}$$
$$= \tfrac{1}{2}$$

Exercise 6G

1. A bag contains 5 black counters and 3 yellow counters. A counter is selected at random from the bag and then replaced. A second counter is then selected from the bag.

First counter	Second counter	Outcome	Probability

(a) Copy and complete the tree diagram, showing all the outcomes and their probabilities.

(b) Calculate the probability that both counters selected are black.

(c) Calculate the probability that both counters selected are yellow.

(d) Calculate the probability that at least one counter is yellow.

2. Two youth clubs join together for a disco. Dales youth club has 28 boys and 32 girls whilst Coseley youth club has 23 boys and 17 girls. Two people are chosen at random, one from each youth cub, to organise the disco.

(a) Draw a tree diagram to show the outcomes and their probabilities.

(b) Use your tree diagram to calculate the probability of
   (i) choosing two girls
   (ii) choosing a boy and a girl.

3. Bill is frequently late for school and his teacher calculates that the probability he will be late on any school day is 0·35. Use a tree diagram to calculate the probability that on three consecutive days
(a) he is late each day
(b) he is not late on any of the days
(c) he is late only once.

4. Denise is good at sport. The probability that Denise will win the form high jump competition is 0·6 and the probability that she will win the 200 metres is 0·2. Draw a tree diagram to show the outcomes when Denise takes part in these two events. Use your tree diagram to calculate the probability that
(a) Denise wins both the high jump and the 200 metres
(b) Denise wins only one of the two events.

5. An ordinary fair dice is rolled twice. Calculate the probability that the dice will land on a 5 on both occasions.

6. Bag A contains 4 yellow counters, 5 red counters and 3 white counters. Bag B contains 3 yellow counters, 5 red counters and 4 white counters. A counter is chosen at random from each bag.
Calculate the probability that
(a) both counters will be white
(b) the counter from bag A will be yellow and the counter from bag B will be red
(c) neither counter will be white.

7. A fair eight-faced dice is numbered 0, 1, 2, 3, 4, 5, 6 and 7. When the dice is rolled the result is the number shown on the upper face. The dice is rolled twice.
What is the probability of obtaining
(a) a number 5 on both rolls
(b) a number less than 3 on both rolls
(c) the same number on both rolls?

8. The probability that a school netball team will win a match is 55%. Draw a tree diagram to show the outcomes for the next three school netball match results. Use your tree diagram to calculate the probability that the school netball team
(a) wins the next three matches
(b) loses the next three matches
(c) wins two out of the next three matches.

6.8 Expected frequency

In this unit you have learned how to calculate the probability of an outcome for different types of event.
You can use this knowledge to estimate the number of times a particular outcome should occur. This is also known as the **expected frequency**.

- For a given number of trials in an experiment:

  Expected frequency = Probability of outcome × Number of trials

Example

A fair coin is tossed 450 times. How many times would you expect to obtain a head?

Assuming equally likely outcomes, $P(\text{Head}) = \frac{1}{2}$.

Expected number of heads $= \frac{1}{2} \times 450 = 225$.

Exercise 6H

1. The probability that someone in the population is right-handed is estimated to be 0·79. Give an estimate for the number of right-handed people in a village with a population of 1500 people.

2. A fair dice is rolled 150 times. How many times would you expect to obtain
   (a) a 5   (b) an odd number   (c) a number smaller than 5?

3. A bag contains 6 balls numbered 1 to 6. A second bag contains 7 coloured balls: 4 black, 2 green and 1 white. A ball is randomly selected from both bags and then returned to the original bag. Copy and complete the table which gives the possible outcomes.

Numbered ball

	1	2	3	4	5	6
Black, B						B6
Black, B						
Black, B		B2				
Black, B	B1					
Green, G				G4		
Green, G						
White, W						

Coloured ball

B6 means Black and 6 are drawn

(a) Use the results table to find the probability of selecting
   (i)   a black ball and a 3
   (ii) a green ball
   (iii) a number above 4.

(b) If this experiment was carried out 450 times, how many times would you expect to obtain
   (i) a white ball
   (ii) a ball numbered 2 or 5?

4. New batteries fitted to cars are known to have a probability of 0·002 of being faulty. The company who supplies these batteries manufactures 2 500 000 each year.
    Estimate the number of batteries produced each year that are liable to be faulty.

5. Bill completed a survey for people entering a post office over a 40-minute time period. He counted 38 men and 62 women entering the post office.
    (a) Estimate the probability that the next person entering the post office will be a woman.
    (b) During the day 1800 people entered the post office. How many of these people would be expected to be men?

6. Two coloured triangular spinners are spun and the results are added together.

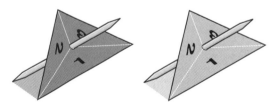

    (a) List all the possible outcomes.
    (b) How many of these outcomes have a total score of 4?
    (c) Estimate how many times a total score of 4 or more would be expected if the spinners were spun together 300 times.

7. Raffle tickets are sold for the school Christmas Fayre. 650 yellow, 400 white and 450 purple tickets are sold.
    All of these tickets are placed in a barrel and tickets are drawn at random from the barrel.
    (a) What is the probability that the first ticket to be drawn is white?
    (b) 30 prizes are given away in the raffle.
        How many prize winners would you expect to have a white ticket?

8. Pupils spend 15 minutes outside a school observing the traffic passing by the school gate. During that time 6 buses, 14 vans, 5 lorries and 45 cars pass by the gate.
   (a) What is the probability that the next vehicle passing the gate will be a lorry?
   (b) If pupils had spent an hour at the gate observing the traffic,
       (i) how many vehicles would be estimated to be seen passing by the gate?
       (ii) how many vehicles would be expected to be cars?
   (c) Another group of pupils spent 15 minutes observing traffic at the school gate and recorded 18 buses passing the gate. How many vans would be estimated to pass by the gate during this 15-minute period?

Summary

1. You understand a probability scale.

2. You can find an estimated probability.

3. You can find the expected probability when outcomes are equally likely.

4. You know the meaning of mutually exclusive events and independent events.

5. You can complete a sample space diagram.

Check out D6

1. Place the following three events on a probability scale.
   (a) I will win the lottery this week.
   (b) I will get up tomorrow.
   (c) The sun will shine tomorrow.

2. You toss a biased dice and have 37 sixes from 50 throws.
   Find an estimate for the probability of getting a six on the next throw.

3. What is the probability of getting
   (a) any queen when picking one card from a pack of playing cards
   (b) an even number when rolling an unbiased dice?

4. If the probability of getting a six on a biased dice is $\frac{1}{3}$, what is the probability of not getting a six?

5. You can travel to meet your friend by bus, car, train or bicycle, and you can arrive earlier or later than expected.
   Complete a sample space diagram to show the possible outcomes.

6. You can find a relative frequency.

6. There are 250 people watching a football match and 72 are female.
What is the relative frequency of a spectator being female?

7. You can estimate the number of successful outcomes.

7. The probability of a marathon runner picking up a drink at a check point is 0.23. 700 people pass the check point. How many drinks are estimated to be needed?

8. You can use a tree diagram to find probabilities.

8. (a) You roll two dice.
What is the probability of getting
(i) 2 sixes (ii) one six (iii) no sixes?

    (b) The probability that Alex uses a bus to go to school is $\frac{2}{3}$. Alternatively he travels by train.
If Alex goes by bus the probability of being late is $\frac{1}{4}$; if he goes by train the probability of being late is $\frac{1}{5}$.
What is the probability of Alex being late?

Revision exercise D6

1. The diagram shows two sets of cards.

Set *A*

     1   **2**   **3**

Set *B*

     2   **3**   **4**

One card is taken from each set at random.
(a) List all the possible outcomes.

(b) The numbers on the cards are added together to give a score.
What is the probability of getting a score of 6?   [SEG]

2. An office has two photocopiers, *A* and *B*.
On any one day

    the probability that *A* is working is 0·8,
    the probability that *B* is working is 0·9.

(a) Calculate the probability that, on any one day, both photocopiers will be working.

(b) Calculate the probability that, on any one day, only one of the photocopiers will be working.   [SEG]

3. The table shows information about a group of adults.

	Can drive	Cannot drive
Male	32	8
Female	38	12

(a) One of these adults is chosen at random.
What is the probability that the adult can drive?

(b) A man in the group is chosen at random.
What is the probability that he can drive?

(c) A woman in the group is chosen at random.
The probability that she can drive is 0·76.
What is the probability that she cannot drive?

(d) Does the information given support the statement:
'More women can drive than men'?   [SEG]
Explain your answer.

4. The table shows information about a group of children.

		Boys	Girls
Wears glasses	**Yes**	5	3
	No	14	10

(a) A boy in the group is chosen at random.
What is the probability that he wears glasses?   [SEG]

(b) A child in the group is chosen at random.
The probability that the child wears glasses is 0·25.
What is the probability that the child does not wear glasses?

5. The table shows the probability for the delivery time of
letters posted first class.

Delivery time (days)	1	2	3 or more
Probability	0·7	0·2	0·1

(a) 100 letters are posted first class.
How many will be delivered in 1 or 2 days?

(b) Two letters are posted first class in different towns.
What is the probability that only one will be delivered
in one day?   [SEG]

6. Two fair spinners are numbered as shown.

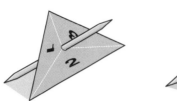 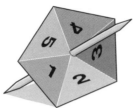

Both spinners are spun once.

(a) Calculate the probability that both spinners land on a 3.

(b) Calculate the probability that both spinners land on an odd number.

(c) Calculate the probability that neither spinner lands on an odd number. [SEG]

7. A sack contains a number of gold and silver discs.
An experiment consists of taking a disc from the sack at random, recording its colour and then replacing it.
The experiment is repeated 10, 50, 100, 150 and 200 times.
The table shows the results.

Number of experiments	10	50	100	150	200
Number of gold discs	3	8	23	30	38

(a) Draw a graph to show how the relative frequency of a gold disc changes as the number of experiments increases.

(b) The sack contains 1000 discs.
Estimate the number of gold discs in the sack. [SEG]

8. The diagram shows two sets of cards.

Set *A*   Set *B*

| 1 | 2 | 3 | | 2 | 4 | 6 |

(a) A card is taken at random from set *A* and another from set *B*.

(i) List all the possible outcomes.

The numbers on the two cards taken are added together to give a score.

(ii) What is the probability of getting a score which is an odd number?

(iii) What is the probability of getting a score which is not an odd number?

(b) The cards in set *A* are red.
The cards in set *B* are blue.
All the cards are shuffled together.
One card is taken at random.
(i)　What is the probability that it is a red 2?
(ii)　What is the probability that it is red or a 2 or
both?　　　　　　　　　　　　　　　[SEG]

9. A fair six-sided spinner has three blank sectors, two sectors
with a 1 and one sector with a 2.
(a)　The spinner is spun twice.
(i)　Copy and complete the tree diagram.

First go　　　　　　　**Second go**

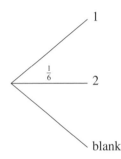

(ii)　What is the probability of getting two blanks?

The spinner is used to play a game called 'Double your money'.
In the game:

getting a blank means you lose;
getting a 1 means you get your money back;
getting a 2 means you get double your money back.

(b)　Tom has two goes.
He pays £1 for each go.
What is the probability that after two goes Tom has
at least £1 more than he started with?　　　　[SEG]

Module 1 Practice Calculator Test

1. The table shows the total distances travelled by different types of vehicles in Great Britain in 1994.

Type of vehicle	Distance (billion km)
Cars	310
Lorries	90
Buses	30
Motorbikes	20
TOTAL	450

Mike wants to draw a pie chart to illustrate these results.

(a) Calculate the angle for the sector that
represents 'Cars'. **(2 marks)**

(b) Draw and label the pie chart for the
data in the table. **(5 marks)**   [SEG]

2. Karl plays a game with a spinner.
The spinner has three equal sections, coloured
red, yellow and blue.

Karl spins the spinner twice.
If both spins land on the same colour, Karl wins 2 tokens.
If exactly one of the spins lands on red, Karl wins 1 token.
For any other result, Karl wins 0 tokens.

(a) Copy and complete the table to show the numbers of
tokens that Karl can win.

		Second spin	
	Red	**Yellow**	**Blue**
Red			
Yellow			
Blue			

First spin

(3 marks)

(b) What is the probability that Karl wins 0 tokens?
(2 marks)   [SEG]

3. Sarah asked 20 men and 20 women
to answer four mental arithmetic
questions and counted how many
correct answers each got. These are
Sarah's results for the 20 men.

(a) Calculate the total number
of correct answers for
the 20 men. **(3 marks)**

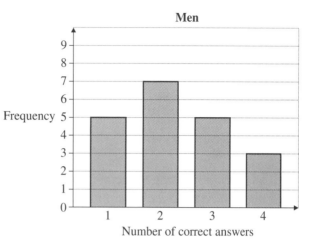

These are Sarah's results for the 20 women.

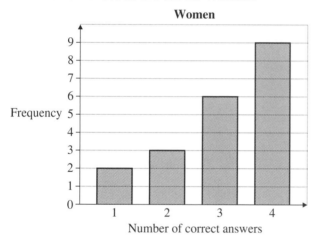

The total number of correct answers for the 20 women is 62.

(b) Write down one difference between the results
for the men and the women. **(1 mark)**

(c) Write down one similarity between the results
for the men and the women. **(1 mark)** [SEG]

4. A café is open for three days per week.
The numbers of iced buns sold in a two-week period were:

21, 16, 11, 24, 12, 17.

Find the first two three-point moving
averages. **(2 marks)** [SEG]

5. Sacha has 3 fair square spinners.
Each spinner is numbered 1, 2, 3 and 4.
He spins all 3 spinners.
What is the probability that he gets exactly
one four? **(4 marks)** [SEG]

MODULE 1

Module 1 Practice Non-calculator Test

1. Zenab recorded the number of different flavours of ice cream in each of 10 ice cream parlours. Her results were

   12   8   8   9   11   12   8   8   9   13

   (a) Use the data to estimate the probability that an ice cream parlour sells 12 or more different flavours.   **(2 marks)**

   The probability that an ice cream parlour sells banana-flavoured ice cream is 0·2.

   (b) Calculate the probability that an ice cream parlour does not sell banana-flavoured ice cream.   **(1 mark)**   [SEG]

2. The two-way table shows the number of credit cards and the number of store cards held by each of 50 shoppers.
   (a) How many of the shoppers had two credit cards and one store card?   **(1 mark)**
   (b) How many of the shoppers had three credit cards?   **(2 marks)**
   (c) How many of the shoppers had exactly one card?   **(1 mark)**   [SEG]

		Number of store cards			
		0	**1**	**2**	**3**
Number of credit cards	**0**	3	2	1	0
	1	5	4	3	1
	2	8	6	4	3
	3	4	3	2	1

3. A teacher asked the pupils in his maths class how long they had spent revising for a maths test.

   He drew a scatter diagram to compare their test results and the time they had spent revising.

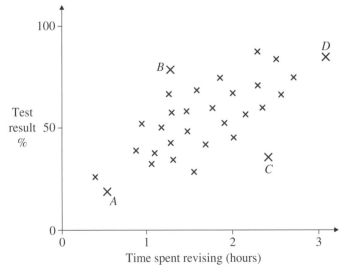

(a) State which point, *A*, *B*, *C* or *D* represents the statement:

    (i) Keith '*Even though I spent a long time revising, I still got a poor test result.*' **(1 mark)**

    (ii) Val '*I got a good test result despite not doing much revision.*' **(1 mark)**

    (iii) Jane '*I revised for ages and got a good test result.*' **(1 mark)**

(b) What does the scatter diagram tell you about the relationship between the time the pupils spent revising and their test results? **(1 mark)**   [NEAB]

4. You want to find out the favourite Bonfire Night food. Design a data collection sheet which could be used. Fill in this data collection sheet as if you had carried out this survey. You should invent suitable data for about 25 people. **(3 marks)**   [NEAB]

5. The cumulative frequency curve of the marks of 120 candidates in an examination is shown.

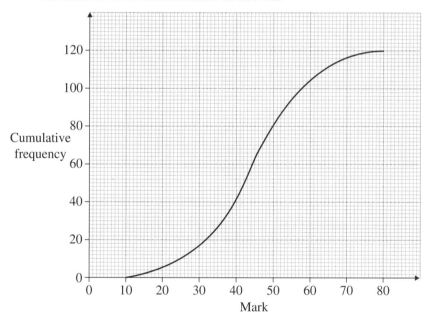

Use the curve to estimate

(a) the median mark **(1 mark)**

(b) the interquartile range of the marks **(2 marks)**

(c) the number of candidates who passed the examination when the pass mark was 48. **(2 marks)**   [SEG]

N1 NUMBER 1

You can use negative numbers to describe direction.

I think we're going two steps forward and three steps back.

Try to think positive!

This unit will show you how to:

- Calculate with decimals
- Recognise types of number
- Calculate with powers
- Find the HCF and LCM
- Use approximation and estimation
- Calculate with directed numbers

1.1 The decimal system

All our numbers are made using the digits: 0, 1, 2, 3, 4, 5, 6, 7, 8, 9.
There are 10 digits in total so our number system uses base 10.
This is called the **decimal system**.

● A digit in a number has place value and face value.
  For example in 35, the 3 has a face value of 3 but a place
  value of 30.

You can use a place value diagram to help you read large numbers.

Each place is 10 times the size of the previous place. ←——————

M	HTh	TTh	Th	H	T	U

Millions   Thousands   Hundreds

Each place is a tenth the size of the previous place. ——————→

Example

Write these numbers in words.

  (a) 12 403   (b) 1 012 487

Draw a place value diagram:

(a)

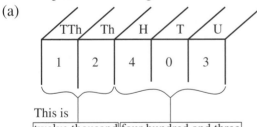

TTh	Th	H	T	U
1	2	4	0	3

This is
twelve thousand four hundred and three

(b)

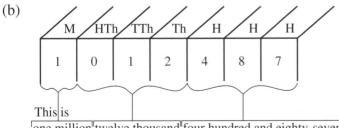

M	HTh	TTh	Th	H	H	H
1	0	1	2	4	8	7

This is
one million twelve thousand four hundred and eighty-seven

MODULE 3

Exercise 1A

1. Write in words
   (a) 340   (b) 580   (c) 2130   (d) 6802   (e) 21 005

2. Write in digit form
   (a) two thousand and twenty-four
   (b) three hundred and seventeen
   (c) nine thousand three hundred and seven
   (d) eight thousand eight hundred and thirty
   (e) one million twenty thousand and fifty-six.

3. In the number 3287, what does
   (a) the digit 2 represent   (b) the digit 8 represent
   (c) the digit 3 represent?

4. Write in words
   (a) 9412   (b) 4210   (c) 2764   (d) 9327   (e) 2100

5. Write in digit form
   (a) two million and sixty thousand   (b) three hundred thousand
   (c) ninety thousand seven hundred and forty-three
   (d) twenty-six thousand and five.

1.2 Types of number

There are lots of different patterns in number. Some people spend their whole lives studying these patterns as they often occur in nature too.

This 100 square shows the pattern made by the numbers in the three times table:

1	2	3	4	5	6	7	8	9	10
11	12	13	14	15	16	17	19	19	20
21	22	23	24	25	26	27	28	29	30
31	32	33	34	35	36	37	38	39	40
41	42	43	44	45	46	47	48	49	50
51	52	53	54	55	56	57	58	59	60
61	62	63	64	65	66	67	68	69	70
71	72	73	74	75	76	77	78	79	80
81	82	83	84	85	86	87	88	89	90
91	92	93	94	95	96	97	98	99	100

The picture on the front cover of this book shows such a pattern in nature – you will find out more about this pattern on page 271.

MODULE 3

Such patterns often have special names you need to know:

There is more about negative numbers on page 153.

- **Integers** are whole numbers. They can be positive or negative:
  ..., ⁻4, ⁻3, ⁻2, ⁻1, 0, 1, 2, 3, 4, ... are integers.
- Positive integers: 1, 2, 3, 4, ... are also called **natural numbers**.
- A **factor** is a number that divides exactly into another number. For example, 2 and 3 are factors of 6.
- Any number with a factor of 2 is an **even number**: 2, 4, 6, 8, ... Integers that are not even are called **odd numbers**: 1, 3, 5, 7, ...
- A **prime number** has no factors except for 1 and itself. For example, the only factors of 7 are 1 and 7 so 7 is **prime**.
- A **multiple** is the result of multiplying two numbers together. For example $6 \times 8 = 48$, so 48 is a multiple of 6 and a multiple of 8.
  A multiple of 3 is any number in the 3 times table: 3, 6, 9, 12, ...
- A **square number** is the result of multiplying any number by itself.
  For example: $1 \times 1 = 1$ and $3 \times 3 = 9$, so 1 and 9 are square numbers.

Note:
The area of a square of side 3 cm is
$3 \text{ cm} \times 3 \text{ cm} = 9 \text{ cm}^2$

3 cm | 9 cm²

3 cm

MODULE 3

Exercise 1B

1. From the list ⁻12, ⁻4, 2, 5, 11, 14, 21, 24, write down
   (a) the negative integers
   (b) the even numbers
   (c) the prime numbers
   (d) the factors of 10
   (e) the multiples of 8.

2. From the list 4, 7, 11, 16, 25, 31, write down
   (a) the odd numbers
   (b) the prime numbers
   (c) the multiples of 8
   (d) the factors of 32
   (e) the square numbers.

3. From the list 5, 9, 14, 21, 35, 41, write down
   (a) the even numbers
   (b) the prime numbers
   (c) the multiples of 7
   (d) the factors of 42
   (e) the square numbers.

4. From the list 5, 7, 10, 16, 24, 42, write down
   (a) the even numbers
   (b) the prime numbers
   (c) the multiples of 6
   (d) the factors of 48
   (e) the square numbers.

5. From the list 11, 13, 15, 22, 35, 44, write down
   (a) the odd numbers
   (b) the prime numbers
   (c) the multiples of 11
   (d) the factors of 66
   (e) the square numbers.

6. From the list ⁻5, ⁻2, 6, 10, 12, 21, write down
   (a) the negative numbers
   (b) the odd numbers
   (c) the prime numbers
   (d) the multiples of 3.

1.3 Powers, roots, surds and reciprocals

A square number is a whole number multiplied by itself:
$5 \times 5 = 25$, so 25 is a square number.

You can write a square number in a short way using a power:

$$5^2 = 25$$

2 is called the **power** or **index**.

You say 5 to the power of 2, or 5 squared.

In a similar way you can write $5 \times 5 \times 5 = 125$ in shorthand as:

$$5^3 = 125$$

3 is the power or index and means you multiply 5 by itself
3 times.

You say 5 to the power of 3, or 5 cubed.

● You can use an index number to show how many times a
  number should be multiplied by itself:

$$3^4 = 3 \times 3 \times 3 \times 3 = 81$$

You say 3 to the power of 4.

Note:

5^3 is called 5 cubed
because the volume of a
cube of side 5 cm is
5 cm × 5 cm × 5 cm.
See page 386.

Finding roots

- You can work backwards from a number to find its root.

For example, if $5^2 = 25$ then $\sqrt[2]{25} = 5$.

You say the square of 5 is 25, the square root of 25 is 5.

Note:
$\sqrt[2]{}$ is usually just written as $\sqrt{}$.

Example

Find (a) the cube root of 64

(b) the square root of 121

(c) $\sqrt[5]{32}$

(a) $4 \times 4 \times 4 = 64$ so the cube root of 64 is 4.

(b) $11 \times 11 = 121$ so the square root of 121 is 11.

(c) $2 \times 2 \times 2 \times 2 \times 2 = 32$ so $\sqrt[5]{32} = 2$.

Hint:
Imagine a cube of volume 64.

Hint:
Imagine a square of area 121.

Surd form

- The square root symbol is called a surd.

You can use factors to find the square root of a number.
If you have a repeated factor, you can simplify the square root.

Example

Find the square root of these numbers.
Leave your answers in surd form.

(a) 24

(b) 32

(c) 98

(a)
$24 = 2 \times 2 \times 2 \times 3$
$\sqrt{24} = \sqrt{2 \times 2} \times \sqrt{2 \times 3}$
$\quad = 2\sqrt{6}$

(b)
$32 = 2 \times 2 \times 2 \times 2 \times 2$
$\sqrt{32} = \sqrt{2 \times 2} \times \sqrt{2 \times 2} \times \sqrt{2}$
$\quad = 2 \times 2\sqrt{2}$
$\quad = 4\sqrt{2}$

(c)
$98 = 2 \times 7 \times 7$
$\sqrt{98} = \sqrt{2} \times \sqrt{7 \times 7}$
$\quad = 7\sqrt{2}$

Reciprocals

The reciprocal of a number is the result when 1 is divided by it.

The reciprocal of 5 is $\frac{1}{5}$, or $0\cdot2$.

The reciprocal of $\frac{1}{4}$ is $\frac{1}{\frac{1}{4}}$, or 4.

Exercise 1C

1. Find the value of

(a) 3^4 (b) 2^3 (c) $(^-6)^2$ (d) $(\frac{1}{2})^2$

MODULE 3

2. Find the positive square root of

(a) 81   (b) 225   (c) 144   (d) 169

3. Find the value of

(a) $\sqrt[3]{8}$ (b) $\sqrt[4]{81}$ (c) $\sqrt[3]{125}$ (d) $\sqrt[3]{\frac{1}{8}}$

4. Find the reciprocal of

(a) 4   (b) 10   (c) $\frac{1}{7}$ (d) $\frac{1}{5}$ (e) 0·25   (f) $\frac{2}{3}$

5. Find

(a) $\sqrt{16} + 5^2$ (b) $2^4 \times \sqrt{81}$ (c) $2^3 + 3 - 4^2$

6. Find the square root of these numbers.
Leave your answers in surd form.

(a) 20   (b) 48   (c) 72   (d) 160

1.4 HCF and LCM

You can split a number into its prime factors. This makes it easier to find the **highest common factor** (HCF) and the **lowest common multiple** (LCM).

> You will need to use the HCF and LCM when you work with fractions – see Unit N2.

A factor tree can help you find the prime factors of a number. Here are the factor trees for 30 and 36.

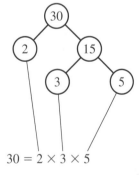

$30 = 2 \times 3 \times 5$

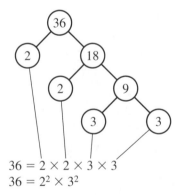

$36 = 2 \times 2 \times 3 \times 3$
$36 = 2^2 \times 3^2$

The highest common factor is the highest factor that a set of numbers has in common.

To find the HCF you multiply all the factors the numbers have in common.

To find the highest common factor of 36 and 30, list all the factors they have in common: a 2 and a 3. The HCF is $2 \times 3 = 6$.

The lowest common multiple of a set of numbers is the smallest number they will all divide into.

To find the LCM you multiply all the factors except for the ones that occur in all the numbers.

To find the LCM of 30 and 36: list the factors of 30, then the factors of 36 leaving out any common factors:

Leave out the common factors of 2 and 3.

$$2 \times 3 \times 5 \times 2 \times 3$$
$$= 180$$

Exercise 1D

1. Express the following numbers as a product of prime numbers.
   (a) 24   (b) 42   (c) 96   (d) 112   (e) 72

2. Find the HCF of
   (a) 24 and 54   (b) 36 and 70   (c) 55 and 33
   (d) 36 and 48   (e) 84 and 70   (f) 28 and 152

3. Find the LCM of
   (a) 25 and 35   (b) 16 and 24   (c) 6 and 20
   (d) 32 and 30   (e) 18 and 50   (f) 70 and 40

4. A lighthouse flashes every 40 seconds and another lighthouse flashes every 35 seconds. At noon they both flash at the same time. What is the time when they again both flash at the same time?

5. Find the HCF of the numbers 72, 96, 144.

1.5 The four rules – mental methods

You should be able to use the four rules: $+, -, \times, \div$ on whole numbers.

Here are some words you should recognise and understand:

+	−	×	÷
Add	Subtract	Times	Divide
Sum	Minus	Multiply	Share
Total	Difference	Product	Quotient
Altogether	More than		Between

When the numbers are small, you should be able to work out the sums in your head.

> **Remember:**
> Use a number line of it helps.

Example 1

Find the difference between 243 and 127.
Break the sum into smaller parts you can do in your head:

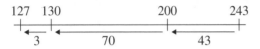

So the difference is $43 + 70 + 3 = 116$.

Example 2

Find 19×34.

19×34 is the same as $20 \times 34 - 34$.

$2 \times 34 = 68$, so $20 \times 34 = 680$.
$680 - 34 = 646$, so $19 \times 34 = 646$.

Exercise 1E

1. From the list 7, 11, 15, 23, 36, 46,
   write down two numbers which
   (a) have a sum of 30
   (b) have a difference of 25
   (c) have a product of 105
   (d) have a quotient of 2.

2. From the list 18, 24, 32, 36, 66, 76,
   write down two numbers which
   (a) have a sum of 100
   (b) have a difference of 40
   (c) have a quotient of 2.0.

3. From the list 12, 14, 19, 21, 36, 48,
   write down two numbers which
   (a) have a sum of 60
   (b) have a difference of 12
   (c) have a sum of 40
   (d) have a quotient of 4
   (e) have an HCF of 7.

4. From the list 8, 12, 24, 36, 64, 100,
  write down two numbers which
  (a) have a sum of 60
  (b) have a difference of 24
  (c) have a product of 288
  (d) have a quotient of 3.

5. From the list 9, 18, 45, 130, 135, 270,
  write down two numbers which
  (a) have an HCF of 18
  (b) have an LCM of 90
  (c) have a product of 162.

1.6 The four rules – paper methods

When the numbers are larger you need to be able to work out
problems without a calculator so you need to use paper methods.

+	−	×	÷
$4537 + 896$	$4537 - 896$	576×23	$962 \div 13$
Line up the units:	Line up the units:	Line up the units:	

So $4537 + 896 = 5433$ So $4537 - 896 = 3641$ So $576 \times 23 = 13\,248$ So $962 \div 13 = 74$

Exercise 1F

Answer these questions **without** using a calculator.

1. Find the sum of
  (a) 545, 782, 176, 53
  (b) 2309, 396, 521, 387
  (c) 7831, 256, 219, 6832
  (d) 328, 176, 483, 93, 781
  (e) 527, 402, 90, 1043, 2023

2. Find the difference between
  (a) 796 and 243   (b) 857 and 436   (c) 1413 and 758
  (d) 6498 and 879   (e) 3125 and 1747

MODULE 3

3. Without the aid of a calculator, multiply
   - (a) 36 by 9
   - (b) 236 by 8
   - (c) 892 by 7
   - (d) 745 by 35
   - (e) 843 by 37
   - (f) 531 by 48
   - (g) 457 by 57
   - (h) 492 by 62
   - (i) 297 by 87

4. Divide
   - (a) 96 by 6
   - (b) 84 by 7
   - (c) 147 by 7
   - (d) 442 by 17
   - (e) 210 by 14
   - (f) 377 by 13
   - (g) 611 by 47
   - (h) 624 by 48
   - (i) 728 by 28
   - (j) 986 by 34
   - (k) 703 by 37
   - (l) 980 by 28

5. (a) Add the numbers
   - (i) 74, 35, 141
   - (ii) 27, 81, 259
   - (iii) 38, 41, 512

   (b) (i) Subtract 84 from 219.
   - (ii) Subtract 35 from 184.
   - (iii) From 1294 subtract 701.

   (c) Find the total of
   - (i) 24, 35 and 294
   - (ii) 75, 81 and 402
   - (iii) 15, 28 and 1001.

1.7 BODMAS

A group of students tried to work out the answer to

$$3 + 2 \times 5 - 4 \div 2$$

Here is some students' working:

$3+2 \quad = 5$	$3+2 \times 5$	$3 + 2 \times 5$	$3 + 2 = 5$
$5 \times 5 \quad = 25$	$3 + 10 \quad = 13$	$3 + 10 \quad = 13$	$5 - 4 = 1$
$25 - 4 = 21$	$13 - 4 \quad = 9$	$13 - 4 \div 2 =$	$5 \times 1 = 5$
$21 \div 2 = \mathbf{11 \cdot 5}$	$9 \div 2 \quad = \mathbf{4 \cdot 5}$	$13 - 2 \quad = \mathbf{11}$	$5 \div 2 = \mathbf{2 \cdot 5}$

There is only one correct answer to the sum.

The right answer is 11!

To make sure you always get the right answer to a long and complicated sum, you use the BODMAS rule.

- **BODMAS** tells you the order you should use the four rules in sums:

   B(rackets)   powers **Of**   **D**ivide   **M**ultiply   **A**dd   **S**ubtract

Example

(a) Work out $2 + 3 \times 4 - 6 \div 3$
(b) Use brackets to make this sum true: $6 \times 9 - 5 \div 8 = 3$
(c) Find $2 \times (4 + 1)^3 \div 10$

(a) $2 + 3 \times 4 - 6 \div 3$

Using BODMAS, do $\div$ first:	$2 + 3 \times 4 - 2$
Then $\times$:	$2 + 12 - 2$
Then $+$ and $-$:	$14 - 2 = \mathbf{12}$

> **Note:**
> You can actually do $\times$ and $\div$ in any order to make the sum easier to do in your head.

(b) By trial and error: $6 \times (9 - 5) \div 8 = 3$
    Check: $6 \times 4 \div 8 = 24 \div 8 = 3$

(c) $2 \times (4 + 1)^3 \div 10$

Using BODMAS, brackets:	$2 \times 5^3 \div 10$
Powers of:	$2 \times 125 \div 10$
$\times$ and $\div$:	$250 \div 10 = \mathbf{25}$

Exercise 1G

Find the value of

1. $7 + 4 \times 3$
2. $8 \times 5 - 4$
3. $9 \times 3 + 5$
4. $(3 + 5) \times 4$
5. $5 \times (7 + 2)$
6. $8 \div (12 \div 3)$
7. $6 \div (5 - 3)$
8. 4 of $3 + 5(8 + 2)$
9. $20 + (4 - 2) \times 6$
10. $16 - 3 \times (5 + 7)$

1.8 Place value in decimals

Decimal numbers show parts of a whole number. They are also part of the decimal system and you can show them on a place value diagram.

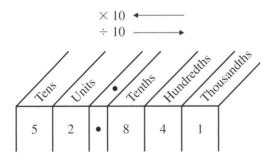

The 4 has a place value of 4 hundredths

You say 3·64 as 'three point six four'.
This is only sixty-four if it is pence!

Remember: 3·64 is between 3 and 4

Adding and subtracting decimals

You can add or subtract decimals without a calculator in the same way that you work with whole numbers.

For example, to find the sum of 4·6 and 13·7 you can use a number line:

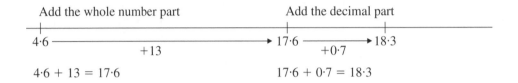

Add the whole number part

Add the decimal part

4·6 ————— +13 ————— → 17·6 ——— +0·7 ——→ 18·3

4·6 + 13 = 17·6

17·6 + 0·7 = 18·3

When the numbers are larger and you need to use a paper method, you must remember to line up the whole number part, otherwise you will get the wrong answer.

Example

Work out
(a) the sum of 17·86 and 21·5
(b) the difference between 527·3 and 159·19

(a) Line up the units:

$$
\begin{array}{r}
1\ 7\cdot 8\ 6 \\
+\ 2\ 1\cdot 5 \\
\hline
3\ 9\cdot 3\ 6 \\
\end{array}
$$

$6 + 0 = 6$
$8 + 5 = 13$
$7 + 1 + 1 = 9$
$1 + 2 = 3$

(b) Line up the units:

$$
\begin{array}{r}
5\ 2\ 7\cdot 3\ 0 \\
-\ 1\ 5\ 9\cdot 1\ 9 \\
\hline
3\ 6\ 8\cdot 1\ 1 \\
\end{array}
$$

$10 - 9 = 1$
$2 - 1 = 1$
$17 - 9 = 8$
$11 - 5 = 6$
$4 - 1 = 3$

Exercise 1H

Without using a calculator, find the values of

1. $17 \cdot 8 + 47 \cdot 2$ 2. $23 \cdot 5 + 72 \cdot 1$

3. $83 \cdot 42 + 17 \cdot 23$ 4. $23 \cdot 24 + 34 \cdot 9 + 17 \cdot 89$

5. $19 \cdot 34 + 24 \cdot 56 + 29 \cdot 5$ 6. $34 \cdot 089 + 35 \cdot 2 + 71 \cdot 56$

7. $34 \cdot 6 - 17 \cdot 2$ 8. $39 \cdot 1 - 16 \cdot 8$

9. $23 \cdot 71 - 12 \cdot 98$ 10. $378 \cdot 2 - 165 \cdot 82$

11. $713 \cdot 83 - 257 \cdot 09$ 12. $34 \cdot 23 - 20 \cdot 58$

1.9 Multiplying and dividing decimal numbers

When you need to multiply or divide decimal numbers it is often easier to treat them as if they are whole numbers.

Multiplication	Division
(a) $6 \cdot 7 \times 2$ This is similar to $67 \times 2 = 134$. There is 1 decimal place in the question so there will be 1 decimal place in the answer: $$6 \cdot 7 \times 2 = 13 \cdot 4$$ $$\text{1 d.p.} \qquad \text{1 d.p.}$$ Check: $6 \cdot 7$ is between 6 and 7 so the answer should be between 12 and 14. (b) $12 \cdot 3 \times 0 \cdot 02$ This is similar to $123 \times 2 = 246$. There are 3 decimal places in the question so there will be 3 decimal places in the answer: $$12 \cdot 3 \times 0 \cdot 02 = 0 \cdot 246$$ $$\text{1 d.p.} + \text{2 d.p.} = \text{3 d.p.}$$	(a) $12 \cdot 6 \div 3$ This is the same as $126 \div 10 \div 3$ So $12 \cdot 6 \div 3 = 126 \div 3 \div 10$ $\qquad\qquad\qquad = 42 \div 10$ $\qquad\qquad\qquad = 4 \cdot 2$ (b) $12 \cdot 3 \div 0 \cdot 02$ When both numbers are decimals it is easiest to multiply both numbers by 10 until the divisor is a whole number: $12 \cdot 3 \div 0 \cdot 02$ $= 123 \div 0 \cdot 2$ $= 1230 \div 2$ $= 615$ (c) $6 \cdot 132 \div 0 \cdot 015$ $= 61 \cdot 32 \div 0 \cdot 15$ $= 613 \cdot 2 \div 1 \cdot 5$ $= 6132 \div 15$ $= 408 \cdot 8$ $\qquad$ $\begin{array}{r} 408 \cdot 8 \\ 15\overline{)6132 \cdot 0} \\ \underline{60} \\ 132 \\ \underline{120} \\ 12\ 0 \\ \underline{12\ 0} \end{array}$

Exercise 1I

Without using a calculator, find the value of

1. $23\cdot4 \times 6$	**2.** $56\cdot2 \times 9$
3. $286\cdot6 \times 7$	**4.** $39\cdot6 \div 6$
5. $29\cdot4 \div 7$	**6.** $215\cdot2 \div 8$
7. 30×2000	**8.** 60×3000
9. 300^2	**10.** 20^3
11. $0\cdot5 \times 0\cdot003$	**12.** $0\cdot3 \times 0\cdot04$
13. $0\cdot002 \times 0\cdot05$	**14.** $3 \div 0\cdot006$
15. $0\cdot4 \div 0\cdot016$	**16.** $0\cdot03 \div 0\cdot0002$

1.10 Approximate answers

There are some calculations that are best done using a calculator.

For example, to work out $12\,971 \div 23\cdot3$ you would take a whole page to work it out on paper and you could easily make a mistake, so it is better to use a calculator.

When you use a calculator, it is easy to get the wrong answer so it is important to have an idea of roughly what the answer should be.

You can get a rough idea of what an answer should be using rounding.

12 971 is quite close to 10 000.
23·3 is quite close to 20.
$12\,971 \div 23\cdot3$ should be roughly $10\,000 \div 20 = 500$.
If your answer is a long way off that estimate then you should check again.
Rounding in this way is called rounding to 1 significant figure (s.f.).

> When it is exactly half way, you always round up!

Example

Round these numbers to 1 significant figure.

(a) 19·735	(b) 12 699·3	(c) 0·002 76	(d) 150
(a) 19·735	(b) 12 699·3	(c) 0·002 76	(d) 150
is between	is between	is between	is between
19 and 20.	10 000 and 20 000.	0·002 and 003.	100 and 200.
It is closer to 20.	It is closer to 10 000.	It is closer to 0·003.	It is exactly half way.
So 19·735 =	So 12 699·3 =	So 0·002 76 =	So 150 =
20 to 1 s.f.	10 000 to 1 s.f.	0·003 to 1 s.f.	200 to 1 s.f.

MODULE 3

Exercise 1J

1. By rounding each of the numbers to one significant figure, find approximate answers for

   (a) $\dfrac{39 \cdot 1 \times 18 \cdot 4}{78 \cdot 1}$ (b) $\dfrac{79 \cdot 2 \times 20 \cdot 9}{49 \cdot 2}$

   (c) $\dfrac{21 \cdot 4 \times 69 \cdot 3}{71 \cdot 1}$ (d) $\dfrac{218 \times 48 \cdot 1}{19 \cdot 3^2}$

2. Find the approximate value of

   (a) $\dfrac{289 \times 721}{31 \cdot 1}$ (b) $\dfrac{289 \times 72 \cdot 1}{31 \cdot 1}$ (c) $\dfrac{289 \times 72 \cdot 1}{31 \cdot 1} \times (0 \cdot 0205)^2$

3. Find the approximate cost of 307 small bottles of water which cost 29p each.

4. Find the approximate cost of 212 cans of coke which cost 38p each.

5. A pack of 72 Christmas cards cost £8·49.
   Find the approximate cost of one card.

6. Francesca sells ice creams on a beach. She sells 389 ice creams at a cost of 72 pence each.
   Estimate how much money she receives.

7. Isobella sells bagels at a market. She sells 478 in a day at a cost of 19·90 French francs each.
   Estimate how much, in francs, she receives.

1.11 More rounding

If you work out 12 971 ÷ 23·3 using your calculator, the display shows 556·695 279.

You can round this number in many different ways:

To 1 s.f.:   556·695 279 is between 500 and 600.
             It is nearer 600 $\longrightarrow$ 600 to 1 s.f.
To 2 s.f.:   556·695 279 is between 550 and 560.
             It is nearer 560 $\longrightarrow$ 560 to 2 s.f.
To 3 s.f.:   556·695 279 is between 556 and 557.
             It is nearer 557 $\longrightarrow$ 557 to 3 s.f.
To the nearest whole number: 12.5265 is between 12 and 13.
             It is nearer 13 $\longrightarrow$ 13 to the nearest whole number.

To 1 decimal place (d.p.):   12.5265 is between 12.5 and 12.6.
             It is nearer 12.5 $\longrightarrow$ 12.5 to 1 d.p.

To 2 d.p.: 12·5265 is between 12·52 $\longrightarrow$ 12·53.

It is nearer 12·53 $\longrightarrow$ 12·53 to 2 d.p.

To 3 d.p.: 12·5265 is between 12·526 and 12·527.

It is exactly half way between, so round up $\longrightarrow$ 12·527 to 3 d.p.

Exercise 1K

Give the following numbers to the degree of accuracy specified.

1. 37·481 (2 d.p.)   **2.** 4·847 (2 d.p.)   **3.** 27·387 (2 d.p.)

4. 113·471 (1 d.p.)   **5.** 27·397 (1 d.p.)   **6.** 28·997 (1 d.p.)

7. 37·495 (2 d.p.)   **8.** 30·698 (2 d.p.)   **9.** 39·912 (1 d.p.)

10. 37·48 (3 s.f.)   **11.** 28·741 (3 s.f.)   **12.** 375·21 (2 s.f.)

13. 2991 (2 s.f.)   **14.** 20·374 (3 s.f.)   **15.** 0·000 748 (2 s.f.)

16. 0·008 92 (2 s.f.)   **17.** 0·008 92 (1 s.f.)   **18.** 0·034 007 8 (3 s.f.)

1.12 Appropriate accuracy

You are often told in an exam question how accurate your answer should be.

There are occasions though where you will need to decide for yourself.

Reading the question again often helps you to give a sensible answer.

Example

47 students travel by minibus to Birmingham to visit a museum.

Each minibus can hold 15 students.

How many minibuses do they need?

47 ÷ 15 is just over 3.

On a calculator, 47 ÷ 15 is 3·133 333 333.

Reading the question again, it is clear that they will need a whole number of minibuses and that 3 would be too few.

They need 4 minibuses.

Exercise 1L

1. Packets of biscuits contain 8 biscuits. How many packets should you buy to ensure each of 36 people can have at least one biscuit?

2. Roses cost £6 for a bunch of ten. Marge wants to buy 47 roses. How many bunches does she need to buy and how much do these cost?

MODULE 3

3. The price of 10 cans of coke is £2·89.
Find the cost of one can.

4. Sausage rolls are sold as 'buy one, get the second half price'. Each pack contains 50 sausage rolls, and they cost £1·99 per pack. How much does one sausage roll cost when you buy 2 packs?

5. Packets of jam tarts cost £1·07, and contain six jam tarts. What is the cost of each tart?

6. There are 568 people on a cruise liner who wish to go on a tour of an island. Each coach can carry 46 passengers. How many coaches are needed?

1.13 Directed numbers

A negative sign can be used to show direction.

The thermometer shows ⁻5°C
which means 5 degrees below freezing

This number line shows the directed numbers from ⁻10 to +10

You can use it to add and subtract simple directed numbers

Example

Work out
(a) ⁻10 + 3   (b) 7 − 15   (c) ⁻1 − 9

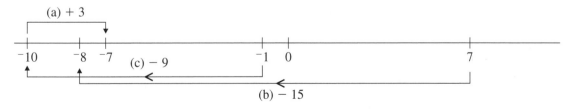

(a) ⁻10 + 3 = −7   (b) 7 − 15 = −8   (c) ⁻1 − 9 = ⁻10

You can use directed numbers to describe your overdraft or money that you owe.

Jules has £120 in her bank account. She pays in her wage of £96. She then writes a cheque for £295 for a midi system.	Jules borrows £50 from her mum to buy a top-up card. She promises to pay her back when she gets her wage.	She works extra hours so she can pay her mum back. Her wage this week is £120.	She still has an overdraft and she works extra hours again so she can buy the CDs she wants.
£120 + 96 − 295 = overdraft, £79	overdraft − £50 = total amount she owes, £129	amount owed + £120 = overdraft, £9	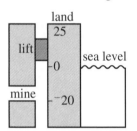

Adding and subtracting a negative number

John works underground. He uses a lift to get to work.

The land is 25 metres above sea level

Sea level is at 0 metres

The mine is 20 metres below sea level

John gets in the lift and goes down 55 metres:

$$25 - 55 = {}^-30,$$ so he is now 30 metres below sea level.

The lift has gone too far so he goes back up 10 metres.
This is the equivalent of subtracting $^-10$ metres:

$$- {}^-10 = {}^+10$$

- Subtracting a positive number is the same as adding a negative number.

$$- {}^+2: \quad 3 + {}^-2 = 1$$

Hint:
The signs are different.
$- + = + -$

- Subtracting a negative number is the same as adding a positive number.

$$- {}^-2: \quad 3 - {}^-2 = 3 + {}^+2 = 5$$

Hint:
The signs are the same.
$- - = + +$

Exercise 1M

1. Find the value of
   (a) $8 + ({}^-7)$ (b) $7 + ({}^-3)$ (c) $6 + ({}^-9)$
   (d) $^-5 + 8$ (e) $^-9 + ({}^-8)$

2. Beryl has an overdraft of £17·96 and she pays £56 into her account.
   What is the new balance on her bank account?

3. John has £74 in his bank account and he withdraws £120.
   What is the balance on his bank account after this transaction?
4. The surface of the Dead Sea is 1128 feet below sea level.
   Angela is in a hot air balloon, 345 feet above the surface of
   the Dead Sea. What is Angela's height above sea level?
5. A mine shaft is 3000 m deep. The surface of the mine is 261
   metres above sea level.
   What is the height of the bottom of the mine shaft?
6. At midday in Paris the temperature was 3° above freezing.
   At midnight the temperature had dropped 12°.
   What was the temperature at midnight?

1.14 Multiplying directed numbers

Maya is learning to drive. She is practising her hill starts.

There are a number of moves she can make:

Up the hill forwards	Up the hill backwards	Down the hill forwards	Down the hill backwards
Her car is facing in a positive direction. She travels in a positive direction. The overall effect is positive. $+ \times + = +$	Her car is facing in a negative direction. She travels in a negative direction. The overall effect is positive. $- \times - = +$	Her car is facing in a negative direction. She travels in a positive direction. The overall effect is negative. $- \times + = -$	Her car is facing in a positive direction. She travels in a negative direction. The overall effect is negative. $+ \times - = -$

- When you multiply two directed numbers:
  - If the two signs are the same, the result is positive:
    $$^-2 \times {}^-3 = 6 \text{ and } 2 \times 3 = 6$$
  - If the two signs are different, the result is negative:
    $$^-2 \times 3 = {}^-6 \text{ and } 3 \times {}^-2 = {}^-6$$

Note that you can extend this to more than two directed numbers:

If there are an even number of negative signs, the result is positive:
$$^-2 \times {}^-3 \times 4 = 24$$

If there are an odd number of negative signs, the result is negative:
$$^-2 \times {}^-3 \times {}^-4 = {}^-24$$

Exercise 1N

Find the value of these.

1. (a) $^-6 \times 4$
   (b) $8 \times {}^-5$
   (c) $^-3 \times {}^-7$
   (d) $^-4 \times {}^-6$

2. (a) $^-11 \times 5$
   (b) $^-8 \times {}^-6$
   (c) $^-5 \times {}^-3$
   (d) $7 \times {}^-4$

3. (a) $3 \times 8 \times 4$
   (b) $^-3 \times 7 \times {}^-5$
   (c) $2 \times {}^-5 \times 4$
   (d) $^-5 \times 3 \times {}^-2$

4. (a) $^-2 \times {}^-3 \times {}^-4$
   (b) $^-3 \times {}^-1 \times {}^-5$
   (c) $^-2 \times {}^-4 \times {}^-7$
   (d) $^-2 \times {}^-2 \times {}^-3$

5. (a) $(^-2)^2$
   (b) $(^-3)^3$
   (c) $(^-2)^2 + (^-4)^3$
   (d) $(^-3)^3 + 1^3$

Summary

1. You can recognise the different types of numbers.

2. You can find powers, roots, reciprocals and surds.

3. You can find HCFs and LCMs.

4. You can use the four rules
   (a) with simple numbers, in your head
   (b) with more complicated numbers, using a calculator or on paper.

5. You can use the BODMAS rule.

6. You can calculate with decimal numbers.

7. You can work out roughly what an answer should be.

8. You can decide what degree of accuracy to give your answer to.

9. You can work with directed numbers.

Check out N1

1. From the list 5, 8, 11, 17, 22, 25, write down
   (a) the prime numbers
   (b) the square numbers
   (c) the even numbers
   (d) the multiples of 4
   (e) the factors of 66.

2. Find
   (a) 11^2 (b) 4^3 (c) 2^{12}
   (c) $\sqrt{36}$ (e) $\frac{1}{\frac{1}{4}}$

3. (a) Find the HCF of 36 and 42.
   (b) Find the LCM of 30 and 24.

4. (a) Find the value of
      (i) $3742 + 891$
      (ii) $3742 - 1786$
   (b) Find the value of
      (i) 726×39 (ii) $756 \div 27$

5. Work out $6 + 3 \times 4$

6. Find the value of
   (a) $37 \cdot 42 + 8 \cdot 9$
   (b) $37 \cdot 42 - 11 \cdot 874$

7. Use an estimate to find an approximate value of 489×41

8. Give the value of
   $\dfrac{37 \cdot 41}{29 \cdot 34}$ to an appropriate degree of accuracy.

9. (a) Find the temperature 10 °C colder than 7 °C.
   (b) Find £17·28 − £35·71

MODULE 3

Revision exercise N1

1. (a) What is the next number in each of these sequences?
   (i) 3, 6, 11, 18, 27
   (ii) 8, 4, 2, 1, $\frac{1}{2}$
   (b) Work out $\sqrt{7}$.
       Give your answer correct to 2 decimal places.
   (c) Work out 7^3.   [SEG]

2. Use your calculator to find the value of
$$\frac{8\cdot27^2}{9\cdot41 + 2\cdot84}$$

   Give your answer to an appropriate degree of accuracy.   [SEG]

3. (a) Calculate $5 \times 7\cdot4^2$.
   (b) Calculate $\sqrt{\dfrac{(9\cdot8)^3}{0\cdot39}}$.

   (c) $m = 3 \times 5^2$ and $n = 3^2 \times 5$.
       (i) What is the lowest common multiple of m and n?
       (ii) What is the highest common factor of m and n?   [SEG]

4. (a) Calculate $\dfrac{89\cdot6 \times 10\cdot3}{19\cdot7 + 9\cdot8}$.

   (b) Do not use your calculator in this part of the question.
       By using approximations show that your answer to (a)
       is about right. You must show all your working.   [SEG]

5. (a) Write 72 as a product of prime factors.
   (b) Work out $\dfrac{81 \times \frac{1}{3}}{\frac{1}{16} \times 8}$.   [SEG]

6. (a) Use approximations to estimate the value of $\dfrac{9\cdot67^2}{0\cdot398}$.

   You must show all your working.

   (b) (i) p and q are prime numbers.
            Find the values of p and q when $p^3 \times q = 24$.
       (ii) Write 18 as a product of prime factors.
       (iii) What is the lowest common multiple of 24 and 18? [SEG]

7. (a) Write down the exact value of $(\sqrt{6})^4$.
   (b) Calculate the value of $2^a \times a^2$, when $a = {}^-2$.
   (c) Calculate $\sqrt{\dfrac{3\cdot9}{(0\cdot6)^3}}$.   [SEG]

N2 NUMBER 2

Money calculations often involve fractions and percentages.

Actually I've already had a double-glazing quote for £2000

Hmm, we could do it for a fraction of the cost

Actually $\frac{11}{10}$

This unit will show you how to:

- Calculate with fractions
- Calculate with percentages

Before you start:

You should know how to...	Check in N2
1. Find the HCF and LCM	**1.** Find the HCF and LCM of 36 and 42.
For example, find the HCF and LCM of 12 and 18.	
$12 = 2 \times 2 \times 3 \qquad = 2^2 \times 3$ $18 = 2 \times 3 \times 3 \qquad = 3^2 \times 2$ $\text{HCF} = 2 \times 3 \qquad \text{LCM} = 2^2 \times 3^2$ $\qquad = 6 \qquad\qquad\qquad = 36$	
2. Use the BODMAS rule	**2.** Without using a calculator, find
For example, $12 - 6 \div 3$ $\qquad\qquad = 12 - 2$ $\qquad\qquad = 10$	(a) $2 + 3 \times 4$ (b) $3 \times (5 - 4)$ (c) $\dfrac{2 + 4}{3 - 1}$

2.1 Fractions of a whole

A fraction describes a part of a whole.

The top number is the numerator. It shows how many parts you have.

$$\frac{5}{8}$$

The bottom number is the denominator. It shows how many parts there are altogether.

You name a fraction by its denominator. This table shows some commonly used names.

Denominator	2	3	4	5	6	8	10	100	1000
Unit fraction	$\frac{1}{2}$	$\frac{1}{3}$	$\frac{1}{4}$	$\frac{1}{5}$	$\frac{1}{6}$	$\frac{1}{8}$	$\frac{1}{10}$	$\frac{1}{100}$	$\frac{1}{1000}$
Name	Half	Third	Quarter	Fifth	Sixth	Eighth	Tenth	Hundredth	Thousandth

Example

What fraction of each shape is shaded? unshaded?
Give your answers using fractions and in words.

(a)   (b) 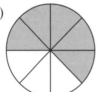 (c)

(a) There are 4 parts so the fraction is quarters.
    3 parts are shaded. That is $\frac{3}{4}$ or three quarters.
    1 part is unshaded. That is $\frac{1}{4}$ or one quarter.

(b) There are 8 parts so the fraction is eighths.
    5 parts are shaded. That is $\frac{5}{8}$ or five eighths.
    3 parts are unshaded. That is $\frac{3}{8}$ or three eighths.

(c) There are 10 parts so the fraction is tenths.
    7 parts are shaded. That is $\frac{7}{10}$ or seven tenths.
    3 parts are unshaded. That is $\frac{3}{10}$ or three tenths.

Exercise 2A

1. Find the fraction of the shape which is not shaded.
   Give your answer (a) using fractions
                    (b) in words.

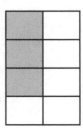

2. Find the fraction of the circle which is not shaded.
Give your answer (a) using fractions
(b) in words.

3. Find the fraction of the shape which is not shaded.
Give your answer as a fraction.

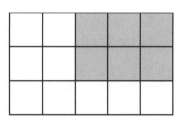

4. Find the fraction of the shape which is not shaded.
Give your answer (a) using fractions
(b) in words.

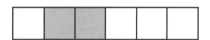

5. Find the fraction of the shape which is not shaded.
Give your answer (a) using fractions
(b) in words.

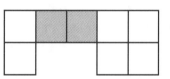

MODULE 3

2.2 Equivalent fractions

These two diagrams show the same fraction:

$\frac{2}{5}$ is shaded.

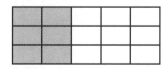

$\frac{6}{15}$ is shaded.

$\frac{2}{5}$ and $\frac{6}{15}$ are equivalent fractions. They show the same fraction of a whole.

$$6 \div 3 = 2 \quad 2 \times 3 = 6$$
$$15 \div 3 = 5 \quad 5 \times 3 = 15$$

You find equivalent fractions by multiplying or dividing both the numerator and denominator by the same number.

Example

(a) Find three fractions equivalent to $\frac{3}{4}$.

(b) Simplify $\frac{16}{36}$ as far as possible by dividing.

(a) Multiply numerator and denominator by 2, 3 and 4:

$$3 \times 2 = 6 \quad 3 \times 3 = 9 \quad 3 \times 4 = 12$$
$$4 \times 2 = 8 \quad 4 \times 3 = 12 \quad 4 \times 4 = 16$$

so $\frac{3}{4} = \frac{6}{8} = \frac{9}{12} = \frac{12}{16}$

(b) $16 \div 2 = 8 \qquad 8 \div 2 = 4$

$36 \div 2 = 18 \qquad 18 \div 2 = 9$

so $\frac{16}{36} = \frac{8}{18} = \frac{4}{9}$

4 and 9 have no common factors so $\frac{4}{9}$ is in its simplest form.

- To express a fraction in its **simplest form** you divide the numerator and denominator by their highest common factor.

> Simplest form is also called simplest terms or lowest terms.

Exercise 2B

1. Each diagram has a number of parts shaded. Write down at least two equivalent fractions to describe the shaded part in each diagram.

(a)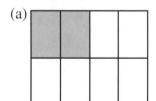

(b)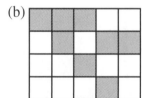

(c)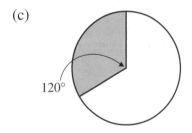

$120°$

(d)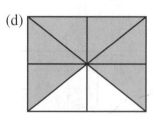

2. Write down three fractions equivalent to

(a) $\frac{1}{4}$ (b) $\frac{2}{7}$ (c) $\frac{7}{9}$ (d) $\frac{4}{5}$ (e) $\frac{5}{12}$

3. Copy and complete these sets of equivalent fractions.

(a) $\frac{3}{5} = \frac{?}{10} = \frac{?}{15} = \frac{?}{25}$ (b) $\frac{3}{7} = \frac{?}{14} = \frac{?}{28} = \frac{?}{35}$ (c) $\frac{5}{6} = \frac{?}{42}$

(d) $\frac{2}{3} = \frac{8}{?}$ (e) $\frac{4}{9} = \frac{28}{?}$ (f) $\frac{9}{10} = \frac{45}{?}$

(g) $\frac{2}{5} = \frac{?}{40}$ (h) $\frac{7}{8} = \frac{42}{?}$

4. Write down each of these fractions in their simplest form.

(a) $\frac{8}{32}$ (b) $\frac{9}{21}$ (c) $\frac{25}{40}$ (d) $\frac{27}{36}$ (e) $\frac{40}{48}$

5. Mrs. Jones bought a large box of crisps from the supermarket. The box contains 32 packets. At the end of the week there were 8 packets left in the box.

(a) What fraction of the box of crisps remained uneaten by the end of the week? Give your answer in the simplest form.

(b) What fraction of the box of crisps had been eaten by the end of the week? Give your answer in the simplest form.

6. A film lasts for 45 minutes. What fraction of the film is left after

(a) 15 minutes

(b) 25 minutes?

Give each answer in its lowest terms.

2.3 Fractions greater than 1

You can have fractions that show amounts that are greater than a whole.

$1\frac{3}{4}$ means $\frac{4}{4}$ and $\frac{3}{4}$ which is $\frac{7}{4}$ in total.

- A **mixed number** has a whole number part and a fraction part.
- An **improper fraction** has a numerator larger than the denominator.

> An improper fraction is also called a top heavy fraction.

Example

(a) Write $2\frac{5}{8}$ as an improper fraction.

(b) Write $\frac{33}{7}$ as a mixed number.

(a) $2\frac{5}{8} = \frac{8}{8} + \frac{8}{8} + \frac{5}{8} = \frac{21}{8}$

(b) 7 goes into 33 four whole times remainder 5

so $\frac{33}{7} = 4\frac{5}{7}$

Exercise 2C

1. Change these mixed numbers to improper fractions.

(a) $1\frac{3}{10}$ (b) $4\frac{1}{2}$ (c) $2\frac{3}{5}$ (d) $4\frac{5}{9}$

(e) $7\frac{3}{4}$ (f) $4\frac{11}{15}$ (g) $3\frac{7}{8}$ (h) $5\frac{3}{7}$

2. Change each of these improper fractions to a mixed number.

(a) $\frac{7}{2}$ (b) $\frac{19}{4}$

(c) $\frac{29}{5}$ (d) $\frac{39}{10}$

(e) $\frac{23}{6}$ (f) $\frac{57}{12}$

(g) $\frac{41}{11}$ (h) $\frac{51}{7}$

3. Write down two improper fractions equivalent to each of the mixed numbers.

(a) $1\frac{4}{10}$

(b) $2\frac{3}{12}$

(c) $4\frac{1}{4}$

4. Copy and complete each improper fraction to make an equivalent fraction.

(a) $1\frac{4}{5} = \frac{?}{10}$

(b) $2\frac{1}{4} = \frac{?}{12}$

(c) $3\frac{2}{5} = \frac{?}{20}$

5. Change each of these improper fractions to a mixed number where the fraction is in its lowest terms.

(a) $\frac{15}{6}$

(b) $\frac{27}{18}$

(c) $\frac{30}{8}$

(d) $\frac{42}{12}$

2.4 Finding fractions of a whole

To find a half, $\frac{1}{2}$ of a quantity, you divide by 2.
To find a third, $\frac{1}{3}$ of a quantity, you divide by 3.
To find a quarter, $\frac{1}{4}$ of a quantity you divide by 4.
And so on.

Example 1

Find
(a) $\frac{1}{4}$ of £16   (b) $\frac{1}{10}$ of 23 metres   (c) $\frac{1}{8}$ of 24 ounces

(a) £16 ÷ 4 = £4   (b) 23 metres ÷ 10 = 2·3 metres   (c) 24 ounces ÷ 8 = 3 ounces

To find more than one part, first find one part then multiply by the number of parts you want.

Example 2

Find

(a) $\frac{3}{4}$ of £28   (b) $\frac{3}{20}$ of 160 metres   (c) $\frac{5}{8}$ of 32 kg

(a) $\frac{1}{4}$ of £28	(b) $\frac{1}{20}$ of 160 metres	(c) $\frac{1}{8}$ of 32 kg
$= £28 \div 4$	$= 160 \text{ metres} \div 20$	$= 32 \text{ kg} \div 8$
$= £7$	$= 8 \text{ metres}$	$= 4 \text{ kg}$
so $\frac{3}{4}$ of £28	so $\frac{3}{20}$ of 160 metres	so $\frac{5}{8}$ of 32 kg
$= 3 \times £7$	$= 3 \times 8 \text{ metres}$	$= 5 \times 4 \text{ kg}$
$= £21$	$= 24 \text{ metres}$	$= 20 \text{ kg}$

Exercise 2D

1. Calculate

   (a) $\frac{1}{8}$ of 72   (b) $\frac{5}{6}$ of 48   (c) $\frac{4}{9}$ of 54 centimetres

   (d) $\frac{5}{12}$ of £180   (e) $\frac{4}{5}$ of 570 cars   (f) $\frac{7}{15}$ of 195 people

2. Brian checks the time keeping of buses on the route by his road and $\frac{3}{8}$ of the 192 buses he checked were on time. How many of these buses were on time?

3. Marion is given £95 for her birthday. She saves $\frac{4}{5}$ of it. How much of her birthday money did Marion save?

4. Basia delivers 168 newspapers on her paper round. On Sunday $\frac{5}{7}$ of the newspapers have a supplement with the paper. How many supplements does she deliver?

5. Clive observes the colours of 240 cars in a car park. $\frac{5}{12}$ of the cars are silver. How many are silver?

2.5 Adding and subtracting fractions

You can add and subtract the same types of fractions – fractions with the same denominator – by just adding the numerators.

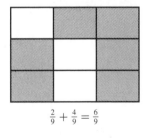

$$\frac{2}{9} + \frac{4}{9} = \frac{6}{9}$$

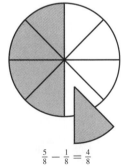

$$\frac{5}{8} - \frac{1}{8} = \frac{4}{8}$$

When the denominators are different you must make them the same before you add or subtract.

For example, to add together $\frac{2}{3}$ and $\frac{1}{8}$:

- First find the least common multiple of the denominators:
$$3 \times 8 = 24$$

- Next find equivalent fractions with the denominator 24:
$$2 \times 8 = 16 \quad 1 \times 3 = 3$$
$$3 \times 8 = 24 \quad 8 \times 3 = 24$$

- Finally, add the fractions:
$$\frac{16}{24} + \frac{3}{24} = \frac{19}{24}$$

> To add or subtract mixed numbers, first change them to improper fractions. Remember to change the answer back to a mixed fraction!

Exercise 2E

Do not use a calculator in questions 1–4.

1. Work out
   - (a) $\frac{2}{7} + \frac{3}{7}$
   - (b) $\frac{5}{8} + \frac{1}{8}$
   - (c) $\frac{3}{10} + \frac{9}{10}$
   - (d) $\frac{5}{8} + \frac{3}{4}$
   - (e) $\frac{1}{4} + \frac{1}{2}$
   - (f) $\frac{1}{3} + \frac{1}{4} + \frac{5}{12}$

2. Work out
   - (a) $1\frac{1}{4} + 3\frac{1}{8}$
   - (b) $\frac{3}{4} + 4\frac{7}{8}$
   - (c) $3\frac{11}{16} + 1\frac{3}{8}$
   - (d) $3\frac{1}{2} + 1\frac{5}{8}$
   - (e) $2\frac{5}{12} + 3\frac{3}{4}$
   - (f) $1\frac{7}{10} + 1\frac{2}{3}$

3. John weighs two large apples. The first weighs $\frac{3}{10}$ kg and the second $\frac{9}{25}$ kg. What is the total weight of these apples?

4. In a class $\frac{1}{8}$ of the pupils travel to school by bus and $\frac{3}{5}$ of the pupils travel to school by car. What fraction of the class travel to school by bus or car?

5. Check all your answers to questions 1–4 using the fraction button on your calculator.

Do not use a calculator in questions 6–9.

> If you are not sure how to use the fraction button on your calculator, look ahead to page 170.

6. Work out
   - (a) $\frac{5}{6} - \frac{4}{6}$
   - (b) $\frac{13}{16} - \frac{3}{16}$
   - (c) $\frac{5}{7} - \frac{2}{7}$
   - (d) $\frac{3}{4} - \frac{1}{2}$
   - (e) $\frac{7}{12} - \frac{1}{4}$
   - (f) $\frac{9}{10} - \frac{2}{5}$

7. Work out
   - (a) $1\frac{1}{2} - \frac{3}{10}$
   - (b) $4\frac{4}{9} - 2\frac{1}{3}$
   - (c) $3\frac{2}{3} - 2\frac{2}{5}$
   - (d) $5\frac{7}{9} - 2\frac{1}{3}$
   - (e) $4\frac{3}{8} - 2\frac{5}{6}$
   - (f) $7\frac{4}{7} - 4\frac{3}{5}$

8. A box containing biscuits has a total weight of $1\frac{7}{8}$ kg. The tin weighs $\frac{1}{20}$ kg when empty.
   What is the weight of the biscuits on their own?

9. A piece of wood is $2\frac{1}{4}$ metres long. A length of $\frac{5}{8}$ metre is cut off one end of this piece of wood.
   How much of the original piece of wood remains?

10. Check all your answers to questions 6–9 using the fraction button on your calculator.

2.6 Multiplying and dividing fractions

Multiplying fractions

To multiply fractions together simply multiply the numerators and multiply the denominators.

Example 1

Work out

(a) $\frac{2}{3}$ of $\frac{4}{5}$

(b) $1\frac{1}{4} \times 2\frac{3}{5}$

(a) $\frac{2}{3} \times \frac{4}{5} = \dfrac{2 \times 4}{3 \times 5} = \frac{8}{15}$

(b) First change to improper fractions then multiply.

$$1\frac{1}{4} \times 2\frac{3}{5} = \frac{5}{4} \times \frac{13}{5} = \dfrac{5 \times 13}{4 \times 5} = \frac{65}{20} = 3\frac{5}{20} \text{ or } 3\frac{1}{4}$$

> Remember to simplify if possible after you multiply.

Multiplying by cancelling

Sometimes you can 'cross cancel' when multiplying. This example shows you what this means:

$\dfrac{5}{_2\,\cancel{6}} \times \dfrac{^1\cancel{3}}{20}$ — 3 and 6 have a common factor of 3

$\dfrac{^1\cancel{5}}{6} \times \dfrac{3}{_4\,\cancel{20}}$ — 5 and 20 have a common factor of 5

$\dfrac{^1\cancel{5}}{_2\,\cancel{6}} \times \dfrac{^1\cancel{3}}{_4\,\cancel{20}} = \dfrac{1 \times 1}{2 \times 4} = \dfrac{1}{8}$

Dividing fractions

- To divide by a fraction you:
  - Invert the second fraction, that is you turn it upside down.
  - Multiply by the inverted fraction.

MODULE 3

Example 2

Find

(a) $24 \div \frac{2}{5}$ (b) $\frac{1}{3} \div \frac{5}{6}$ (c) $3\frac{1}{5} \div \frac{4}{5}$

(a) $24 \div \frac{2}{5}$ (b) $\frac{1}{3} \div \frac{5}{6}$ (c) $3\frac{1}{5} \div \frac{4}{5}$

$\quad = \overset{12}{\cancel{24}} \times \dfrac{5}{\cancel{2}_1}$ $= \dfrac{1}{\cancel{3}_1} \times \dfrac{\overset{2}{\cancel{6}}}{5}$ $= \dfrac{\overset{4}{\cancel{16}}}{\cancel{5}_1} \times \dfrac{\overset{1}{\cancel{5}}}{\cancel{4}_1}$

$\quad = 60$ $= \frac{2}{5}$ $= 4$

Exercise 2F

Do not use a calculator in questions 1–5.

1. Work out

   (a) $\frac{1}{2} \times \frac{3}{4}$ (b) $\frac{4}{7} \times \frac{5}{8}$ (c) $\frac{2}{3} \times \frac{2}{5}$ (d) $\frac{3}{8} \times \frac{4}{9}$

   (e) $\frac{1}{3} \times \frac{6}{7}$ (f) $\frac{9}{10} \times \frac{11}{18}$ (g) $\frac{4}{5} \times \frac{7}{8}$ (h) $\frac{11}{20} \times \frac{15}{16}$

2. Work out

   (a) $1\frac{1}{2} \times \frac{3}{8}$ (b) $2\frac{1}{4} \times \frac{2}{7}$ (c) $6\frac{3}{10} \times 2\frac{1}{7}$ (d) $3\frac{3}{4} \times 3\frac{3}{5}$

   (e) $1\frac{1}{2} \times 2\frac{1}{2}$ (f) $1\frac{3}{4} \times 2\frac{2}{5}$ (g) $1\frac{3}{5} \times 1\frac{1}{6}$

3. Work out

   (a) $2\frac{3}{4} \times 3\frac{1}{3}$ (b) $\frac{4}{5}$ of $2\frac{1}{4}$ (c) $\frac{2}{3}$ of $4\frac{1}{5}$

   (d) $\frac{3}{10}$ of $5\frac{5}{9}$ (e) $\frac{5}{8}$ of $2\frac{2}{15}$

4. Work out

   (a) $\frac{6}{7}$ of 42 pints   (b) $\frac{4}{5}$ of 225 people

   (c) $\frac{3}{16}$ of 640 toys   (d) $\frac{5}{12}$ of 1368 cars

5. A painter takes $1\frac{1}{3}$ hours to paint a picture. In one week he paints 34 pictures.
   How long does he take to paint these pictures?

6. Check all your answers to questions 1–5 using the fraction button on your calculator.

Do not use a calculator in questions 7–10.

7. Work out

   (a) $\frac{1}{5} \div \frac{1}{2}$ (b) $\frac{3}{5} \div \frac{1}{6}$ (c) $\frac{3}{8} \div \frac{9}{16}$ (d) $\frac{8}{9} \div 4$

   (e) $\frac{3}{8} \div \frac{2}{3}$ (f) $\frac{7}{12} \div \frac{5}{18}$ (g) $\frac{24}{25} \div \frac{8}{15}$ (h) $\frac{9}{20} \div \frac{7}{10}$

MODULE 3

8. Work out

   (a) $1\frac{1}{3} \div 1\frac{1}{2}$ (b) $2\frac{3}{4} \div 4\frac{1}{8}$ (c) $3\frac{1}{5} \div 4\frac{4}{5}$

   (d) $3\frac{1}{3} \div 5\frac{1}{5}$ (e) $2\frac{1}{4} \div 1\frac{4}{5}$ (f) $5\frac{2}{3} \div 1\frac{5}{6}$

9. A large paint tin contains $10\frac{1}{2}$ litres. How many containers taking $1\frac{3}{4}$ litres each can be filled from the large tin?

10. A plant grows $\frac{3}{8}$ centimetre every day. How many days will it take to grow $22\frac{1}{2}$ centimetres extra in height?

11. Check your answers to questions 7–10 using the fraction button on your calculator.

2.7 Changing fractions to decimals

You can change a fraction to a decimal by dividing.

$$\tfrac{1}{4} = 1 \div 4 = 0.25$$

$$\tfrac{5}{8} = 5 \div 8 = 0.625$$

You should recognise all these fraction and decimal equivalents.

Fraction	Decimal	Fraction	Decimal
$\frac{1}{2} = \frac{2}{4} = \frac{4}{8} = \frac{5}{10}$	0·5	$\frac{1}{5} = \frac{2}{10}$	0·2
$\frac{1}{3}$	0·333 333 333 333	$\frac{2}{5} = \frac{4}{10}$	0·4
$\frac{2}{3}$	0·666 666 666 666	$\frac{3}{5} = \frac{6}{10}$	0·6
$\frac{1}{4} = \frac{2}{8}$	0·25	$\frac{4}{5} = \frac{8}{10}$	0·8
$\frac{3}{4} = \frac{6}{8}$	0·75	$\frac{1}{10}$	0·1
$\frac{1}{8}$	0·125	$\frac{3}{10}$	0·3
$\frac{3}{8}$	0·375	$\frac{7}{10}$	0·7
$\frac{5}{8}$	0·625	$\frac{9}{10}$	0·9
$\frac{7}{8}$	0·875	$\frac{1}{100}$	0·01

To change a decimal to a fraction you use the place value table:

For example:

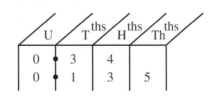

$$0.34 = \tfrac{34}{100} = \tfrac{17}{50}$$

$$0.135 = \tfrac{135}{1000} = \tfrac{27}{200}$$

MODULE 3

Recurring decimals

$\frac{1}{3} = 1 \div 3 = 0{\cdot}333\,333\,333\,3\ldots$

The decimal goes on for ever. It is a recurring decimal.
You can write a recurring decimal simply by using a dot like this:

$$\frac{1}{3} = 0{\cdot}\dot{3} \qquad \frac{2}{3} = 0{\cdot}\dot{6}$$

$$\frac{1}{6} = 0{\cdot}166\,666\,666\,6\ldots = 0{\cdot}1\dot{6}$$

$$\frac{2}{11} = 0{\cdot}181\,818\,181\,8\ldots = 0{\cdot}\dot{1}\dot{8}$$

Exercise 2G

1. Change each of these decimals into a fraction.

   (a) 0·3   (b) 0·4   (c) 0·7   (d) 0·9

2. Express each of these fractions as a decimal.

   (a) $\frac{1}{4}$ (b) $\frac{2}{5}$ (c) $\frac{3}{4}$ (d) $\frac{2}{10}$

3. Change each of these decimals into a fraction.

   (a) 0·48   (b) 0·28   (c) 0·64   (d) 0·92

4. Express each of these fractions as a decimal.

   (a) $\frac{1}{7}$ (b) $\frac{1}{30}$ (c) $\frac{1}{12}$ (d) $\frac{1}{15}$

5. Change each of these decimals into a fraction, expressing the fraction in its lowest terms.

   (a) 0·375   (b) 0·0625   (c) 0·48   (d) 0·9625

2.8 Using the calculator

You can use a calculator to work out fraction problems.
Remember you must also be able to work them out on paper or in your head.

The fraction button on your calculator usually looks like this:

You input fractions like this:

$\frac{3}{8}$

$1\frac{2}{3}$

The button will also change mixed numbers to improper
fractions and vice versa:

Input $1\frac{2}{3}$ ⟶ press a^{b/c} again ⟶ you should see $\frac{5}{3}$ ⟶ press a^{b/c} again ⟶ it should show $1\frac{2}{3}$

Exercise 2H

1. Change each of these to an improper fraction.

(a) $3\frac{1}{2}$ (b) $5\frac{1}{4}$ (c) $7\frac{1}{5}$ (d) $4\frac{1}{3}$

2. Change each of these to a mixed number.

(a) $\frac{5}{2}$ (b) $\frac{7}{5}$ (c) $\frac{11}{6}$ (d) $\frac{24}{7}$

3. Change each of these to a mixed number and to a decimal.

(a) $\frac{9}{4}$ (b) $\frac{11}{5}$ (c) $\frac{33}{6}$ (d) $\frac{19}{2}$

4. Express each of these as a fraction.

(a) 3·5   (b) 7·4   (c) 11·2   (d) 9·25

5. Express each of these as a fraction in its simplest form.

(a) $2\frac{15}{25}$ (b) $3\frac{6}{20}$ (c) $4\frac{12}{16}$ (d) $7\frac{10}{35}$

2.9 Percentages

Percentages are often used in everyday life.

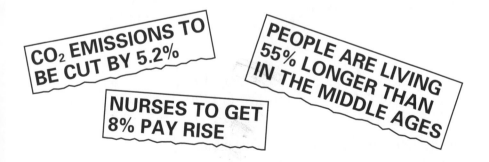

CO$_2$ EMISSIONS TO BE CUT BY 5.2%

PEOPLE ARE LIVING 55% LONGER THAN IN THE MIDDLE AGES

NURSES TO GET 8% PAY RISE

A percentage is a fraction out of 100. The symbol % means
'out of 100'. For example 43% means $\frac{43}{100}$.

Percentages are widely used because they make fractions of quantities easy to compare.

For example, $\frac{3}{4} = 75\%$ and $\frac{4}{5} = 80\%$.

It is much easier to compare 75% and 80% than $\frac{3}{4}$ and $\frac{4}{5}$!

Calculating with percentages

To find a percentage of an amount, first see whether you recognise the percentage. If not, change the percentage to a fraction.

Example 1

Find

(a) 30% of £120

(b) 25% of 40 metres

(c) 23% of £1270

(a) 10% of £120 = £12

So 30% of £120 = 3 × £12

= £36

(b) 25% is $\frac{1}{4}$.

$\frac{1}{4}$ of 40 metres

= 10 metres

(c) 23% of £1270

= $\frac{23}{100}$ × £1270

= £292·10

- Tax rates are expressed using percentages.
  The usual rate of value added tax (VAT) is 17·5%.
- To find the VAT in your head
  - first find 10%
  - then halve that to find 5%
  - then halve that to find 2·5%.
- 17·5% = 10% + 5% + 2·5%

Example 2

Find 17·5% of £220.

10% of £220	= £220 ÷ 10	= £22
5% of £220	= £22 ÷ 2	= £11
2·5% of £220	= £11 ÷ 2	= £5·50
17·5% of £220	= £22 + £11 + £5·50	= £38·50

Exercise 2I

1. Find

   (a) 25% of £50
   (b) 20% of £32
   (c) 30% of £91
   (d) 10% of £90
   (e) 15% of £70
   (f) 28% of £170
   (g) 8% of £60
   (h) 7% of £42
   (i) 34% of £60

2. A tower block contains 200 flats. Of these, 30% have a blue front door. How many flats have a blue front door?

3. A plane can carry 238 passengers. 27% of the seats are empty. How many seats are empty?

4. 32 400 spectators watch a football match. Of these, 54% are male. How many spectators are male?

5. Jason repairs his car and receives a bill for £80.
VAT at 17·5% is added to this bill.
How much is the total which Jason has to pay?

2.10 Fraction, decimal and percentage equivalents

Fractions, decimals and percentages can be used to show the same amounts.
You need to recognise these fraction, decimal and percentage equivalents:

Fraction	Decimal	Percentage	Fraction	Decimal	Percentage
$\frac{1}{2} = \frac{2}{4} = \frac{4}{8} = \frac{5}{10}$	0·5	50%	$\frac{1}{8}$	0·125	12·5%
$\frac{1}{3}$	0·3	$33\frac{1}{3}$% or 33·3%	$\frac{3}{8}$	0·375	37·5%
$\frac{2}{3}$	0·6	$66\frac{2}{3}$% or 66·6%	$\frac{5}{8}$	0·625	62·5%
$\frac{1}{4}$	0·25	25%	$\frac{7}{8}$	0·875	87·5%
$\frac{3}{4}$	0·75	75%	$\frac{1}{10}$	0·1	10%
$\frac{1}{5} = \frac{2}{10}$	0·2	20%	$\frac{3}{10}$	0·3	30%
$\frac{2}{5} = \frac{4}{10}$	0·4	40%	$\frac{7}{10}$	0·7	70%
$\frac{3}{5} = \frac{6}{10}$	0·6	60%	$\frac{9}{10}$	0·9	90%
$\frac{4}{5} = \frac{8}{10}$	0·8	80%	$\frac{1}{100}$	0·01	1%

To change an unfamiliar percentage into a decimal or a fraction you just need to remember that % means out of 100.

Example
(a) Write 22·5% as a decimal and as a fraction.
(b) Write 125% as a fraction and as a decimal.

(a) As a decimal: 22·5% means $\qquad$ $22·5 \div 100 = 0·225$

As a fraction: 22·5% means $\qquad$ $\frac{22.5}{100}$

Multiply to get rid of the decimal: $\frac{225}{1000} = \frac{45}{200} = \frac{9}{40}$

[Check: $9 \div 40 = 0·225$]

(b) As a fraction: 125% means $\qquad$ $\frac{125}{100} = \frac{25}{20} = \frac{5}{4} = 1\frac{1}{4}$

As a decimal: 125% means $\qquad$ $125 \div 100 = 1·25$

Exercise 2J

1. Convert each of these percentages into (i) a fraction (ii) a decimal.
   (a) 20%   (b) 30%   (c) 55%   (d) 35%   (e) 22%

2. Convert each of these decimals into (i) a percentage (ii) a fraction.
   (a) 0·3   (b) 0·7   (c) 0·15   (d) 0·35   (e) 0·58

3. Write each of these fractions as (i) a percentage (ii) a decimal.
   (a) $\frac{3}{4}$ (b) $\frac{2}{5}$ (c) $\frac{1}{10}$ (d) $\frac{3}{20}$

Summary

1. You can find equivalent fractions.

2. You can change mixed numbers to improper fractions and back.

3. You can find fractions of a quantity.

4. You can calculate with fractions.

5. You can convert between fractions, decimals and percentages.

Check out N2

1. Express $\frac{3}{5}$ as $\frac{?}{25}$.

2. (a) Express $\frac{37}{8}$ as a mixed number.
   (b) Express $2\frac{1}{5}$ as an improper fraction.

3. Find (a) $\frac{3}{5}$ of £27
   (b) $\frac{1}{3}$ of £39·60
   (c) $\frac{1}{4}$ of £18·20

4. Find (a) $\frac{3}{4} + \frac{2}{5}$ (b) $\frac{3}{5} - \frac{2}{7}$
   (c) $\frac{2}{3} \times 5$ (d) $\frac{3}{4} \times \frac{7}{12}$
   (e) $\frac{2}{5} \times 1\frac{1}{2}$ (f) $\frac{3}{4} \div \frac{6}{11}$

5. (a) Convert 40% to (i) a fraction
   (ii) a decimal.
   (b) Convert 0.3 to (i) a fraction
   (ii) a percentage.

Revision exercise N2

1. Andrew sees two different advertisements for the same pair of designer trainers

Train 'n' Sports

Our Price 40% off
Recommended
price of £84

Run 'n' Sports

Our Price
$\frac{1}{3}$ off
Recommended
price of £84

Calculate the final cost of the trainers in
(a) Train'n'Sports
(b) Run'n'Sports.
(c) Evaluate $\frac{2}{3} - \frac{1}{5}$, giving your answer as a fraction. [SEG]

2. (a) The cost of 6 medium eggs is 48 pence.

    (i) How much will 10 medium eggs cost?

    (ii) Small eggs cost $\frac{7}{8}$ of the price of medium eggs.
    How much will 6 small eggs cost?

    (iii) Large eggs cost 25% more than medium eggs.
    How much will 6 large eggs cost?

  (b) An egg weighs 57 g to the nearest gram.
    What is the minimum weight of the egg? [SEG]

3. Taka sees two different advertisements for the same CD Rom.

<table>
<tr><td>

Games A-go-go

Our Price

*15% off Recommended
Price
of £47*

</td><td>

*Computing
Companion*

Our Price
$\frac{1}{6}$ off Recommended Price
of
£47

</td></tr>
</table>

Calculate the final cost of the CD Rom in

(a) Games A-go-go

(b) Computing Companion. [SEG]

4. A Munch Crunch bar weighs 21 g.
Each bar contains the following nutrients.

Protein	1·9 g
Fat	4·7 g
Carbohydrate	13·3 g
Fibre	1·1 g

(a) What percentage of the bar is fat?
    Give your answer to an appropriate degree of accuracy.

(b) What is the ratio of protein to carbohydrate?
    Give your answer in the form $1 : n$. [SEG]

N3 NUMBER 3

Measurements are meaningless unless you know the units that they refer to. Spacecraft have been lost through using the wrong units.

I can't understand it. All my calculations were correct!

Yes, the numbers were right. But you used the wrong units!

This unit will show you how to:

- Use the metric system
- Convert between metric and imperial measures
- Calculate with time
- Calculate with speed and density

Before you start:

You should know how to...	Check in N3

1. Multiply and divide by 10, 100, 1000
 For example,
 $5 \cdot 829 \times 100$
 $= 5\,8\,2 \cdot 9$
	1. (a) Multiply
	     (i) 2·34 by 1000
	     (ii) 20·269 by 100
	   (b) Divide
	     (i) 2891 by 100
	     (ii) 347 by 1000

2. Give answers to an appropriate degree of accuracy	**2.** Give to the nearest penny
	   (a) £34 ÷ 73
	   (b) £86 ÷ 493

3.1 The metric system

Most quantities are now measured using the metric system.

- Lengths are measured in metres and centimetres.
- Weights are measured in grams and kilograms.
- Capacities are measured using litres and millilitres.

The metric system is easy to use because, like our number system, it works in base 10.

If you can multiply and divide by 10, 100, 1000, and so on then you can easily convert between different measures.

Multiplying by 10, 100, 1000

- When you multiply by 10, the digits move 1 place to the left.

  10 has 1 zero

  $56 \times 10 = 560$

- When you multiply by 100, the digits move 2 places to the left.

  100 has 2 zeros

  $234 \times 100 = 23\ 400$

- When you multiply by 1000, the digits move 3 places to the left.

  1000 has 3 zeros

  $12 \cdot 3 \times 1000 = 12\ 300$

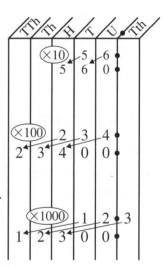

Dividing by 10, 100, 1000

- When you divide by 10, the digits move 1 place to the right.

  10 has 1 zero

  $56 \div 10 = 5 \cdot 6$

- When you divide by 100, the digits move 2 places to the right.

  100 has 2 zeros

  $236 \div 100 = 2 \cdot 36$

- When you divide by 1000, the digits move 3 places to the right.

  1000 has 3 zeros

  $1900 \div 1000 = 1 \cdot 9$

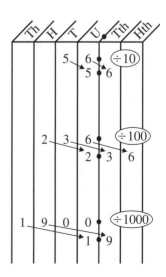

MODULE 3

Exercise 3A

1. Multiply
   (a) 783 by 10
   (b) 384 by 100
   (c) 295 by 10 000
   (d) 347 by 100

2. Divide
   (a) 394 by 10
   (b) 2748 by 1000
   (c) 4120 by 10 000
   (d) 29 by 100

3. Multiply
   (a) 74·2 by 100
   (b) 25·7 by 1000
   (c) 41·34 by 10
   (d) 8·7501 by 1000

4. Divide
   (a) 34·2 by 100
   (b) 71·8 by 1000
   (c) 0·28 by 10
   (d) 0·034 by 1000

5. Work out each of these.
   (a) 74 002 ÷ 100
   (b) 2·413 × 100
   (c) 0·024 ÷ 10
   (d) 0·000 34 × 100

3.2 Metric lengths

The basic metric unit of length is the metre (m).

A metre is about half the height of a door.
You would use a measuring tape to measure a metre.

Everyday lengths are often given in miles or inches.
You will find out more about these imperial measures on page 182.

This will help you to estimate lengths in metres.

There are 100 centimetres (cm) in a metre.
Your ruler is marked in cm.

There are 1000 m in 1 kilometre (km).
You'd measure this using a trundle wheel.

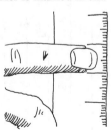

1 cm is about the width of your little finger.

1 km is about $2\frac{1}{2}$ times the distance around a football pitch.

You can measure very small lengths using millimetres (mm).
There are 10 mm in 1 cm.
That means there are 1000 mm in 1 m.

In summary:

- 10 mm = 1 cm
- 100 cm = 1 m
- 1000 m = 1 km

so

- 1 km = 1000 m = 100 000 cm = 1 000 000 mm

or

- 1 mm = 0·1 cm = 0·001 m = 0·000 001 km

> The millimetre got its name from the millipede which has about 1000 legs! And a centipede has about 100 legs!

To change between units:

units get bigger ———→ numbers get smaller ———→ divide

230 mm ———→ 23 cm ———→ 0·23 m ———→ 0·000 23 km

$\div 10$ $\div 100$ $\div 1000$

multiply ◄——— numbers get bigger ◄——— units get smaller

12 000 mm ◄——— 1200 cm ◄——— 12 m ◄——— 0·012 km

$\times 10$ $\times 100$ $\times 1000$

MODULE 3

Exercise 3B

Convert these lengths into the units required.

1. 2·3 m into cm

2. 31·4 cm into m

3. 1487 mm into

    (a) cm   (b) m

4. 24·7 mm into cm

5. 3·92 km into m

6. 254 mm into

    (a) m   (b) km

7. 489 m into

    (a) cm   (b) km

3.3 Metric weights

The basic metric unit of weight is the gram (g).
It is very light.

A teaspoon of sugar weighs about 1 gram.

1000 g = 1 kilogram (kg).
A bag of sugar weighs 1 kg.

1000 kg = 1 tonne (t).
A small car weighs a tonne!

A car is very heavy – a tonne is 1 000 000 grams!

There is a smaller weight than a gram – it is used to measure
very small things such as traces of chemicals or drops of blood.
You may have used the measure in Science.

1 g = 1000 milligrams (mg).

In summary:

- 1000 mg = 1 g
- 1000 g = 1 kg
- 1000 kg = 1 t

> **Remember:**
> 1000 mm = 1 m
> 1000 m = 1 km

Remember:

As the units get smaller the numbers get bigger so you multiply.
$0.02 \text{ t} = 0.02 \times 1000 \text{ kg} = 20 \text{ kg} = 20 \times 1000 \text{ g} = 20\,000 \text{ g}$
$= 20\,000 \times 1000 \text{ mg} = 20\,000\,000 \text{ mg}$

As the units get bigger the numbers get smaller so you divide.
$8700 \text{ mg} = 8700 \div 1000 \text{ g} = 8.7 \text{ g} = 8.7 \div 1000 \text{ kg} = 0.0087 \text{ kg}$
$= 0.0087 \div 1000 \text{ t} = 0.000\,008\,7 \text{ t}$

Exercise 3C

Convert these weights into the units required.

1. 278 g into kg

2. 394 mg into g

3. 7·4 g into
   (a) kg   (b) mg

4. 2·9 tonnes into
   (a) kg   (b) g

5. One pound is 453 grams.
   Express this weight in
   (a) kg   (b) mg

3.4 Metric capacity

Capacity is the amount of space a 3-D shape can hold.
The space may be taken up by

● a solid
● a liquid or
● a gas.

In any container, the amount of space stays the same but the
measure used changes depending on what is in the container.

For GCSE you need to know about liquid and solid measures.

Liquid measure

The basic metric measure for liquid capacity is the litre (l).
A bottle of soft drink holds 1 litre.

1 l = 1000 millilitres (ml)   1 l = 100 centilitres (cl)
A can of soft drink holds 330 ml.   A glass is measured in cl.
                                      A wine glass holds about 10 cl.

Solid measure

The equivalent solid measure for 1 litre is
1000 cubic centimetres (cm^3).
It measures the number of centimetre cubes that fit into the space.

The capacity of a car engine is measured in cm³.
A small car engine holds 1000 ccs or 1000 cm³.

You will find out more
about cm³ in the section
on volume on page 386.

In summary:

- 1000 ml = 1000 cm³ = 1 l
- 100 cl = 1 l
- 10 ml = 1 cl

Remember:
1000 mm = 1 m   1000 mg = 1 g
100 cm = 1 m
10 mm = 1 cm

Exercise 3D

1. Convert
   (a) 1748 g into kilograms
   (b) 3·45 km into metres
   (c) 2·85 kg into grams
   (d) 41·25 cl into litres
   (e) 89·487 m into cm
   (f) 924 800 mm into kilometres.

2. A bottle contains 75 cl of juice.
   How much is this in litres?

3. Two cables are 347·2 m and 810 cm in length.
   What is their combined length in metres?

4. A bag of flour contains 1·14 kg.
   Joan makes a cake and there is 1·074 kg of flour left.
   How many grams of flour have been used?

5. A roll of material is 13·4 m in length. After the next
   customer has taken some there is 12·34 m left.
   How much material was cut off?
   Give your answer
   (a) in metres
   (b) in millimetres.

3.5 Imperial measures

We still use some imperial measures.

Many people measure:

- heights in feet and inches
- weights in pounds and ounces
- long distances in miles
- capacity in pints and gallons.

The common imperial measures are:

Length	Weight	Capacity
feet, inches, yards and miles	ounces, pounds and stones	pints and gallons
12 inches (in) = 1 foot (ft) 3 feet = 1 yard 1760 yards = 1 mile	16 ounces (oz) = 1 pound (lb) 14 pounds (lb) = 1 stone	8 pints = 1 gallon

Example

Josh is 5 ft 7 in.
How many inches is this?

$5\,ft = 5 \times 12\,in = 60\,in$
so $5\,ft\,7\,in = 60\,in + 7\,in = 67\,in.$

5 ft 7 in is 67 inches.

> Using imperial measures is not as easy as using metric as you can see, but remember that as the units get bigger, the numbers get smaller so you divide and as the units get smaller, the numbers get bigger and so you multiply.

MODULE 3

Exercise 3E

1. Convert

    (a) 3 ft 9 inches into inches
    (b) 4 gallons into pints
    (c) 94 inches into feet and inches
    (d) 11 stone 4 pounds into pounds
    (e) 9 pounds into ounces
    (f) 7 feet 8 inches into inches
    (g) 84 pints into gallons
    (h) 1·1 miles into feet.

2. A petrol can contains 2 gallons.
   How many pints does it contain?

3. The dimensions of a room are 11 ft 3 inches by 9 ft 10 inches.
   Convert these dimensions into (a) feet   (b) inches.

4. A 14 inch TV has a screen which is 14 inches wide and
   10·5 inches high.
   What are the dimensions in feet?

5. A playground is 120 yards by 70 yards.
   What are the dimensions in feet?

3.6 Metric and imperial equivalents

For your exam you need to know the rough equivalents between some of the metric and imperial measures.

You should know that:

Length (short)	Length (long)	Weight	Capacity
1 inch = 2·54 cm	5 miles = 8 km	1 kg = 2·2 lb	1 gallon = 4·5 l

Example

Brenda weighs 9 stone 3 lb.
Roughly how much does she weigh in kilograms?
The measure linking weights is 1 kg = 2·2 lb.
To convert her weight to kg you must first convert it to lb.
1 stone = 14 lb
9 stone = 9 × 14 lb = 126 lb
9 stone 3 lb = 126 lb + 3 lb = 129 lb

Using the unitary method:
2·2 lb = 1 kg
so 1 lb = 1 ÷ 2·2 kg = 0·45 kg
so 129 lb = 129 × 0·45 kg = 58·05 kg.

There is more about the unitary method on page 33.

Exercise 3F

1. Find the approximate metric value of
   (a) 7 inches
   (b) 2 feet 3 inches
   (c) 9 feet 8 inches
   (d) 4.2 pounds
   (e) 12 ounces
   (f) 4 stone 3 pounds
   (g) 2·8 gallons
   (h) 7·6 gallons.

2. Find the approximate imperial value of
   (a) 32 cm
   (b) 4·8 m
   (c) 17 km
   (d) 8·3 km
   (e) 210 g
   (f) 4·2 kg
   (g) 70 litres
   (h) 94 litres.

3. The distance by road from Paris to Berlin is 1047 kilometres.
   Find the approximate value of this distance in miles.

4. A packet weighs 7·8 pounds.
   What is the approximate weight in kilograms?

5. Henry grows 14·2 kg of tomatoes.
   Approximately, what is this weight in pounds?

MODULE 3

3.7 Time

Time does not use the metric system. There are:

- 24 hours in a day
- 60 minutes in an hour, and
- 60 seconds in a minute.

> This makes it difficult to use a calculator when you calculate using time.

Time can be measured on a 12-hour scale:

- You use am for times before midday.
- You use pm for times after midday.

Time can also be measured on a 24-hour scale. Instead of starting again at 1 pm after midday, you carry on. This 24-hour scale shows the equivalent pm times.

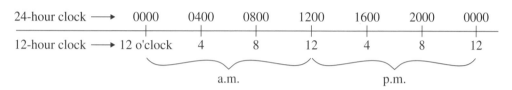

You need to be able to use the 24-hour clock to read timetables, to set the video or your mobile phone clock, and for many other everyday activities.

For times past midday you just:

- add 12 to pm hours on the 12-hour clock, and
- subtract 12 from the hour on the 24-hour clock.

Calculating with time

As time is not metric you cannot use a calculator for time.

- To work out changes in time you should:
  - use a time line, and
  - consider the hours and minutes separately.

> A time line is like a number line.

Example

Amy left home at 0850 and arrived in Birmingham at 1415.
How long did her journey take?

Draw a time line.

0850————+5 hours————→1350—+10 min→1400—+15 min→1415

      Work out the hours first   Then work out the minutes

Her journey took 5 hours and 25 minutes.

MODULE 3

Exercise 3G

1. Express these times in 24-hour clock mode.

   (a) 3.15 am

   (b) 5.20 am

   (c) 3.20 pm

   (d) 5.40 pm

   (e) half past two in the afternoon

   (f) quarter past one in the morning

   (g) ten to eight in the morning

   (h) quarter to six in the evening.

2. Express these times in am, pm mode

   (a) 0820

   (b) 0945

   (c) 1640

   (d) 1820

   (e) 0015

   (f) 2310

3. John worked from 9 am to 2.45 pm.
   How many hours did he work?

4. Sarah worked from 8.30 am to 1.15 pm.
   How many hours did Sarah work?

5. Alistair worked from 8.30 am to 4.30 pm with a lunch
   break of 1 hour. How long did Alistair work?

6. Haseeb worked from 8.15 am to 5.05 pm with a lunch break
   of 30 minutes. How long did Haseeb work?

7. Steff worked from 8.30 am to 5.15 pm with a lunch break
   of 30 minutes. How long did Steff work?

8. Ben caught the 1743 train from Bournemouth and it arrived
   at London at 2016. How long did the train journey take?

9. (a) Kath walked 15 minutes to the station. She left home at
       8.50 am and the train left at 9.28 am.
       How long did Kath wait at the station?

   (b) The train arrived at Kath's destination at 1.12 pm.
       How long did the train journey take?

10. Matt arrived at an airport at 7.50 am, two and a half hours
    before his plane took off. The flight took 3 hours 45
    minutes. When did the plane land?

3.8 Compound measures

Compound measures use two or more different types of measure.

$$\text{Speed} = \frac{\text{Distance}}{\text{Time}} \quad \text{uses length and time.}$$

This is the same as Speed × Time = Distance.

Density $= \dfrac{\text{Weight}}{\text{Volume}}$ uses weight and capacity.

There is more about formulae on page 234.

This is the same as Density $\times$ Volume $=$ Weight.
Both of these measures have the same sort of formula: $a = \frac{b}{c}$
You can use a triangle to work out how to rearrange the formulae.

Speed

Distance $=$ Speed $\times$ Time

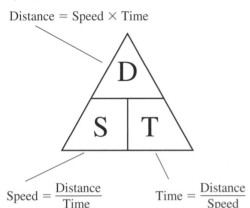

Speed $= \dfrac{\text{Distance}}{\text{Time}}$ Time $= \dfrac{\text{Distance}}{\text{Speed}}$

Density

Weight $=$ Density $\times$ Volume

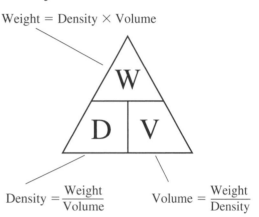

Density $= \dfrac{\text{Weight}}{\text{Volume}}$ Volume $= \dfrac{\text{Weight}}{\text{Density}}$

The units you use will depend on the measures you are using.

$\dfrac{\text{miles}}{\text{hours}}$ is miles per hour, written mph.

$\dfrac{\text{grams}}{\text{cm}^3}$ is grams per cm^3, written g/cm^3 or g cm^{-3}.

Example

What units would you use for
(a) speed if the time is measured in hours and the distance in kilometres
(b) speed if the time is measured in seconds and the distance in metres
(c) distance and the time if the speed is in miles per hour
(d) density if the volume is in kg and the volume is in m^3?

(a) speed $= \dfrac{\text{distance}}{\text{time}} = \dfrac{\text{km}}{\text{hours}}$ or km per hour, written km/h

(b) speed $= \dfrac{\text{distance}}{\text{time}} = \dfrac{\text{metres}}{\text{seconds}} =$ metres per second or m/s or m s^{-1}

(c) speed $= \dfrac{\text{miles}}{\text{hours}} = \dfrac{\text{distance}}{\text{time}}$ so distance $=$ miles and time $=$ hours

(d) density $= \dfrac{\text{weight}}{\text{volume}} =$ kg/m^3 $=$ kg per m^3

Exercise 3H

1. Liz travels 180 miles on a motorway in 5 hours.
   What is Liz's average speed?

2. A train travels 45 miles in $1\frac{1}{2}$ hours.
   What is its average speed?

3. A plane travels 5 hours at 525 mph.
   How far does it fly?

4. A car travelled $3\frac{1}{2}$ hours at 92 km/h.
   How far did it travel?

5. A plane travels 1740 miles at 510 mph.
   How long, in hours and minutes, is the flight?

6. A train travels from London to Edinburgh, a distance of 413 miles.

   (a) The train's average speed was 45 mph.
      How long did the journey take?

   Bill travels the journey by car at an average speed of 51 mph.

   (b) How long does Bill take?

7. A ferry travels 30 miles in 1 hour 49 minutes.
   What is its average speed?

8. The weight of a container is 4860 kg and its volume is 1754 cm³. Find its density in kg/cm³.

9. It takes 4 minutes to put 75 litres of petrol into a car.
   Find the rate of flow in litres per minute.

10. Bev is paid £31·56 for 6 hours work.
    How much is she paid for one hour?

11. The weight of a litre of a liquid is 1132 g.
    Find the density of the liquid in grams per cm³.
    You may use 1 litre = 1000 cm³.

12. The density of a block of wood is 0·8 g per cm³.
    Its weight is 2·3 g. Find its volume.

Summary

1. You can convert from one metric measure to another.

2. You can convert from one imperial measure to another.

3. You can convert between metric and imperial measures.

4. You can do calculations involving time.

5. You can do calculations involving compound measures.

Check out N3

1. Convert
   (a) 375 cm into metres
   (b) 2·1 litres into centilitres.

2. Convert
   (a) 3 ft 4 ins into inches
   (b) 2 stones 3 pounds into pounds.

3. Convert
   (a) 5 kg into pounds.
   (b) 10 miles into kilometres.
   (c) Convert 3 ft into centimetres.

4. Find how long it is between
   (a) 5.40 pm and 9.10 pm
   (b) 11.20 am and 5.15 pm

5. Find the speed if you travel
   (a) 56 miles in 2 hours
   (b) 72 miles in $2\frac{1}{4}$ hours.
   (c) Find the time taken, in hours and minutes, to travel 258 miles at 60 mph.

MODULE 3

Revision exercise N3

1. (a) A recipe for plum jam states:
       2 kg of plums and 2 kg of sugar are needed to make
       3·6 kg of jam.
       Kevin makes 4·5 kg of jam.
       How many kilograms of plums does he need?
   (b) Kevin puts the jam into 1 lb jars.
       How many jars are needed for 4·5 kg of jam?

2. (a) A year ago Martin was 1·60 m tall.
       He is now 4% taller.
       Calculate his height now.
       Give your answer in centimetres.
   (b) Martin now weighs 58 kg.
       A year ago he weighed 51 kg.
       Calculate the percentage increase in his weight.
       Give your answer to an appropriate degree of accuracy.

       [SEG]

3. Strawberries cost £1·50 for 1 lb.

(a) Estimate, to the nearest £, the cost of buying 2 kg of strawberries.

(b) Gooseberries cost 30% per pound more than strawberries.
Calculate the cost of a pound of gooseberries.

(c) John buys 500 g of strawberries.
The weight of the strawberries is correct to the nearest 10 g.
What is the minimum weight of the strawberries? **[SEG]**

4. (a) A taxi left Russell Square at 1643.
It arrived at Waterloo station 22 minutes later.
At what time did the taxi arrive at Waterloo station?
Give your answer in 12-hour clock time.

(b) Part of a railway timetable is shown.

London Waterloo	1630	1645	1715	1745	1830	1850
Southampton	1739	1810	1825	1859	1940	2018
Bournemouth	1812	1831	1856	1929	2011	2101
Poole	1825	1905	1907	1942	2023	2116
Weymouth	1913	–	1953	2028	2111	–

George catches the 1745 train from London Waterloo to
Bournemouth.
How long does the journey take? **[SEG]**

5. The diagram shows the distances, in miles, between some
junctions on the M4.

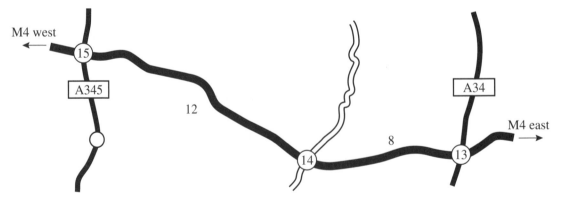

A bus is travelling west on the M4.
At 1140 it passes junction 13 and at 1152 it passes junction 14.

(a) Calculate the average speed of the bus in miles per hour.

Between junctions 14 and 15 the bus travels at an average
speed of 60 miles per hour.

(b) Calculate the time when the bus passes junction 15. **[SEG]**

6. (a) John is 8·4 kg heavier than Alan.
The sum of their weights is 133·2 kg.
How heavy is Alan?

(b) Before starting a diet Derek weighed 80 kg.
He now weighs 8 kg less.
Calculate his weight loss as a percentage of his previous
weight.

(c) Sarah weighs 54 kg.

(i) Sarah's weight has been given to the nearest kilogram.
What is the minimum weight she could be?

(ii) What is Sarah's weight in pounds?   [SEG]

7. On a Saturday 1·5 million copies of a newspaper are printed.

(a) Write 1·5 million in standard form.

(b) Each copy of the newspaper has 80 pages.
Calculate the total number of pages printed on a Saturday.
Give your answer in standard form.

(c) The total weight of the newspapers is 3×10^5 kg.
Calculate the weight of one newspaper.
Give your answers in grams.   [SEG]

8. Sheila lives 6 kilometres from the beach.
She jogs from her home to the beach at an average speed of
10 km/h.
She gets to the beach at 10:00.
Calculate the time when she left home.   [SEG]

9. A publisher prints $1·25 \times 10^6$ copies of a magazine.
Each magazine consists of 18 sheets of paper.

(a) Calculate the number of sheets of paper needed to print all the
magazines. Give your answer in standard form.

To make the magazine, the sheets of paper are folded as shown.

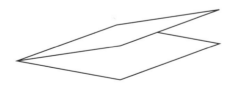

(b) The height of a pile of magazines is 79·1 cm.
The pile contains 232 magazines.
Calculate, in centimetres, the thickness of one sheet of
paper.   [SEG]

N4 NUMBER 4

When you go shopping in a supermarket, you should be able to work out mentally what is the best purchase.

This unit will show you how to:

- Understand wages and taxes
- Calculate profit and loss
- Calculate with interest and credit
- Decide on the best buy from a selection
- Convert between currencies

Before you start:

You should know how to...	Check in N4
1. Calculate a fraction and a percentage of an amount For example, $\frac{2}{3}$ of 51 is $\frac{2}{3} \times 51 = \dfrac{2 \times \cancel{51}^{17}}{\cancel{3}_1}$ $= 34$	**1.** Find (a) $\frac{2}{5}$ of £72 (b) $\frac{1}{3}$ of £42 (c) 20% of £38 (d) 37% of £45
2. Find a unitary cost	**2.** Eight grapefruit cost £2·56. What is the cost of one grapefruit?

4.1 Wages and salaries

Most people are paid for the work they do. They may receive cash in hand, a wage or a salary.

- A **wage** is paid weekly and is usually paid at an hourly rate.
  Wage = Number of hours worked × Hourly rate of pay
- A **salary** is paid monthly and is usually paid at an annual rate.
  A monthly salary will be $\frac{1}{12}$ of the annual salary.

Example 1

Joe works 14 hours a week at a burger bar and is paid £4·15 per hour. Find his weekly wage.
Joe's wage is calculated as:

$$\begin{aligned} \text{Wage} &= \text{Number of hours worked} \times \text{Rate of pay} \\ \text{Wage} &= 14 \times £4\cdot15 \\ &= £58\cdot10 \end{aligned}$$

Example 2

One week, Zoe received £188·25 for her week's work. She is paid £5·02 per hour. How many hours did Zoe work that week?

$$\begin{aligned} \text{Number of hours worked} &= \frac{\text{Weekly wage}}{\text{Rate of pay per hour}} \\ &= \frac{£188\cdot25}{£5\cdot02} \\ &= 37\cdot5 \text{ hours} \end{aligned}$$

So Zoe worked $37\frac{1}{2}$ hours that week.

Exercise 4A

1. Ben works 11 hours per week in a burger bar. He is paid £4·15 per hour. How much is his weekly pay?

2. Fatima works 14 hours per week in a supermarket. She is paid £3·90 per hour. How much is her weekly pay?

3. Avril works $17\frac{3}{4}$ hours per week and is paid £5·12 per hour. How much is her weekly pay?

4. Carl is paid £4·74 per hour for each of the $19\frac{1}{3}$ hours that he works in a week. How much is he paid per week?

5. Asif works 12 hours 20 minutes in a newsagent. He is paid £4·05 per hour. How much is he paid?

MODULE 3

6. Helen is paid £4·20 per hour and works 8 hours 40 minutes. How much is she paid?

7. John works from 8.30 am until 5 pm, with a one hour unpaid lunch break. He is paid £4·50 per hour. How much is he paid for this day's work?

8. Jill works from 8.45 am until 4.45 pm, and has a half-hour unpaid lunch break. She is paid £4·80 per hour. How much is she paid for this day's work?

9. Claire is paid £115·64 for her week's work in a restaurant. She is paid £4·72 per hour. How many hours has Claire worked?

10. (a) Peter is paid £135·72 for his week's work. He is paid £4·64 per hour. How many hours has he worked?
    (b) Peter has a pay rise, and is paid £152·29 when he works $32\frac{1}{3}$ hours. How much is his hourly increase in pay?

4.2 Overtime

Sometimes when you work more than your set number of hours per week you earn overtime.

Overtime is also paid when employers find it hard to get staff to work, for example on a Sunday or Bank Holiday.

- Common overtime rates are:
  - double time – you earn 2 × the normal hourly rate, and
  - time and a half – you earn 1·5 × the normal hourly rate.

You can only earn overtime on the 'over' hours you work. You will get your normal hourly rate for your normal working hours.

> You are more likely to get overtime if you earn a wage rather than a salary. Some employers give 'time off in lieu' which means extra time off instead of extra pay.

Example

Lynne is paid a basic rate of £5·08 per hour. Her standard working week is 38 hours. In one week Lynne also works 8 hours in the evenings for which she is paid overtime at time and a half, and 5 hours on Sunday for which she is paid double time. Find Lynne's gross pay for that week.

Lynne's overtime rate at time and a half is £5·08 + ($\frac{1}{2}$ × £5.08)   = £7·62
Lynne's overtime rate of pay on Sunday is £5·08 × 2   = £10·16
Lynne's basic pay for the 38-hour week is 38 × £5·08   = £193·04
Lynne's overtime pay for the 8 hours evening work is 8 × £7·62   = £60·96
Lynne's pay for the five hours she worked on Sunday is 5 × £10·16 = £50·80
So Lynne's gross pay for the week is £193·04 + £60·96 + £50·80   = £304·80

Exercise 4B

1. Philip works in a burger bar. His basic rate of pay is £3·75 per hour. On Sunday he is paid double time. Philip works 5 hours on Sunday. How much is he paid?

2. Ingrid works in a hotel. On Saturday evening, she is paid double time. Her basic rate of pay is £4·20 per hour.
   How much is she paid when she works for 3 hours and 20 minutes on Saturday evening?

3. James works $5\frac{1}{2}$ hours on Saturday, and is paid overtime at time and a half. His basic pay is £4·10 per hour.
   How much is he paid for that Saturday?

4. Kelly works in a supermarket, and her basic pay is £4·26 per hour. One Saturday, she works $6\frac{1}{2}$ hours and is paid overtime at time and a half. What is her pay for that Saturday?

5. Elaine is paid a basic rate of £4·78 per hour. Her standard working week is 37 hours. In one week Elaine also works 7 hours in the evenings for which she is paid overtime at time and a half, and 6 hours on Sunday for which she is paid double time. Find Elaine's gross pay for that week.

6. Mark is paid a basic rate of £5·16 per hour. His standard working week is 39 hours. In one week Mark also works 4 hours in the evenings for which he is paid overtime at time and a half, and 8 hours on Sunday for which he is paid double time. Find Mark's gross pay for that week.

7. Shelley's standard working week is 38 hours, and her basic rate of pay is £4·38 per hour. In one week, she works additional hours, and is paid overtime at time and a half. Her pay for that week is £192·72. How many hours overtime does Shelley work?

8. Asif normally works 37 hours in a week, and is paid £155·40. In one week, he works additional hours in the evening, and is paid overtime at time and a half. His pay for that week is £176·40. How many hours overtime does he work?

MODULE 3

4.3 Income tax

The government takes income tax from your wage or salary, to pay for services.

There is a small amount of money you can earn before you pay tax.

The thresholds at which you start to pay tax and at which the rate of tax increases change each year in the Budget.

In 2001, the thresholds were:

Unless you are self-employed, your income tax will normally be deducted from your wage or salary.

Annual income	Rate of tax
Up to £4535	0%
From £4535 to £6415	10%
From £6415 to £33 935	23%
Over £33 935	40%

The tax year starts at the beginning of April each year and finishes at the end of March the following year.

Calculating your tax is easy if you take it in steps.

The 0% threshold is different if you are married or a pensioner. You can check the current tax rates on the Inland Revenue's website: www.inlandrevenue.gov. uk

Example

Zoe is a self-employed website designer.
In the current tax year she earned £31 207.
Calculate how much tax she owes the Inland Revenue.

From £4535 to £6415 she pays 10% tax,
that is 10% of £(6415 − 4535) = £188
From £6415 to £31 207 she pays 23% tax,
that is 23% of £(31 207 − 6415) = £5702·16
Her total tax bill is £5702.16 + £188 = **£5890·16**

Exercise 4C

For the questions in this exercise use the income tax rates in the table above.

1. Harry earns £5290 in a year, and has a tax-free allowance of £4535. Find
   (a) his taxable income
   (b) the amount he pays in income tax in the year.

2. Chloe earns £5828 in a year, and has a tax-free allowance of £4535. Find the amount of income tax she pays annually.

3. Mary is paid £109 per week, and has a tax-free allowance of £4535. Find how much income tax she pays in a year.

4. Bev is paid £454 per month, and has a tax-free allowance of £4535. How much does Bev pay annually in income tax?

5. Greg is paid £461 per month, and has a tax-free allowance of £4535. Find how much he pays in income tax each month.

6. Sara is paid £2175 per month, and has a tax-free allowance of £4535. Find how much she pays in income tax each month.

7. Glenda is paid £11 370 per year. She has a tax-free allowance of £4535. Find the amount of income tax she pays per year.

8. Charles is paid £237 per week, and has a tax-free allowance of £4535. Find
   (a) his annual taxable income
   (b) the income tax he pays per year.

9. Edna is paid £295 per week, and has a tax-free allowance of £4535. Find
   (a) her annual taxable income
   (b) the income tax she pays per year.

10. Troy is paid £2151 per month, and has a tax-free allowance of £4535. Find
    (a) his annual taxable income
    (b) the income tax he pays per month.

4.4 Value added tax

Value added tax (VAT) is a tax that is added to the retail price of goods and services.

As for income tax, VAT is not included in the basic price of an item but is added by the retailer. Usually the price tag or bill already includes VAT.

Many small businesses can claim the VAT paid back from the Inland Revenue so they need to be able to find out how much VAT they have paid.

VAT is currently 17·5% on most goods and services.

You need to be able to calculate VAT with or without a calculator.

> VAT on electricity and gas use is 5%.
> It is 0% on children's clothes.

MODULE 3

Example 1

Find the cost of these items including VAT.

(a) Computer + printer
    Price = £699 + VAT

(b) Computer + printer + scanner
    Price = £1070 + VAT

(a) £699 + 17·5% of £699
    = 117·5% of £699
    = 1·175 × £699
    = £821·33

(b) £1070 + 17·5% of £1070
    10% of £1070 = £107
    so   5% of £1070 = £ 53·50
    2·5% of £1070 = £ 26·75
    so 17·5% of £1070 = £187·25
    Price including VAT is £1257·25

- To calculate the price including VAT you multiply by 1·175:
  Price before VAT × 1·175 = Price including VAT
- So to find the price without VAT, you divide by 1·175:
  Price before VAT = Price including VAT ÷ 1·175

Example 2

A widescreen TV costs £450 including VAT.
Find the price before VAT.

Price before VAT = Price including VAT ÷ 1·175
Price before VAT = £450 ÷ 1·175 = £382·98

Exercise 4D

1. Tony receives a gas bill for £80, plus VAT at 5%.
   How much is
   (a) the VAT
   (b) the total gas bill?

2. Jamie receives an electricity bill for £140 plus VAT at 5%.
   How much is the total bill?

3. Peter receives a gas bill for £73·51 plus VAT at 5%.
   How much is the total bill?

4. Caroline receives an electricity bill for £92·56 plus VAT at
   5%. How much is the total bill?

5. Frank buys a computer costing £749 plus VAT. VAT is levied
   at 17·5%. Find
   (a) the VAT on the computer
   (b) the total cost of the computer.

6. Kelli buys an upgrade for her computer costing £128 plus
   VAT at 17·5%. Find
   (a) the VAT on the upgrade
   (b) the total cost of the upgrade.

MODULE 3

7. A DIY store sells fencing posts at £4·22 each. VAT at $17\frac{1}{2}\%$ is charged in addition. What is the cost inclusive of VAT?

8. A wholesaler sells soap powder at £16·32 plus VAT at $17\frac{1}{2}\%$. Find the price inclusive of VAT.

9. Jim receives a bill from a solicitor for £384·70. VAT is charged at $17\frac{1}{2}\%$ on this amount.
How much does Jim pay the solicitor?

10. A garage bill for a repair to a car is for £382·35 inclusive of VAT at $17\frac{1}{2}\%$. How much is the VAT?

11. The cost of refurbishing a kitchen is £9275 inclusive of VAT at $17\frac{1}{2}\%$. What was the total cost before VAT was added?

12. A gas bill is for £131·74. This includes the cost of VAT at 5%. How much is the VAT?

4.5 Profit and loss

A retailer makes money by selling most goods for more than they cost. This is profit.

Sometimes it is worth making a loss on some goods just to get customers in the shop to spend on other goods.

- Profit or less = Selling price − Cost price
- Percentage profit or loss $= \dfrac{\text{Profit or loss}}{\text{Cost price}} \times 100\%$

Example

Joan buys 12 pairs of jeans from the wholesalers for £300 and sells them for £36 a pair.
What is her percentage profit on one pair?

The cost price per pair is £300 ÷ 12 = £25.
Her profit per pair is £36 − £25 = £11.

$$\% \text{ Profit} = \frac{\text{Profit}}{\text{Cost price}} \times 100\%$$

$$= \frac{11 \times \overset{4}{\cancel{100}}}{\underset{1}{\cancel{25}}}\%$$

$$= 44\% \text{ per pair}$$

Exercise 4E

1. A market trader buys a pair of jeans for £12·50 and then sells them for £17. What is
   (a) his profit
   (b) his percentage profit?

2. A shopkeeper buys a pair of shoes for £30 and sells them at £48. What is her percentage profit?

3. A farm shop sells daffodils at 30p per bunch of 12 flowers. The daffodils cost the shop $1\frac{1}{2}$p each. What is the shop's percentage profit?

4. Pauline buys dresses at £20 each. She sells them at £37 each.
   (a) What is her percentage profit?
   In a sale, she reduces the selling price to £17.
   (b) What is the percentage loss that she makes on each dress sold in the sale?

5. A trader buys 350 CDs at £8 each and then sells them at £23 each. To clear his stock, he sells the last fifty at a discount of 40%.
   (a) How much is the new selling price of each CD?
   (b) How much in total does the trader receive from the sale of the 350 CDs?

6. A shopkeeper buys 200 cauliflowers at 30p each. He sells 120 at 69p each, and then reduces the price by $\frac{1}{3}$. At the end of the day, he has only 10 cauliflowers left, which he throws away. Find
   (a) the reduced selling price
   (b) the total amount of money received by selling the cauliflowers
   (c) the percentage profit made on the 200 cauliflowers.

7. A trader buys 420 books at £1·20 each and then sells them at £1·99 each. To clear his stock, he sells the last twenty at a discount of 30%.
   (a) How much is the new selling price of each book?
   (b) How much in total does the trader receive from the sale of the 420 books?

4.6 Interest and savings

If you invest money in a bank or building society, you are paid
interest by the bank or building society.
Conversely, if you borrow money, you pay interest to the bank
or building society.

The Bank of England sets the base interest rate. Banks and
building societies use the base rate to work out their own rates.

The rate paid for savings is usually below the base rate.
The rate charged for borrowing is usually higher than the base rate.

Savings

Many people save some of their earnings – for a holiday, to buy
a house or a car, for a rainy day …

You are paid interest on savings in one of two ways:

1. Simple interest
This is calculated on the original sum you invest, called the **principal**.
It depends on the interest rate and the number of years you invest.

$$\text{Simple interest} = \frac{\text{Principal} \times \text{Interest rate} \times \text{Time in years}}{100} = \frac{PRT}{100}$$

2. Compound interest
This is calculated each year.
The amount of interest you earn is added to the principal and
becomes the new principal each year.
This is far more common than simple interest.

Example

Amit invests £300 for three years at 5·2% per annum.
Calculate what it would be worth after three years if he is paid
(a) simple interest.
(b) compound interest.

(a) Simple interest $= \dfrac{PRT}{100}$

$$= \frac{300 \times 5 \cdot 2 \times 3}{100}$$

$$= £46 \cdot 80$$

So after 3 years Amit's investment is worth £346·80.

(b) Compound interest
   At the end of year 1, the interest is 5·2% of £300 = £15·60
   In year 2 the new balance is £315·60 (= 105·2% of £300)
   At the end of year 2, the balance is 105·2% of £315·60 = £332·01
   At the end of year 3, the balance is 105·2% of £332·01 = £349·27

Amit has earned £2·47 more interest under the compound interest system.

Notice that in the compound interest example, you can get the same result by repeatedly multiplying by 105·2%, that is 3 times for 3 years.

After 3 years at 5·2% interest, Amit's £300 is worth
£300 × 1·052 × 1·052 × 1·052 = £349·27

You could write this calculation like this:

$$£300 \times \left(1 + \frac{5·2}{100}\right)^3 = £349·27$$

In general, the formula for calculating the **new** amount A when compound interest is added over T years is:

$$A = P \times \left(1 + \frac{R}{100}\right)^T$$

Note:
The number in the brackets is called the **multiplier**.

Exercise 4F

1. Mark invests £480 at 3% simple interest for 5 years.
   Find the interest which Mark makes.

2. Liz invests £1780 at 5·2% simple interest for 4 years.
   Find the interest which Liz makes.

3. Vicky invests £2300 and obtains £340·40 interest. The interest is paid as simple interest after 5 years.
   What rate of interest did Vicky get for her money?

4. Henry obtains £46 interest in two years when he invests his money at 4·3% interest. This interest is paid as simple interest. Find the amount of money that Henry invested.

5. Kate invests £5200 and is paid £470·08 in interest. The interest is paid as simple interest after 4 years.
   What rate of interest did Kate get for her money?

6. Carl invests his money at 3·2% simple interest. After 2 years he is paid £24 in interest.
   How much did Carl invest?

MODULE 3

7. Tim invests £370 at 4% interest. The interest is compounded annually. Find the interest earned in 3 years.

8. Susan invests £1250 at 5% interest. The interest is compounded annually. Find the interest earned in 2 years.

9. £3000 is invested at 8% per annum interest. The interest is compounded every 6 months.
Find the interest earned in 2 years.

10. £5000 is invested at 6% per annum interest. The interest is compounded every 4 months.
Find the interest earned in 1 year.

11. £4000 is invested at 5% per annum interest. The interest is compounded every 6 months.
Find the interest earned in 18 months.

12. £900 is invested at 4% per annum interest. The interest is compounded every 3 months.
Find the interest earned in 15 months.

13. £8000 is invested at 3% per annum interest. The interest is compounded every 6 months.
Find the interest earned in 10 years.

14. £1800 is invested at 6% per annum interest. The interest is compounded every 4 months.
Find the interest earned in 10 years.

15. £2100 is invested at 4·4% per annum interest. The interest is compounded every 6 months.
Find the interest earned in 8 years.

16. £48 000 is invested at 4·6% per annum interest. The interest is compounded every 3 months.
Find the interest earned in 12 years.

17. £1900 is invested at 4% per annum interest. The interest is compounded every three months.
Find the interest earned in 15 years.

18. £8000 is invested at 4·3% per annum interest. The interest is compounded every six months.
Find the interest earned in 10 years.

19. £9800 is invested at 6·42% per annum interest. The interest is compounded every four months.
Find the interest earned in 10 years.

4.7 Interest and borrowing

People borrow money from banks and building societies by way of a

- loan
- credit card account
- mortgage.

Interest on an amount borrowed is usually worked out using compound interest.

> Using a credit card is the simplest and most popular way to borrow money. It is also the most expensive!

Example 1

Melanie borrows £400 and is charged interest at 1·12% per month. Calculate how much she owes after 2 years.

The interest is charged per month and the time is in years. The units must be the same so change the years to months:

2 years is 24 months.

1·12% interest = 101·12% total

Melanie will owe £400 × 1·0112²⁴

$$= £522 \cdot 58$$

> The rate of interest may be given monthly but the best way to compare how much it will cost is to look at the annual percentage rate: APR. The lower the APR the better the deal.

Buying on credit

Sometimes when you buy goods you can pay over a period of time.

The goods may be available on interest-free credit, in which case you only pay the cost price.

Usually though you have to pay interest if you pay over a period.

Example 2

Kevin wants to buy a computer on credit. The computer is on sale at a cash price of £899. Kevin agrees to pay a deposit of £99 and to repay the remainder over three years at the rate of £31 per month.

Find (a) the total credit price
(b) the extra amount Kevin has to pay for credit
(c) the extra which Kevin pays as a percentage of the amount he borrows.

(a) The monthly repayments are £31

Kevin pays 36 repayments = 36 × £31 = £1116

Total credit price = Deposit + Total monthly repayments

= £99 + £1116

= £1215

(b) The extra amount paid is the total credit price − the cash price

= £1215 − £899

= £316

(c) Kevin had to borrow the difference between the cash price and the deposit which he paid.

He borrows £899 − £99 = £800

Kevin pays $\frac{316}{800} \times 100\%$

= 39·5% extra

Exercise 4G

1. Melanie buys a minidisc player on credit. Its cash price is £210. The credit terms are a deposit of £65 and 12 monthly payments of £15. Find
    (a) the total credit price
    (b) the extra paid for credit.

2. Kevin buys a mountain bike that is on sale at £149·95. The credit terms are a deposit of £39·95 and 12 monthly payments of £11. Find
    (a) the total credit price
    (b) the extra paid for credit.

3. Shaun buys a trombone with a cash price of £3050. The credit terms are a deposit of 20% and 36 monthly payments of £90. Find
    (a) the total credit price
    (b) the extra paid for credit.

4. Hazel buys a tennis racket that is on sale for £199. The credit terms are a deposit of 25% and 24 monthly payments of £7. Find
    (a) the total credit price
    (b) the extra paid for credit.

MODULE 3

5. Caroline buys a set of golf clubs. The cash price of the golf clubs is £499. The credit terms are a deposit of 30% and 36 monthly payments of £11. Find

   (a) the total credit price

   (b) the extra paid for credit.

6. Jerome buys a digital camera that is on sale for £299·99. The credit terms are a deposit of 20% and 36 monthly payments of £8. Find

   (a) the total credit price

   (b) the extra paid for credit.

7. Lisa buys a camcorder that is on sale at £259·99. The credit terms are a deposit of 30% and 24 monthly payments of £8·20. Find

   (a) the total credit price

   (b) the extra paid for credit.

8. Bob and Sarah book a holiday costing £290 each. They pay a deposit of £75 each and repay the remainder in six monthly instalments of £37 each. Find

   (a) the total credit price

   (b) the extra paid for credit.

4.8 Best buys

Some supermarkets show you the comparative prices for similar items. Usually though, you need to be able to work out what is the best buy for yourself.

Example

Jam is sold in three different sizes:

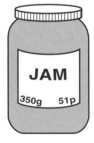
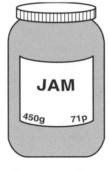

Which is the best value for money?

You want to know which jar has the lowest cost per gram.
First work out how much 1 gram costs for each jar:

350 g costs 51p	450 g costs 71p	750 g costs 120p
1 g costs 51p ÷ 350	1 g costs 71p ÷ 450	1 g costs 120p ÷ 750
1 g costs 0·1457p	1 g costs 0·1578p	1 g costs 0·16p

The 350 g jar has the lowest cost per gram so it is the best value
for money.

(Hint: you can multiply all the amounts by 100 so that you
compare the prices for 100 g if you prefer to work with larger
numbers:

100 g costs 14·57p	100 g costs 15·78p	100 g costs 16p

It is now easier to see that the 350 g jar is the best value.)

Exercise 4H

1. Orange juice is sold in two sizes: one-litre packs costing
   72p, and a 2·4-litre pack costing £1·70.
   Find which is the better buy.

2. Packs of file paper are sold in two sizes. 40 sheets cost 74p,
   and 100 sheets cost £1·79. Which size is the better buy?

3. Video tapes are sold in different packs. A pack of 4 video
   tapes costs £4·99, and a pack of 5 tapes costs £6·19.
   Which is the better buy?

4. Paint is sold in two different size tins. $2\frac{1}{2}$ litres costs £13·49,
   and 10 litres costs £51. Which is the better buy?

5. Coke is sold in two sizes. A two-litre bottle costs £1·49, and
   a 0·75-litre bottle costs 51p. Which size is the better buy?

6. Bottled water is sold in two sizes. The 500 ml size costs
   32p, and the 1·25 litre size costs 79p.
   Which is the better buy?

7. Tomato ketchup is sold in three sizes. The 450 g size costs
   84p, the 200 g size costs 41p, and the 1400 g size costs
   £2·79. Which is the best buy?

8. A breakfast cereal is sold in two sizes. A packet containing
   36 biscuits costs £1·45, and a packet containing 48 biscuits
   costs £1·99. Which is the better buy?

9. Honey is sold in two sizes. A jar containing 450 grams costs 39 French francs, and a 200 g jar costs 18 French francs. Which is the better buy?

10. Bathroom tiles are sold in two different packs. A pack containing 36 tiles costs £9·99, and a pack containing 50 tiles costs £14·49. Which is the better buy?

4.9 Foreign exchange rates

The currency in the UK is sterling and uses the symbols £ and p.

When you go abroad you have to use a different currency. Exchange rates for foreign currencies change every day.

You can find up-to-date exchange rates at www.Expedia.co.uk

In Europe there is a new currency called the euro, which you will use when you go to Europe and may soon be used every day in the UK.

Here are some exchange rates for major tourist destinations.

Country	Currency	Exchange rates (to nearest penny)
USA	Dollar ($)	£0·69
Europe	Euro (€)	£0·63
Australia	Australian dollar (A$)	£0·37
Jamaica	Jamaican dollar (J$)	£0·02
India	Rupee (Rs)	£0·01
Thailand	Baht (Bt)	£0·02
Turkey	Turkish lira (TL)	£0·00
Israel	New shekel (NIS)	£0·16

Example

Deirdre goes to New York for a shopping weekend.
She takes $300 spending money.
How much is this in sterling?

$1 = £0·69
$300 = 300 × £0·69
     = £207

Exercise 4I

1. Charles pays $14·70 for a CD. The exchange rate is $1·47 to £1. How much does the CD cost in pounds?

2. A trip in a cable car in Switzerland costs 47·30 Swiss francs. The exchange rate is 2·58 Swiss francs to £1. What is the cost of the cable car trip in pounds?

3. A drink in Canada costs $3·49. The exchange rate is 2·28 Canadian dollars to £1. What is the cost of the drink in pounds?

4. A train fare in Japan is 3200 yen. The exchange rate is 155·80 yen to £1. What is the cost of the train fare in pounds?

5. A trip to Ayers Rock costs 231 Australian dollars. The exchange rate is 2·71 Australian dollars to the £. Find the cost of the trip in pounds.

6. An ice cream in Denmark costs 23·1 kroner. The exchange rate is 12.5 Danish kroner to the £. Find the cost of the ice cream in pounds.

7. The hire of a sunbed for a day in Cyprus costs 4·99 Cyprus pounds. The exchange rate is 0·942 Cyprus pounds to the £. Find the cost of the trip in pounds.

8. A meal in Turkey costs 9 758 000 lire. The exchange rate is 945 500 Turkish lire to £1. What is the cost of the meal in pounds?

9. The entrance to a club in Lithuania is 99 litas. The exchange rate is 6·45 litas to £1. What is the cost of the entrance in pounds?

10. A boat cruise in Thailand costs 229 baht. The exchange rate is 58·76 baht to £1. What is the cost of the boat cruise in pounds?

11. A hotel room in Cape Town costs 199 rand. The exchange rate is 10·57 rand to £1. What is the cost of the hotel room in pounds?

12. Ron and Sue buy dinner in the USA. Their meal costs $25 each. In addition, they have to pay a tax of 6·25% on the total. They also pay a 15% service charge. The exchange rate is $1·47 to £1.

    (a) How much is the total cost of the dinner in dollars?

    (b) What is the total cost in pounds?

MODULE 3

Summary

1. You can work out wages and salaries.

2. You can work out overtime payments.

3. You can work out income tax payments.

4. You can calculate VAT.

5. You can work out the profit or loss on a sale.

6. You can work out
(a) simple interest
(b) compound interest.

7. You can find which is a best buy.

8. You can do calculations involving exchange rates.

Check out N4

1. Find the weekly wage if Avril works $38\frac{1}{2}$ hours and is paid £4·24 per hour.

2. Find the overtime earned when you work 3 hours 20 minutes at time and a half. Your normal pay is £5·10 per hour.

3. Philip earns £210 per week and has a tax free allowance of £4385. The rate of tax is 10p in the £ on the first £1520 of taxable income and 22p in the £ on the remainder. Find the income tax paid.

4. (a) Find the VAT charged on a gas bill of £132·48. The rate of VAT is 5%.
(b) Find the total cost of a washing machine costing £328·50 plus VAT at 17·5%.

5. A book is bought at £9·09 and sold at £14·38.
What is the percentage profit?

6. (a) Sue invests £900 at 4% simple interest for 3 years.
What is the interest earned?
(b) Henry invests £3000 for 8 years in an account which pays 3% interest every 6 months. What is the interest earned?

7. Porridge is sold in two different sized packs: a 1 kilogram pack at £2·99 and a 600 gram pack at £1·83.
Which is the better value?

8. (a) A CD player costs $49·95. The exchange rate is $1·49 to £1. Find the cost of the CD player in pounds.
(b) A meal in Norway costs £11. The exchange rate is 13·5 krone to £1. Find the cost of the meal in krone.

Revision exercise N4

1. (a) Richard buys 8 bars of toffee.
He pays with a £5 note.
He gets £2·04 change.
How much is a bar of toffee?

(b) The diagram shows the weights and prices of two sticks
of rock.

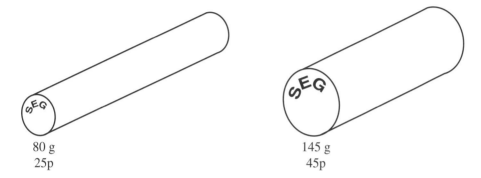

80 g   145 g
25p   45p

Which stick of rock gives more grams per penny?
You must show all your working.   [SEG]

2. Gita's basic rate of pay is £3·70 per hour. When Gita works
on Saturday, she is paid at time and a half.
One Saturday Gita works six and a quarter hours.
How much is Gita's pay for this Saturday?   [SEG]

3. Sue is a caretaker. She is paid at the basic rate of £4·36 per hour.

(a) When Sue works overtime, she is paid at one and a half times the
basic rate.
What is her rate of pay per hour for overtime?

(b) Sue is given a pay rise of 13 pence on her basic rate per hour.
Calculate the percentage increase in her basic rate.
Give your answer to an appropriate degree of accuracy.   [SEG]

4. The price of a bottle of red wine is £3·29 and a kilogram of
cheddar cheese costs £4·96.
What is the total cost of twelve bottles of red wine and a
quarter of a kilogram of cheddar cheese?   [SEG]

5. Jack invests £2000 at 7% per annum compound interest.
Calculate the value of his investment at the end of 2 years.   [SEG]

6. (a) An electrician earns £259·92 per week.

   (i) The electrician works 36 hours per week.
       What is his hourly rate of pay?

   (ii) The electrician has 30% of his pay deducted each week.
        How much does he get each week after deductions?

   (b) Once a month the electrician is on call-out duty.
       He gets £20 to be on duty. He is also paid one and a half
       times his hourly rate of pay for each hour he works.
       How much does he earn, before deductions, for a 3 hour
       call-out?   [SEG]

7. Tomato sauce is sold in two sizes.

   A large bottle contains 681 g and costs 66p.
   A small bottle contains 408 g and costs 38p.

   Which size is better value for money?
   You must show all your working.   [SEG]

8. Tina wishes to buy a computer which is on sale at a cash price
   of £699.
   The credit terms are a deposit of £210 and 12 monthly
   repayments of £51·50.

   (a) Find the total credit price.

   (b) To buy the computer on credit, Tina needs a loan.
       The loan is the difference between the cash price and the
       deposit.
       Express the extra amount paid for credit, compared with
       cash, as a percentage of the loan.   [SEG]

9. Ken buys 400 pairs of trainers for £7250.

   He sells $\frac{3}{5}$ of the trainers at £28 a pair.

   Ken then reduces the price to £16·80 a pair.

   He sells 90 pairs at this reduced price.

   A market trader buys the remaining pairs of trainers from
   Ken for £300.

   (a) How much in total does Ken receive from selling the
       trainers?

   (b) Find the percentage profit which Ken made on the
       trainers.   [SEG]

MODULE 3

Module 3 Practice Calculator Test

1. A farmer had 175 sheep.

   (a) $\frac{4}{5}$ of the sheep had lambs.

      How many sheep had lambs? **(1 mark)**

   (b) Of the sheep which had lambs, 35% had two lambs.

      How many sheep had two lambs? **(2 marks)**   [SEG]

2. Elaine buys 0·4 kg of Edam cheese at £4·80 per kilogram and $\frac{1}{4}$ kg of Cheddar cheese. She pays £2·73 altogether.

   How much per kilogram is Cheddar cheese? **(4 marks)**   [SEG]

3. (a) Write $2\frac{1}{5}$ as a decimal. **(1 mark)**

   (b) Place the following numbers in order of size, starting with the smallest.

      $2\frac{1}{5}$ $1·48^2$ $2·15$ $2·015$ $\sqrt{4·56}$ **(3 marks)**   [SEG]

4. Anna prints 300 tickets for a band event which has cost her £950. She sells 220 tickets at £15 each.

   On the day of the event, she reduces the selling price to £10, and is only left with 10 unsold tickets.

   (a) Find the total amount Anna receives from selling the tickets. **(4 marks)**

   (b) Find the percentage profit which Anna made on this band event. **(3 marks)**   [SEG]

5. Scooters can be hired at a cost of £21 per day plus 5 pence per mile travelled.
Mustapha hires a scooter for three days and drives it 136 miles.
Find the cost to Mustapha. **(4 marks)**   [SEG]

6. Use your calculator to find the value of

$$\frac{128·47 + 22·98}{79·11 - 15·67}$$

   Give your answer to 3 significant figures. **(2 marks)**   [SEG]

7. Prove that the product of three consecutive integers is divisible by 6. **(2 marks)**

8. In England £1·012 × 10^{10} is spent on healthcare
per year.
There are 4·71 × 10^7 people in England.
How much per person is spent on healthcare in
England per year?　　　　　　　　　　**(2 marks)**　　　[SEG]

9. A jumper is on sale in a shop at £53·46.
The shopkeeper has added 35% onto its
cost price.
How much did the shopkeeper pay for
the jumper?　　　　　　　　　　　　**(4 marks)**　　　[SEG]

Module 3　Practice Non-calculator Test

1. A 50 gram ball of wool costs 59p.

　(a)　Alex buys 32 balls of wool.

　　　(i)　What is the total weight of this wool
　　　　　in kilograms?　　　　　　　　**(2 marks)**

　　　(ii)　Alex pays for the wool with a £20 note.
　　　　　How much change is she given?　**(3 marks)**

　　　(iii)　The 32 balls of wool are either red or
　　　　　white.
　　　　　The number of red balls to the number
　　　　　of white balls is 5 : 3.
　　　　　How many red balls did she buy?　**(3 marks)**

　(b)　The weight of each ball of wool is accurate
　　　to the nearest 10 g.
　　　What is the minimum weight of one ball?　**(1 mark)**　　[SEG]

2. (a)　Work out $\frac{2}{5}$ of 12.　　　　　　　　**(2 marks)**

　(b)　Write down the value of $3^2 + \sqrt{16}$.　　**(2 marks)**

　(c)　Write down

　　　(i)　0·03^2　　　　　　　　　　　**(2 marks)**

　　　(ii)　16^0　　　　　　　　　　　　**(1 mark)**

　(d)　Find an approximate value of $\dfrac{5·81}{12·3 + 18·2}$

　　　Give your answer in its simplest form.　**(3 marks)**　　[SEG]

3. A college party of 38 travel to London by minibus to watch an international hockey match.
Each minibus can carry 15 passengers.
How many minibuses travel to London?   **(3 marks)**   [SEG]

4. A shop normally sells a camera at £84.
In a sale its price is reduced by $\frac{1}{3}$.
Find its price in the sale.   **(3 marks)**

5. The distance from Paris to the island of Guadeloupe
is 4200 miles.
A plane averages 500 miles per hour.
How long does the plane take for the journey?
Give your answer in hours and minutes.   **(4 marks)**   [SEG]

6. $u = 6 \times 10^8$ $v = 4 \times 10^6$

Evaluate uv.
Give your answer in standard form.   **(3 marks)**

MODULE 3

AS1 ALGEBRA 1

To solve equations you need to know about balance.

This unit will show you how to:

- Add, subtract, multiply and divide using algebra
- Use indices in algebra
- Expand and factorise expressions
- Solve linear equations
- Use formulae

Before you start:

You should know how to...	Check in AS1
1. Calculate with indices For example, $2^5 \div 2^3$ $= 2^{5-3}$ $= 2^2$	**1.** Find the value of (a) $3^2 \times 3^5$ (b) $3^6 \div 3^4$
2. Multiply directed numbers For example, $^-8 \times 3 = ^-24$ $^- \times ^+ = ^-$	**2.** Write down the value of (a) $4 \times ^-3$ (b) $^-5 \times 2$ (c) $^-6 \times ^-5$

1.1 Introduction to algebra

Algebra is a branch of mathematics in which you use letters to represent numbers. Two of its many uses are:

Algebra is used to form the instructions that control robots used in manufacturing processes, such as car production.

Weather and surveillance satellites all have their orbits calculated using algebraic formulae and equations.

Writing simple expressions

You can use letters to represent amounts that you do not know. This is called forming an algebraic expression.

Example

A bus starts its journey from the bus station.
You cannot see all the people on the bus so you call the number of passengers p.

Another bus waiting at the bus station has the same number of passengers, p, as the first bus.
These two buses have a total of $p + p$ or $2 \times p$ passengers on them.
In algebra you usually write $2 \times p$ as $2p$.

One of the buses leaves the bus station.
At the first bus stop four people get onto this bus.
You now have $p + 4$ people on this bus.

MODULE 5

Exercise 1A

1. (a) A bus has p people travelling on it.
   At the next bus stop 5 people get off the bus.
   How many people are now left on the bus?
   (b) There are six buses in the bus station and each bus has p passengers. How many passengers, in total, are there on all the buses?

2. (a) A shop sells bags containing s sweets per bag.
   You buy four bags of sweets.
   How many sweets have you bought?
   (b) You open one bag and take out 5 sweets.
   How many sweets, in total, are now left?
   (c) You give three of the bags of sweets away to friends.
   How many sweets do you now have left for yourself?

3. You buy packs of stickers costing 25 pence for each pack.
   How much do you pay for n packs of stickers?

4. You cook b biscuits as part of your food technology lesson.
   You share these with your three friends so each of you receives the same amount of biscuits.
   How many biscuits do you each receive?

5. There are 9 pieces of chewing gum in a packet.
   How many pieces of gum are there in
   (a) 3 packets
   (b) 15 packets
   (c) g packets?

6. A child is c years old.
   (a) How old will the child be in four years time?
   (b) How old was the child two years ago?
   (c) How old will the child be in x years time?

In questions 7–13 write the statements as one algebraic expression.

7. Eggs are sold in boxes of six. How many eggs will you buy if you purchase b boxes, all full of eggs?

8. What is the sum of five times x and three times y?

9. Brian has a piece of wood *m* centimetres long. Clive has a piece of wood which is longer than Brian's piece. Clive's piece of wood is *n* centimetres long. By how much is Clive's piece of wood longer than Brian's?

10. What is the total weight of 5 letters weighing *w* grams each?

11. Anne-Marie buys a piece of ribbon *r* metres long and cuts it into 9 equal pieces. How long is each piece?

12. What is the total cost of 3 CDs at £*x* each and 5 tapes at £*y* each?

13. Robert has £25 for his birthday. He buys *t* ties costing £*s* each.
    (a) How much does he pay for his ties?
    (b) How much change will he have after making his purchases?

1.2 Addition and subtraction of algebraic terms

In algebra, quantities like *x*, *y*, 2*a*, 3*ab* and p^2 are called **terms**. Like terms contain the same letters.

2*a* and 3*a* are like terms.   2*a* and 3*b* are not like terms.

The letters are the same   The letters are different

An **expression** is a collections of terms that have been added or subtracted, for example: $x + y$, $2x + 3y$ and $4a + 3b - c$.

Expressions can be simplified if they contain like terms. This is called **collecting like terms**.

These expressions have been simplified:

$b + b = 2b$

$5c - 2c = 3c$

Example
Simplify (a) $3a + 4b + 2a + 3b + a$
           (b) $4x + 5y + 3 - 3x + 2y - 6 + 3y$

Remember:
a means 1*a*.

MODULE 5

(a) $3a + 4b + 2a + 3b + a$
$= 3a + 2a + a + 4b + 3b$ Rearrange with like terms together.
$= 6a + 7b$

(b) $4x + 5y + 3 - 3x + 2y - 6 + 3y$
$= 4x - 3x + 5y + 2y + 3y + 3 - 6$ Rearrange with like terms together.
$= x + 10by - 3$

Exercise 1B

Simplify these expressions.

1. $4a + 2a$ **2.** $7b - b$

3. $4c - 3c + 2c$ **4.** $6d - 4d - 3d$

5. $4e + 2 - 3e - 5$ **6.** $3t + 4s - 2t + s$

7. $a + 3a - 5a + 2$ **8.** $3b + 4c - 2b + 5c$

9. $6 - 3x - 2c - 4$ **10.** $8a - 3b - 4a + 5b - 2c$

11. $c + d - 2c + 3d + 4c - 3d$ **12.** $4 - 7c + 5b - 6 + 9c - 5b$

13. $6 + 4x - 5y + 3x - 7 + 2y$ **14.** $2a - 3b + 4c - 4a + b + 5c$

15. $5 - 2a + b + a - 2b + a - 4$ **16.** $4x - 3y - z - 5x + 4y - 2z$

1.3 Multiplication and division of algebraic terms

Algebra is a language, with rules and conventions. Here are some of them.

For multiplication:

$1 \times a$	or	$a \times 1$ are both written as a
$3 \times a$	or	$a \times 3$ are both written as $3a$
$a \times b$	or	$b \times a$ are both usually written as ab

$$3a \times 2b \times 4c \; = \; 3 \times a \times 2 \times b \times 4 \times c$$
$$= \; 3 \times 2 \times 4 \times a \times b \times c$$
$$= \; 24abc$$

> **Note:**
> You put the number before the letters and put the letters in alphabetical order.

For division:

$b \div 2$ is written as $\frac{b}{2}$ or $\frac{1}{2}b$

$x \div y$ is written as $\frac{x}{y}$

Example

Simplify (a) $2 \times a \times 6 \times 4$
               (b) $4 \times x \times 10 \div y \div 5 \times z$
               (c) $(10x) \times (^-3y) \div (^-5z)$

(a) $2 \times a \times b \times 4 = 2 \times 4 \times a \times b$ Regroup the terms.
$$= 8 \times ab$$
$$= 8ab$$

(b) $4 \times x \times 10 \div y \div 5 \times z = 4 \times 10 \div 5 \times x \div y \times z$
$$= 8 \times \frac{xy}{z}$$
$$= \frac{8xy}{z}$$

(c) $(10x) \times (^-3y) \div (^-5z)$ $= \dfrac{10 \times (^-3)}{(^-5)} \times \dfrac{x \times y}{z}$
$$= 6 \times \frac{xy}{z}$$
$$= \frac{6xy}{z}$$

Exercise 1C

Simplify these expressions.

1. $3 \times a$ **2.** $5 \times 4 \times b$

3. $2a \times 4b$ **4.** $3t \times 5 \times 4s$

5. $6g \times 4p \times 5r$ **6.** $4q \times 5y \div 10$

7. $2a \times 3b \div 6c$ **8.** $a \div 2b \times 6c$

9. $(^-3y) \times (4x)$ **10.** $(2p) \div (^-3q) \times 6r$

11. $(12s) \times (^-3t) \times (6r)$ **12.** $(^-3a) \times (^-4b) \times (^-5c)$

13. $(^-x) \times (^-x) \times (^-2x)$ **14.** $(^-2s) \div (^-6t) \times (^-12t)$

1.4 Indices

When you write 7^4 (pronounced '7 to the power 4') the number 4 is called the **index** and shows the number of 7s multiplied together.

There is more about indices on page 140.

$7^4 = 7 \times 7 \times 7 \times 7$

You can apply indices to letters as well as to numbers. For example:

$a^4 = a \times a \times a \times a$

MODULE 5

You can …

- multiply terms with indices either:

  the long way   or   the short way

  $x^2 \times x^3$ $x^2 \times x^3$

  $= (x \times x) \times (x \times x \times x)$ $= x^{(2 + 3)}$

  $= x^5$ $= x^5$

  > **Remember:**
  >
  > x^2 is x squared.
  > x^3 is x cubed.

  The general rule for multiplication is:

  $$x^n \times x^m = x^{(n + m)}$$

- divide terms containing indices either:

  the long way   or   the short way

                                 $\dfrac{x^5}{x^3}$

  $x^5 \div x^3$

  $= \dfrac{x \times x \times \cancel{x} \times \cancel{x} \times \cancel{x}}{\cancel{x} \times \cancel{x} \times \cancel{x}}$ $= x^{(5 - 3)}$

  $= x^2$ $= x^2$

  The general rule for division is:

  $$x^n \div x^m = x^{(n - m)}$$

- raise a power to another power either:

  the long way   or   the short way

  $(x^2)^3 = x^2 \times x^2 \times x^2$ $= x^{(2 \times 3)}$

  $= (x \times x) \times (x \times x) \times (x \times x)$ $= x^6$

  $= x^6$

  The general rule for powers of powers is:

  $$(x^n)^m = x^{(nm)}$$

These rules are also useful:

- $\dfrac{1}{x^n} = x^{-n}$ • $x^0 = 1$

Example

Simplify

(a) $x^3 \times x^4$ (b) $x^5 \div x^2$

(c) $(x^3)^4$ (d) $3x^2 \times 4x^3 \div 12x^4$

(e) $\dfrac{(2x^3)^2 \times 3y^4}{9x^4y^3}$

(a) $x^3 \times x^4$ or $x^3 \times x^4$

     $= (x \times x \times x) \times (x \times x \times x \times x)$ $= x^{(3 + 4)}$

     $= x^7$ $= x^7$

(b) $x^5 \div x^2$

$$= \frac{x \times x \times x \times x \times x}{x \times x}$$

$$= x^3$$

or $x^5 \div x^2$

$$= x^{(5-2)}$$

$$= x^3$$

(c) $(x^3)^4$

$$= x^3 \times x^3 \times x^3 \times x^3$$

$$= x^{(3+3+3+3)}$$

$$= x^{12}$$

or $(x^3)^4$

$$= x^{(3 \times 4)}$$

$$= x^{12}$$

(d) $3x^2 \times 4x^3 \div 12x^4$

$$= \frac{3 \times x^2 \times 4 \times x^3}{12 \times x^4}$$

$$= \frac{3 \times 4}{12} \times \frac{x^2 \times x^3}{x^4}$$

$$= 1 \times x^{(5-4)}$$

$$= x^1 \text{ or } x$$

or $3x^2 \times 4x^3 \div 12x^4$

$$= \frac{3 \times 4}{12} \times x^{(2+3-4)}$$

$$= x$$

(e) $\dfrac{(2x^3)^2 \times 3y^4}{9x^4y^3}$

$$= \frac{2x^3 \times 2x^3 \times 3y^4}{9 \times x^4 \times y^3}$$

$$= \frac{2 \times 2 \times 3}{9} \times \frac{x^3 \times x^3}{x^4} \times \frac{y^4}{y^3}$$

$$= \frac{4}{3}x^{(3+3-4)}y^{(4-3)}$$

$$= \frac{4x^2y}{3}$$

or $\dfrac{(2x^3)^2 \times 3y^4}{9x^4y^3}$

$$= \frac{2^2 \times 3}{9} \times \frac{(x^3)^2 \times y^4}{x^4y^3}$$

$$= \frac{4}{3}x^{(6-4)}y^{(4-3)}$$

$$= \frac{4}{3}x^2y$$

Exercise 1D

Simplify these expressions.

1. $a^2 \times a^5$

2. $b \times b^3 \div b^2$

3. $w^7 \times w^5$

4. $d^5 \div d^4 \times d^3$

5. $t^4 \times t^5 \div t^8$

6. $a^{24} \div a^{15}$

7. $(x^7)^2$

8. $(x^3)^3$

9. $(^-2x)^4$

10. $(4x^2)^3$

11. $(ab)^0$

12. $(x^{-1})^2$

MODULE 5

13. $(^-3a^4)^2$

14. $\dfrac{a^2 \times (2a^3)^4}{20a^{10}}$

15. $8d^5 \div 12d^3$

16. $a^3b^2 \times a^2b^4$

17. $3b^2 \times 4b^3c \times (2c)^3$

18. $(^-3x) \times (4y) \div (^-6y^2)$

19. $\dfrac{7x^2y \times 6xy^3}{3x^3y^2 \times 14y^2}$

20. $\dfrac{2d^6 \times (6d^2)^3}{(3d)^2 \times (2d^3)^3}$

21. $4xy \times 6x^2y \div (^-4z^2)^2$

22. $(^-7w^2)^2 \times (^-8xy^3)^3 \div (4wx^2y)^5$

1.5 Brackets

In algebra you use brackets in exactly the same way as for numbers.

An example of a bracket is $3(a + b)$

$3(a + b)$ means $3 \times (a + b)$

So $3 \times (a + b) = (a + b) + (a + b) + (a + b)$

$3(a + b) = 3a + 3b$

This is called multiplying out, or **expanding** the bracket.
You multiply each term inside the bracket by the term outside.

So $\quad 3(a + b)$

$= 3a + 3b$

Example

Simplify the expressions
(a) $^-3(2a - 6)$
(b) $2(4x + 5) + 3(x - 1)$
(c) $x(x + 3) - 2(x - 2) + x^2$

(a) $^-3(2a - 6) = (^-3) \times 2a - (^-3) \times 6$
$\qquad\qquad\quad = ^-6a - (^-18)$
$\qquad\qquad\quad = 18 - 6a$

(b) $2(4x + 5) + 3(x - 1) = 2 \times 4x + 2 \times 5 + 3 \times x + 3 \times (^-1)$
$\qquad\qquad\qquad\qquad\quad = 8x + 10 + 3x - 3$
$\qquad\qquad\qquad\qquad\quad = 8x + 3x + 10 - 3$
$\qquad\qquad\qquad\qquad\quad = 11x + 7$

(c) $x(x + 3) - 2(x - 2) + x^2 = x \times x + x \times 3 - 2 \times x - 2 \times (^-2) + x^2$
$\qquad\qquad\qquad\qquad\qquad = x^2 + 3x - 2x + 4 + x^2$
$\qquad\qquad\qquad\qquad\qquad = 2x^2 + x + 4$

Exercise 1E

Remove the brackets from these expressions and simplify them, where possible.

1. $4(x + y)$ **2.** $3(2x + 4y)$

3. $5(2x - y)$ **4.** $5(a - b + c)$

5. $p(p + q)$ **6.** $4(3x - 2)$

7. $y(3y - 2)$ **8.** $4y(y - 6)$

9. $2x^2(3x^2 - 2)$ **10.** $2(3r - 1) + 4r$

11. $3(2x + y) + 4(x - 2y)$ **12.** $4(m - n) + 3(2m - n)$

13. $2t(t^2 + t) - t^2$ **14.** $4x - 3(x - y)$

15. $2(2a + b) - 3(a - b)$ **16.** $a(b - c) - a(3 - c)$

17. $5c(4c - 3) - 2(4c - 3)$ **18.** $x(x - 2) - x(2x - 4)$

19. $x^2(1 - x^2) - x(1 - 2x)$ **20.** $2x^3(2x - 5) + 3x^2(2x^2 + 5x)$

1.6 Common factors

You now know that you can remove brackets by multiplying, so that:
$4(n + 3) = 4n + 12$

If you write this in reverse it becomes:
$4n + 12 = 4(n + 3)$

Factorising is the reverse process to removing the brackets.

> You can find out more about factors on page 142.

Example

Factorise
(a) $x^2 + 5x$
(b) $8ab - 12ac$
(c) $x^2y - xyz + xy^3$

(a) $x^2 + 5x = x \times x + 5 \times x$
             $= x \times (x + 5)$ x is the only common factor.
             $= x(x + 5)$

(b) $8ab - 12ac = 4 \times 2ab - 4 \times 3ac$ Each term has 4 as a factor.
               $= 4(2ab - 3ac)$ Each term also has a as a factor.
               $= 4a(2b - 3c)$ So $4a$ is the common factor.

(c) $x^2y - xyz + xy^3 = xy \times x - xy \times z + xy \times y^2$ Each term has both x and y
                  $= xy(x - z + y^2)$ as common factors.

Exercise 1F

1. Complete the factorisation for each of these.

(a) $3a + 3b = 3(\ldots + \ldots)$

(b) $10a - 12b = 2(\ldots - \ldots)$

(c) $12x + 16y = 4(\ldots + \ldots)$

(d) $ab - bc = b(\ldots - \ldots)$

(e) $d^2 + d = d(\ldots - \ldots)$

(f) $2m^2 + 4m = 2m(\ldots + \ldots)$

(g) $6c^3 + 3c^2 = 3c^2(\ldots + \ldots)$

(h) $36x - 27x^2 = \ldots(\ldots - 3x)$

2. Factorise these expressions.

(a) $20x + 8y$

(b) $27a - 33b$

(c) $35p + 49q$

(d) $30x - 24y$

(e) $12a + 8b - 10c$

(f) $16x - 8y + 24z$

(g) $8 - 12x$

(h) $9xy + 12x$

(i) $6a^2 - 9ab$

(j) $x^2 - 3x$

(k) $3p^2 - 9pq + 27p$

(l) $p - p^2$

(m) $48m + 8n - 24x$

(n) $25x^2 - 30y^2$

(o) $7a^2b + 28ab^2$

(p) $2x^2 - 4x$

(q) $2\pi r + \pi rh$

(r) $x^3 + x^2$

1.7 Equations

An **equation** is a statement that includes an $=$ sign, and an unknown to find.

An equation has two sides, a Left-Hand Side (LHS) and a Right-Hand Side (RHS), with the $=$ sign between them.

Example

Which of these are equations?

(a) $x^2 - 5x + 1$ (b) $2x + 3 = 11$ (c) $7x - 1 < 13$

> Remember $<$ means 'less than'.

(a) is not an equation because it does not contain an $=$ sign.

(b) is an equation because it contains an unknown (x) and an $=$ sign.

(c) is not an equation because it contains a $<$ instead of an $=$ sign.

Linear equations

A **linear equation** has no powers. Examples are:

$x + 3 = 9$, $2x - 7 = 12$ and $5x + 9 = 3x - 2$

> $2x^2 - 3 = 5x$ is **not** a linear equation because it contains an x^2 term.

To keep the equation balanced you do the same thing to both sides.

Example 1

Solve $x - 3 = 8$

$x - 3$ balances 8:

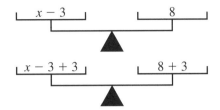

Add 3 to both sides of the equation:

So the solution is $x = 11$

The working could be set out without drawing the balance.

$x - 3 \quad\ = 8$

$x - 3 + 3 = 8 + 3 \qquad$ Add 3 to both sides.

$x \qquad\ \ = 11$

> **Check** your answer by substituting $x = 11$ into the original equation.
> $11 - 3 = 8$
> So your answer is correct.

Example 2

Solve $4x + 9 = 41$

$4x + 9$ balances 41.

Subtract 9 from both sides to get the x term on its own:

Divide both sides by 4 to leave x on its own:

So the solution is $x = 8$.

Without drawing the balance:

$$4x + 9 \qquad = 41$$

Subtract 9 from both sides: $\quad 4x + 9 - 9 = 41 - 9$

$$4x \qquad\ = 32$$

Divide both sides by 4: $\qquad \dfrac{4x}{4} \qquad = \dfrac{32}{4}$

$$x \qquad\ = 8$$

> **Check** your answer:
> $4 \times 8 + 9$
> $= 32 + 9$
> $= 41$
> So it is correct.

Exercise 1G

Solve the following equations.

Check each solution by completing the substitution back into the given equation.

1. $x + 2 = 6$ **2.** $y - 5 = 12$

3. $6 + x = 14$ **4.** $a - 3{\cdot}4 = 8$

5. $b + \frac{1}{2} = 7$ **6.** $2x = 24$

MODULE 5

7. $4y = 30$ **8.** $\frac{1}{2}x = 7$

9. $12a = 72$ **10.** $\frac{1}{3}y = 4{\cdot}5$

11. $x - 7 = {}^{-}6$ **12.** $y + 9 = 5$

13. $2x + 4 = 10$ **14.** $3y - 5 = 19$

15. $9a - 7 = 29$ **16.** $\dfrac{x}{2} + 5 = 24$

17. $8a + 7 = 31$ **18.** $4x - 6 = 8$

19. $\dfrac{a}{3} - 2 = 1$ **20.** $\dfrac{3x}{4} = 9$

21. $y - 4 = 3\frac{1}{2}$ **22.** $2y + 5 = 8$

23. $5x - 6 = 19$ **24.** $\dfrac{x}{2} + 3 = 7$

25. $\frac{5}{7}x = 15$ **26.** $\frac{3}{4}x - 1 = 8$

1.8 Harder equations

Some equations are harder than others because:

- They use brackets.
  You may have to expand these out.

- The unknown letter appears on both sides.
  You will need to bring all the unknowns together.

- They involve algebraic fractions.
  You will need to use fraction rules.

Example 1

Solve the equation $3(2x - 5) = 12$.

Write out the equation: $3(2x - 5) = 12$

Multiply out the bracket: $6x - 15 = 12$

Add 15 to both sides: $6x - 15 + 15 = 12 + 15$

$$6x = 27$$

Divide both sides by 6: $\dfrac{6x}{6} = \dfrac{27}{6}$

$$x = 4\tfrac{1}{2}$$

Example 2

Solve the equation $4x - 7 = 2x + 3$.

$$4x - 7 = 2x + 3$$

Subtract $2x$ from both sides: $4x - 7 - 2x = 2x + 3 - 2x$

$$2x - 7 = 3$$

Add 7 to both sides: $2x - 7 + 7 = 3 + 7$

$$2x = 10$$

Divide both sides by 2: $\dfrac{2x}{2} = \dfrac{10}{2}$

So $\qquad x = 5$

Example 3

Solve the equation $3(2x + 5) - 4(1 - 3x) = {}^-16$.

$3(2x + 5) - 4(1 - 3x) = {}^-16$

$6x + 15 - 4 + 12x = {}^-16$ Multiply out the brackets.

                                  (Remember your rules for multiplying directed numbers.)

$18x + 11 = {}^-16$ Combine like terms on LHS.

$18x + 11 - 11 = {}^-16 - 11$ Take 11 from both sides.

$18x = {}^-27$

$\dfrac{18x}{18} = \dfrac{{}^-27}{18}$ Divide both sides by 18.

$x = {}^-1\frac{1}{2}$

Example 4

Solve the equation $\dfrac{x}{2} + \dfrac{2x - 3}{5} = 3$.

This equation involves algebraic fractions. The best way is to remove the fractions first. In order to achieve this find the lowest common multiple of the denominators of the fractions, then multiply both sides of the equation by this lowest common multiple.

MODULE 5

$$\frac{x}{2} + \frac{2x-3}{5} \qquad = 3 \qquad \text{LCM for 2 and 5 is 10.}$$

(Section N1 gives further work on LCM.)

$$10 \times \frac{x}{2} + 10 \times \frac{2x-3}{5} = 3 = 10 \times 3 \quad \text{Multiply both sides by 10.}$$

$$5x + 2(2x - 3) \qquad = 30$$

$$5x + 4x - 6 \qquad = 30 \qquad \text{Multiply out the brackets.}$$

$$9x - 6 \qquad = 30 \qquad \text{Combine like terms on LHS.}$$

$$9x - 6 + 6 \qquad = 30 + 6 \quad \text{Add 6 to both sides.}$$

$$9x \qquad = 36$$

$$\frac{9x}{9} \qquad = \frac{36}{9} \qquad \text{Divide both sides by 6.}$$

$$x \qquad = 4$$

Exercise 1H

Solve these equations.

1. $3(x + 4) = 12$ **2.** $2(y - 1) = 9$

3. $6(a + 3) = 24$ **4.** $2(3 - 4x) = {}^{-}10$

5. $x + 3(x - 2) = 14$ **6.** $3x + 6 = 21 - 2x$

7. $20 + 4m = 2 + 2m$ **8.** $y + 5 = 8 - y$

9. $13 - 2x = 21$ **10.** $2x - 1{\cdot}8 = 4x - 3{\cdot}4$

11. $5y = 3 - 3(y - 5)$ **12.** $3 - 2(y - 2) = 10$

13. $2(2x + 3) = 3(4x - 2)$ **14.** $3(2a + 3) = 5 - 4(3 - a)$

15. $2(4h - 3) = 3(2h + 1) - 5$ **16.** $7x - 2(3x - 7) = 8 + 5(3 - x)$

17. $\dfrac{x}{2} + 4 = \dfrac{x}{4} + 1$ **18.** $\dfrac{y+3}{4} = \dfrac{y}{5} + 2$

19. $\dfrac{x}{3} - 1 = \dfrac{x}{5} + 1$ **20.** $3(2x - 10) = \dfrac{4x-7}{2}$

21. $\dfrac{2x}{3} = \dfrac{4}{9}$ **22.** $\dfrac{3y}{2} - \dfrac{y}{4} = 4$

23. $\dfrac{2(3a-5)}{5} = {}^{-}4$ **24.** $\dfrac{x}{2} + \dfrac{2(x-1)}{3} - \dfrac{3(2x+1)}{4} = \dfrac{1}{6}$

MODULE 5

1.9 Forming equations to solve problems

Often the problem is given as a worded statement or a diagram and you will be asked to form an equation using this information.

Example 1

A number is multiplied by 4 and then 5 is added and the result is 22. Find the original number.

Let the original number be x.

$$\text{The equation is } x \times 4 + 5 = 22$$

$$\text{or } 4x + 5 = 22$$

$$4x + 5 - 5 = 22 - 5 \qquad \text{Subtract 5 from both sides.}$$

$$4x = 17$$

$$\frac{4x}{4} = \frac{17}{4} \qquad \text{Divide both sides by 4.}$$

$$4 = 4\tfrac{1}{4}$$

The original number was $4\tfrac{1}{4}$.

Example 2

The perimeter of a rectangular garden border is 26 metres. Its length is $2\tfrac{1}{2}$ metres more than its width. Form an equation to find the width of the border, and solve the equation.

Let the width of the border be w metres.

Then the length of the border is $(w + 2\tfrac{1}{2})$ metres.

$$\text{Total perimeter} = 2 \text{ widths} + 2 \text{ lengths}$$

$$2w + 2(w + 2\tfrac{1}{2}) = 26$$

$$\therefore 2w + 2w + 5 = 26 \qquad \text{Expand the bracket.}$$

$$4w + 5 = 26 \qquad \text{Combine like terms.}$$

$$4w + 5 - 5 = 26 - 5 \qquad \text{Subtract 5 from both sides.}$$

$$4w = 21$$

$$\frac{4w}{4} = \frac{21}{4} \qquad \text{Divide both sides by 4.}$$

$$w = 5\tfrac{1}{4}$$

The width of the border is $5\tfrac{1}{4}$ metres.

MODULE 5

Example 3

Brian's father was 27 years old when Brian was born. Now he is four times as old as Brian.

Form an equation to find Brian's age now and solve this equation.

Let Brian be x years old now, then Brian's father is $(x + 27)$ years old now.

$$4 \times \text{Brian's age now} = \text{Father's age now}$$
$$4x = x + 27$$
$$3x = 27$$
$$x = 9$$

Brian is 9 years old now.

Exercise 1I

In questions 1–8 let the unknown number be x, form an equation involving x and solve the equation to find the number.

1. A number is multiplied by 4 and then 7 is subtracted, giving an answer of 33. Find the number.

2. A number is divided by 3 and then 10 is added, giving an answer of 22. Find the number.

3. A number has 5 added to it then the result is multiplied by 6, giving an answer of 108. Find the number.

4. A number is doubled and 5 is subtracted. The result is then divided by 6, giving an answer of 4. Find the number.

5. A number is multiplied by 5 and 7 is subtracted. This gives the same answer as multiplying the number by 3 and adding 12. Find the number.

6. A number has 8 added to it and the result is divided by 3. This gives the same result as subtracting 12 from the number and multiplying that answer by 2. Find the number.

7. A number is divided by 2 and has 3 subtracted from the result. This gives the same answer as adding 2 to the number and then dividing that result by 5. Find the number.

8. A number is multiplied by 7 and has 3 added to it. This gives the same result as multiplying the number by 2 and subtracting this answer from 66. Find the number.

9. The sum of three consecutive numbers is 177. Let the first number be x.
Form and solve an equation in x to find the numbers.

10. The sum of four consecutive odd numbers is 808. Let the first number be x. Form and solve an equation in x.
What is the largest of the four numbers?

11. The perimeter of the rectangle is 42 cm.
Form an equation in x and solve it.

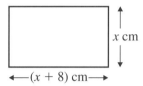

12. The perimeter of the rectangle is 50 cm.
Form an equation in x and solve it.

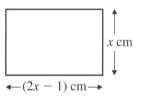

13. The length of a rectangle is five times its width. The perimeter of the rectangle is 54 cm. Let the width be w cm.
Form an equation in w and solve it.
What is the length of the rectangle?

14. The area of the rectangle is 30 cm². Form an equation in x and solve it.

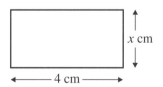

15. John is three times as old as his son Peter. The sum of their ages is 52 years. Let John's age be x years. Form an equation in x and solve it. How old is John?

16. Robert is 10 years older than his sister and he is now twice her age. Let Robert be x years old now. Form an equation in x and solve it. How old is Robert's sister now?

MODULE 5

1.10 Formulae

A **formula** describes a relationship. It can be expressed in words or using algebra.

Formula 1 racing cars are continually changing speed, but you can find their average speed using a formula.

Average speed = Total distance travelled / Time taken

This is a formula: $S = \dfrac{D}{T}$

If a racing car travels 22·5 kilometres in 0·15 hours, it is travelling at a speed of $\dfrac{22 \cdot 5}{0 \cdot 15} = 150$ kilometres per hour.

If a cuboid has a length of l units, a width of w units, and a height of h units, its volume V cubic units will be given by

$V = lwh$

Note:

The units of l, w and h must be the same, for example centimetres.

Example

A college has both full-time and part-time students attending courses. Write down a formula to calculate the total number of students attending the college.

Let T be the total number of students, P be the number of part-time students, and F be the number of full-time students.

The formula is $T = F + P$

Exercise 1J

1. A science class contains s students. If there are g girls and b boys in this class, write down a formula connecting s, g and b.

2. Write down a formula for A, where A m^2 is the area of a square and x m is the length of the side of the square.

3. The area of a parallelogram is found by calculating the product of base length and the perpendicular height. If the area is A m^2, the base length is b m and the perpendicular height is h m, write down a formula for the area of the parallelogram in term of b and h.

4. Write down a formula for s where s km per hour is the constant speed of a car travelling a distance of d km along a motorway for t hours.

5. A rectangle has a length l cm, a width w cm and an area A cm^2. Write down a formula for w in terms of A and l.

6. Write down a formula for calculating the perimeter P cm of a rectangle if the length is l cm and the width is w cm.

7. A triangle has sides of length x cm, y cm and z cm. Write down a formula for the perimeter p where p cm is the perimeter of the triangle.

8. Jayne works in a shop and is paid £x per hour. If she earns £w in one week having worked h hours, write down a formula for her earnings in terms of x and h.

9. A ball of string is B m long. A class of p pupils cuts x pieces of string each s cm long from the ball of string. There is now L m of string remaining on the ball. Write down a formula for L.

MODULE 5

1.11 Using formulae

You can substitute numerical values into a formula.

In the formula $S = \dfrac{D}{T}$ S, D and T are all **variables**. They are quantities that can vary.

If you know two of these variables you can substitute their values into the formula to find the value of the third.

MODULE 5

Example 1

The formula for finding the area of a trapezium is

$$A = \frac{h}{2}(a + b)$$

If $a = 6$ cm, $b = 9$ cm and $h = 4$ cm, calculate A.

$$A = \frac{4}{2} \times (6 + 9)$$

$$= 2 \times 15$$

$$A = 30 \text{ cm}^2$$

Example 2

If $y = 3x^2 - 4x + 2$, calculate y when

(a) $x = 4$ (b) $x = {}^{-}2$

(a) $y = 3x^2 - 4x + 2$ and $x = 4$

$\quad\quad y = 3 \times 4^2 - (4 \times 4) + 2$

$\quad\quad\quad = 48 - 16 + 2$

$\quad\quad y = 34$

(b) $y = 3x^2 - 4x + 2$ and $x = {}^{-}2$

$\quad\quad y = 3 \times ({}^{-}2)^2 - (4 \times {}^{-}2) + 2$

$\quad\quad\quad = 12 + 8 + 2$

$\quad\quad y = 22$

Example 3

A formula for V is given by $V = \frac{1}{3}\pi r^2 h$. Calculate the value of V when $r = 7\cdot5$ and $h = 20$. You may use the π button on your calculator or you may use $\pi = 3\cdot14$.

$$V = \frac{1}{3} \times \pi \times 7\cdot5^2 \times 20$$

$$= 1178\cdot097\,245\,1 \quad\quad \text{[Using calculator } \pi.\text{]}$$

$$= 1180 \text{ (to 3 significant figures)}$$

Note:

Calculator answers at GCSE are usually rounded to 3 significant figure accuracy.

Exercise 1K

Do not use a calculator to answer questions 1–10.

1. If $X = 3(d + 7)$, calculate the value of X when $d = 40$.

2. If $D = 9(w + x)$, calculate the value of D when $w = 6\cdot5$ and $x = 7\cdot5$.

3. If $P = 9 - 2d$, calculate the value of P when
    (a) $d = 2$ (b) $d = 6$ (c) $d = {}^-1$

4. If $S = a(b + 5)$, calculate the value of S when $a = 14$ and $b = 0.2$.

5. If $S = n(a + b)$, calculate the value of S when
    (a) $n = 6$, $a = 4$ and $b = 5$
    (b) $n = 7$, $a = 6$ and $b = {}^-4$
    (c) $n = 1.5$, $a = 14.4$ and $b = 5.6$

6. If $A = 4x^2$, calculate the value of A when
    (a) $x = 3$ (b) $x = {}^-3$

7. If $B = (\dfrac{1}{2y})^2$, calculate the value of B when
    (a) $y = 4$ (b) $y = {}^-10$

8. If $M = \dfrac{2x + y}{3}$, calculate the value of M when
    (a) $x = 6$ and $y = 48$ (b) $x = {}^-6$ and $y = {}^-3$

9. If $A = \dfrac{kx^2}{2y}$, calculate the value of A when $k = 1.25$, $x = 6$
    and $y = 0.5$.

10. If $X = \dfrac{ab}{a - b}$, calculate the value of X when $a = 15$ and
    $b = 12$.

11. Check your answers to questions 1–10 using your calculator.

You may use a calculator to answer questions 12–16.

12. The temperature C (°Celsius) can be changed into
    F (°Fahrenheit) using the formula
    $$F = \frac{9C}{5} + 32$$
    (a) Calculate the value of F when $C = 15$.
    (b) Calculate, to the nearest degree, the value of F when
        $C = 42$.

13. If $X = w^2 + y^2$, calculate the value of X when
    (a) $w = 1{\cdot}9$ and $y = 2{\cdot}6$
    (b) $w = {}^-4$ and $y = {}^-13$

14. If $V = \sqrt{(a - 5b)}$, calculate the value of V when
    (a) $a = 38$ and $b = 4{\cdot}5$
    (b) $a = {}^-2{\cdot}9$ and $b = {}^-3{\cdot}7$, giving your answer to
         3 significant figures.

15. The time period for the swing of a simple pendulum is

given by the formula $T = 2\pi\sqrt{\dfrac{l}{g}}$ where l is the length of

the pendulum and g is the acceleration due to gravity.
Calculate the value of T when $l = 1{\cdot}25$, $g = 9{\cdot}81$ and
$\pi = 3{\cdot}142$, giving your answer to 3 significant figures.

16. If $s = ut + \frac{1}{2}at^2$, calculate the value of s when
    (a) $u = 5{\cdot}5$, $t = 4{\cdot}5$ and $a = 6$
    (b) $u = 0$, $t = 12$ and $a = 1{\cdot}75$

1.12 Standard index form

Standard index form is used to write very large or very small numbers easily.

In order to use standard form notation; you must be able to write powers of 10 in index form.

Note:
Standard index form is often called **standard form** or **scientific notation**.

$$10 = 10^1$$
$$100 = 10 \times 10 = 10^2$$
$$1000 = 10 \times 10 \times 10 = 10^3 \qquad \text{and}$$
$$10000 = 10 \times 10 \times 10 \times 10 = 10^4$$

$$0{\cdot}1 = \tfrac{1}{10} = \tfrac{1}{10^1} = 10^{-1}$$
$$0{\cdot}01 = \tfrac{1}{100} = \tfrac{1}{10 \times 10} \times \tfrac{1}{10^2} = 10^{-2}$$
$$0{\cdot}001 = \tfrac{1}{1000} \times \tfrac{1}{10 \times 10 \times 10} = \tfrac{1}{10^3} = 10^{-3}$$

- A number is in standard index form when it is written as

     $A \times 10^n$

where A is a number between 1 and 10 and n is an integer.
- For any number greater than 1, n is positive.
- For any number less than 1, n is negative.

Changing an ordinary number into standard form

To change a number into standard form:

1. Change the ordinary number into a number between 1 and 10 (*A*).

2. Multiply it by the appropriate power of 10 (10^n).

Example

Write the following numbers in standard form.

    (a) 75 000 000   (b) 0·000 007 5

    (a) 75 000 000 $= 7{\cdot}5 \times 10\,000\,000$
                         $= 7{\cdot}5 \times 10^7$

    (b) 0·000 007 5 $= 7{\cdot}5 \times \frac{1}{1\,000\,000}$
                         $= 7{\cdot}5 \times 0{\cdot}000\,001$
                         $= 7{\cdot}5 \times 10^{-6}$

Note:

In (a) it is 7.5 because it is between 1 and 10. You have to × by 10 000 000 to get 75 000 000.

To change a number **from** standard form:

1. Change 10^n into a multiple of 10.

2. Multiply *A* by the multiple of 10.

Example

Write the following as ordinary numbers.

    (a) $3{\cdot}74 \times 10^4$ (b) $8{\cdot}91 \times 10^{-5}$

    (a) $3{\cdot}74 \times 10^4$ $= 3{\cdot}74 \times 10\,000$
                     $= 37\,400$

    (b) $8{\cdot}91 \times 10^{-5} = 8{\cdot}91 \times \frac{1}{100\,000}$
                     $= 0{\cdot}000\,089\,1$

Using standard form in addition and subtraction

To add or subtract two numbers in standard form, first make sure that they both contain the same power of ten.

Thus, $6{\cdot}8 \times 10^3 + 4{\cdot}1 \times 10^4$ would become $6{\cdot}8 \times 10^3 + 41 \times 10^3$

Example

$$4{\cdot}3 \times 10^7 + 2{\cdot}97 \times 10^5 = 430 \times 10^5 + 2{\cdot}97 \times 10^5$$
$$= 432{\cdot}97 \times 10^5$$
$$= 4{\cdot}3297 \times 10^7$$

Note:

You usually change the larger power into the smaller power.

MODULE 5

Using standard form in multiplication and division

Use the rules of indices to calculate in standard form.

Example 1

$$(4 \times 10^5) \times (8 \times 10^7) = 32 \times 10^{12}$$

$$= 3 \cdot 2 \times 10^{13}$$

Example 2

$$(3 \times 10^7) \div (5 \times 10^{11}) = \frac{3}{5} \times \frac{10^7}{10^{11}}$$

$$= 0 \cdot 6 \times 10^{-4}$$

$$= 6 \times 10^{-5}$$

> Notice that you must turn $0 \cdot 6 \times 10^{-4}$ into standard form.

Exercise 1

1. Copy this table and fill in the missing forms of each number.

Ordinary number	Number between 1 and 10 multiplied by a power of 10	Standard form
700 000	$7 \times 100\,000$	7×10^5
65 000	$6 \cdot 5 \times 10\,000$	
	$4 \cdot 2 \times 1\,000\,000$	
9 050		
		$5 \cdot 8 \times 10^9$

2. Write these numbers in standard form.
   (a) 720 000   (b) 97 000   (c) 595
   (d) 372 000 000   (e) 6 179 5000

3. Write these as ordinary numbers.
   (a) 3×10^3 (b) $1 \cdot 2 \times 10^5$ (c) $6 \cdot 7 \times 10^7$
   (d) $8 \cdot 05 \times 10^6$ (e) $1 \cdot 903 \times 10^4$ (d) $2 \cdot 88 \times 10^1$

4. Calculate:
   (a) $4 \cdot 3 \times 10^5 + 7 \cdot 4 \times 10^4$ (b) $2 \cdot 9 \times 10^6 + 8 \cdot 1 \times 10^5$
   (c) $2 \cdot 84 \times 10^7 + 2 \cdot 9 \times 10^5$

5. Calculate:
   (a) $3 \times 10^5 \times 8 \times 10^{-7}$ (b) $2 \times 10^6 \times 7 \times 10^{-18}$
   (c) $4 \times 10^5 \div 2 \times 10^3$ (d) $4 \times 10^6 \div 8 \times 10^{-7}$
   (e) $2 \times 10^7 \div 5 \times 10^4$

Summary

1. You can write simple algebraic expressions.

2. You can collect like terms.

3. You can add and subtract algebraic terms.

4. You can multiply and divide algebraic terms.

5. You can use indices in algebraic terms.

6. You can expand brackets.

7. You can factorise.

8. You can solve equations.

9. You can form an equation.

Check out AS1

1. There are x books in your bag. You put another 5 books in your bag. How many books have you now in your bag?

2. Simplify
   (a) $2a + 3a$
   (b) $4a - 3b + 2a - b$
   (c) $a - b$
   (d) $3a - 2b - 4c$

3. Simplify
   (a) $4a + 3b - 2a - b$
   (b) $4a + 5b + 7a + 6b + a$

4. Simplify
   (a) $4a^2 \times 3a^3b^2 \times 5a^4b^2$
   (b) $2a^5 \times 6a^2b^3 \div 4a^4b$

5. Find
   (a) $3p^4 \times 7p^9$
   (b) $8p^6 \div 4p^2$

6. Simplify
   (a) $5(2x - 3)$
   (b) $^-4(4x + 7y - 5)$
   (c) $3x^2(2 + 4x - 6x^2)$

7. Factorise
   (a) $4y - 8$
   (b) $3ab - 6ac$
   (c) $3x^2 + 6xy$
   (d) $4x^2 - 8x$

8. Find x when
   (a) $3x + 5 = 11$
   (b) $4x - 7 = x + 8$
   (c) $\frac{2}{3}x - 1 = 7 - 4(x + \frac{1}{2})$.

9. A school bus has x pupils on it.
   When it arrives at the next bus stop, $2x$ pupils get on.
   The bus now has 6 empty seats.
   The bus has 48 seats for passengers.
   Write an equation in x and solve it.

MODULE 5

10. You can substitute in formulae.

10. (a) $y = 2x^2 - 7x + 5$. Find y when $x = 3$.
(b) $A = \pi r^2 h$. $r = 7$, $h = 4$, find A.

You should leave your answer as a multiple of π.

11. You can calculate in standard form.

11. Calculate
(a) $4 \times 10^5 - 9 \times 10^4$
(b) $8 \times 10^6 \div 2 \times 10^3$

Revision exercise AS1

1. (a) A pen costs x pence.
How much will 4 pens cost?
(b) Simplify $3m + 2 + m - 3$.
(c) Solve the equation $2x + 3 = 15$.
(d) Solve the equation $3(x - 1) = 6$.
(e) Solve the equation $x + 2 = 5 - x$.   [SEG]

2. Adrian has three regular polygons: A, B and C.

A has x sides.
B has $(2x - 1)$ sides.
C has $(2x + 2)$ sides.

(a) Write an expression, in terms of x, for the total number of sides of these three polygons.
Write your answer in its simplest form.

The three polygons have a total of 16 sides.
(b) (i) Form an equation and hence find the value of x.
(ii) Use your value of x to find the number of sides of polygon B.   [SEG]

3. A brick weighs x kilograms.
(a) Write an expression, in terms of x, for the weight of 500 bricks.

A builder orders 500 bricks and 2 bags of cement.
The order weighs 1250 kg.
A bag of cement weighs 25 kg.
(b) By forming an equation in terms of x, find the weight of a brick.   [SEG]

4. (a) Simplify $3a - 2a + a$.
(b) What is the value of $x^2 + 5$ when x is $^-3$?
(c) Solve $3(x - 2) = 12$.   [SEG]

5. Solve these equations.

(a) $2(x - 1) = 8$

(b) $3x + 8 = 18 - 2x$ [SEG]

6. (a) Write an expression for the perimeter of this shape.
All lengths are in centimetres.

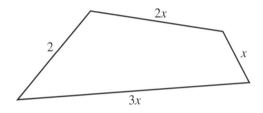

(b) The perimeter of the shape is 44 cm.
What is the value of x? [SEG]

7. (a) (i) Simplify $2a^5 \times 3a^2$.
(ii) Simplify $36a^6 \div 9a^2$.

(b) Factorise completely $3x^2 - 9x$. [SEG]

8. (a) Simplify $2x - x + 1$.

(b) Find the value of $3x + y^2$ when $x = {}^-2$ and $y = 3$. [SEG]

9. Solve these equations.

(a) $5x - 2 = 13$

(b) $3(2x - 1) = 9$ [SEG]

10. (a) Simplify $3a^5 \times 4a^2$.

(b) Simplify $6a^4 \div 2a$. [SEG]

11. Sarah weighs x kilograms.

Her mother weighs $2x$ kilograms.

Her father weighs 21 kilograms more than her mother.

(a) Write an expression, in terms of x, for the weight of her father.

The sum of their weights is 171 kg.

(b) Form an equation and find the value of x. [SEG]

MODULE 5

12. A small paving slab weighs x kilograms

A large paving slab weighs $(2x + 3)$ kilograms.

(a) Write an expression, in terms of x, for the total weight of 16 small slabs and 4 large slabs.
Give your answer in its simplest form.

The total weight of the slabs is 132 kilograms.

(b) Write down an equation and find the value of x. [SEG]

13. (a) Simplify $(2x - 3) + 5$.

(b) Factorise completely $4a - 2ab$.

(c) Solve $5x - 3 = 3x + 7$. [SEG]

14. (a) Simplify the expression $3(3x - 5) - 7$.

(b) Solve the equation $\dfrac{2}{5} = \dfrac{3}{x}$. [SEG]

15. Calculate 4×10^3 times 7×10^{-5}.
Give your answer in standard form.

16. The area of the United Kingdom is 244 018 square kilometres.
(a) Write 244 018 in standard form.
(b) The area of the Earth is $5 \cdot 09 \times 10^8$ square kilometres.
Calculate the area of the United Kingdom as a percentage of the area of the Earth. [SEG]

17. Work out $\dfrac{2 \cdot 7 \times 10^3}{4 \cdot 3 \times 10^{-3}}$, giving your answer in standard form.
  [SEG]

18. The number p written in standard form is 8×10^5.
The number q written in standard form is 5×10^{-2}.

(a) Calculate $p \times q$.
Give your answer in standard form.

(b) Calculate $p \div q$.
Give your answer in standard form. [SEG]

AS2 ALGEBRA 2

Equations can often describe everyday things, like the path traced out by a stone that is thrown.

I bet you can't beat that quadratic curve.

This unit will show you how to:

- Use coordinates
- Describe mappings and functions
- Draw and describe linear graphs
- Draw quadratic graphs
- Draw cubic and reciprocal graphs

Before you start:

You should know how to ...	Check in AS2
1. Calculate with directed numbers For example, $^-4 + 5 = 1$ 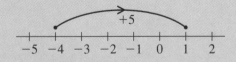	**1.** Find the value of (a) $^-7 + 5$ (b) $^-8 + {}^-3$ (c) $3 \times {}^-4$
2. Substitute in formulae For example, find the value of $y = 2x + 5$ when $x = {}^-3$. $\quad y = 2 \times {}^-3 + 5$ $\qquad = {}^-6 + 5$ $\qquad = {}^-1$	**2.** $y = 4x - 7$ Find y when $x = 3$.

2.1 Coordinates

You can describe the location of a point on a grid by using coordinates.

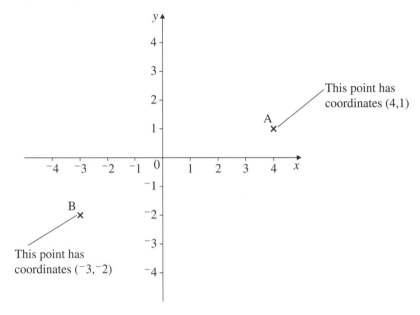

This point has coordinates (4,1)

This point has coordinates (⁻3,⁻2)

Exercise 2A

1. Write down the coordinates of the points labelled A to E on the grid below.

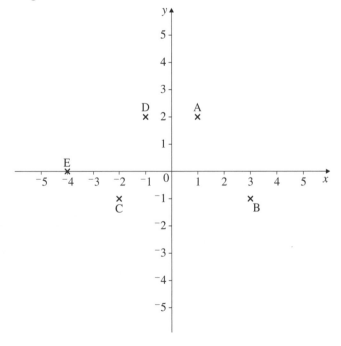

2. Draw axes similar to those used in question 1, with the
same scale for the *x* and *y* axes.
On your grid mark and label the following points.

R = (1, 2)   S = (⁻4, 3)   T = (⁻1, 4)
U = (4, 0)   V = (5, ⁻2)   W = (⁻3, ⁻3)
X = (0, 3)   Y = (⁻3, 0)   Z = (1, ⁻3)

2.2 Mappings and functions

A **mapping** shows how a set of numbers (the input) is
transformed into a second set of numbers (the output).

For example, you could apply a mapping 'add 6' to the input
numbers 1, 3, 5, 7, 9.

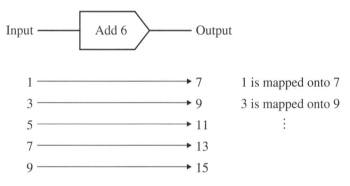

1	→ 7	1 is mapped onto 7
3	→ 9	3 is mapped onto 9
5	→ 11	⋮
7	→ 13	
9	→ 15	

You can use algebra to describe this mapping.

Let *x* be the input. Then *x* is mapped onto *x* + 6.

This is the mapping $x \rightarrow (x + 6)$.

You can illustrate it on a pair of number lines.

Draw two scales to represent the
input and output. Draw arrows to
connect each input value to its output.

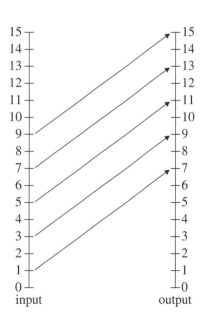

Example

Draw mapping diagrams to illustrate the following for input values $-1, 0, 2, 3$.

(a) $x \rightarrow x + 2$ (b) $x \rightarrow 3x$

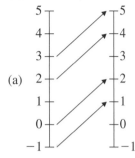

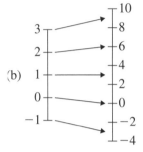

The mapping $x \rightarrow x - 1$ is an example of a **function**.

● A function is a mapping that has a single output value for any given input.

You can draw the graph of a function:

1. First you need to write it as an equation $y = x - 1$.

2. Choose values for x, say $^-1, 0, 2$ and 4.
Calculate the y values in a table:

x	$^-1$	0	2	4
$y = x - 1$	$^-2$	$^-1$	1	3

3. You can plot the coordinates … $\Downarrow$
       $(^-1, ^-2)$, $(0, ^-1)$, $(2, 1)$, $(4, 3)$

4. … to give a graph of the equation $y = x + 1$

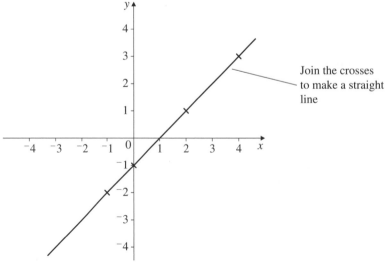

Join the crosses
to make a straight
line

$x \rightarrow x - 1$ is called a linear function and $y = x - 1$ is the equation of the straight line.

Exercise 2B

1. (a) Write the function $x \rightarrow x + 2$ as an equation using x and y.

(b) Make a list of values for the equation in (a) using the values $^-1, 0, 1, 2, 3, 4$ for x.

(c) Draw a graph to show the numbers from your table of values.

Your axis for x should go from $^-1$ to 4 and your axis for y from $^-3$ to 12.

2. Repeat question 1 for the functions

(a) $x \rightarrow 3x$

(b) $x \rightarrow \dfrac{x}{2}$

(c) $x \rightarrow 8 - x$

3. (a) Write each of these functions as an equation using x and y.

(i) $x \rightarrow x + 5$

(ii) $x \rightarrow 2x + 1$

(iii) $x \rightarrow 3x - 1$

(b) Make a table of values for each equation in (a) using the values $^-1, 0, 1, 2, 3, 4, 5$ for x.

(c) Draw separate graphs for each table of values.

Check your y values carefully before drawing your axis.

2.3 Straight-line graphs

Linear equations give linear graphs, which are straight lines.

Example

Draw the graph of the equation $y = 2x - 4$:

● Choose easy whole number values for x, close to zero.

$x = ^-2, ^-1, 0, 1, 2$

● Work out the value of y for each x.

For example, when $x = ^-2$, $y = (2 \times ^-2) - 4 = 8$.

● Put the values in a table:

x	$^-2$	$^-1$	0	1	2
y	$^-8$	$^-6$	$^-4$	$^-2$	0

To remind yourself about linear equations, turn to page 226.

Hint:

You only really need three points to draw a straight line (two for the line, and one to check).

MODULE 5

- Draw a set of axes with x from $^-2$ to 4 and y from $^-8$ to 4, plot the values for each point and draw the line for $y = 2x - 4$.

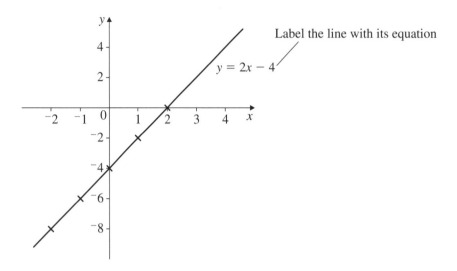

Label the line with its equation

$y = 2x - 4$

Exercise 2C

1. Draw graphs of $y = 4$, $y = {}^-1$, $y = 0$ and $y = 6$ on the same axes. What do these lines have in common?
   Explain your answer.

2. Draw graphs of $x = 5$, $x = 2$, $x = 0$ and $x = 3$ on the same axes. What do these lines have in common?
   Explain your answer.

3. (a) On the same axes, draw the graphs of
   - (i) $y = x + 1$
   - (ii) $y = x - 1$
   - (iii) $y = x + 2$
   - (iv) $y = x$
   - (v) $y = x - 2$
   (b) What do these graphs have in common with each other?
   (c) What is different for each graph?

4. (a) On the same axes, draw the graphs of
   - (i) $y = 2x + 3$
   - (ii) $y = 2x - 1$
   - (iii) $y = 2x + 4$
   - (iv) $y = 2x$
   - (v) $y = 2x - 2$
   (b) What do these graphs have in common with each other?
   (c) What is different for each graph?

5. (a) On the same axes, draw the graphs of
   - (i) $y = 2x + 2$
   - (ii) $y = 4x + 2$
   - (iii) $y = x + 2$
   - (iv) $y = {}^-x + 2$
   - (v) $y = 3x + 2$
   (b) What do these graphs have in common with each other?
   (c) What is different for each graph?

6. (a) On the same axes, draw the graphs of

    (i) $y = 3x - 1$ (ii) $y = x - 1$ (iii) $y = 2x - 1$

    (iv) $y = {}^-x - 1$ (v) $y = \frac{1}{2}x - 1$

  (b) What do these graphs have in common with each other?

  (c) What is different for each graph?

2.4 Gradient

The measure of the steepness of a graph is called the **gradient**.
You can find the gradient of a straight line by choosing two
points on the line and finding the distance up and across.

> The lines drawn in
> questions 3 and 4 of
> Exercise 2C are parallel.
> They have the same
> gradient.

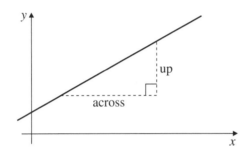

- $\text{Gradient} = \dfrac{\text{Distance up (change in } y \text{ value)}}{\text{Distance across (change in } x \text{ value)}}$

The gradient of a line can be positive, negative or zero.

Example

Find the gradient of the lines AB and CD.

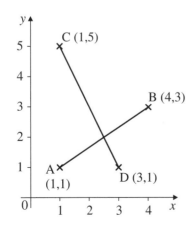

MODULE 5

For AB, work out the distance across and up.

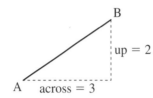

$$\text{gradient AB} = \frac{\text{up}}{\text{across}} = \frac{2}{3} \text{ (an uphill slope)}$$

For CD, work out the distance across and up.

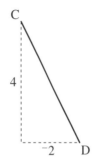

$$\text{gradient CD} = \frac{4}{^-2} = {}^-2$$

Exercise 2D

1. Work out the gradients of these lines.

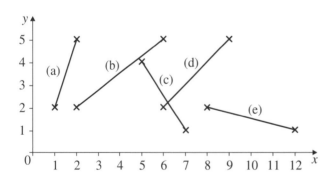

2. Sketch each pair of coordinate points and find the gradient of the straight line joining them.
   (a) (4, 2) and (6, 8)
   (b) (0, 3) and (4, 4)
   (c) (⁻4, 7) and (⁻7, 4)

(d) $(^-1, 4)$ and $(3, 1)$
(e) $(2, 3)$ and $(5, 5)$
(f) $(3, 1)$ and $(^-2. ^-3)$
(g) $(4, 8)$ and $(^-6, 3)$
(h) $(^-2, 5)$ and $(2, ^-1)$

2.5 Intercept

- The **y-intercept** for a line is the point where the graph crosses the y-axis.

Example

Find the y-intercept for the line $2y = x - 5$.
When a straight line cuts the y-axis, $x = 0$
so substitute the value $x = 0$ into the equation $2y = x - 5$.

$\therefore \quad 2y = 0 - 5 = ^-5$

$\qquad y = ^-\frac{5}{2} = ^-2\frac{1}{2}$

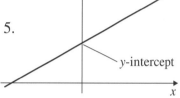

The line $2y = x - 5$ cuts the y-axis at $(0, \ ^-2\frac{1}{2})$ so the intercept value is $^-2\frac{1}{2}$.

Exercise 2E

Find the intercept on the y-axis for each of these lines.

1. $y = x + 4$

2. $2y = x - 2$

3. $y = x$

4. $x + y = 6$

5. $2y + 3x = 9$

6. $y = 2x$

7. $2y + x = 5$

8. $\frac{1}{2}y = 3x + 4$

2.6 General equation of a straight-line graph

The general equation of a straight line is:

$$y = mx + c$$

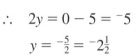

m is the gradient c is the y-intercept

MODULE 5

Example 1

Find the equation of the line shown.

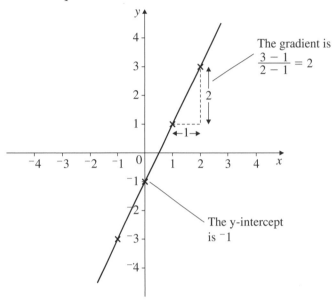

Note:
You can choose **any** two points on a straight line to find the gradient.

So $m = 2$ and $c = {}^-1$.
The equation of this line is $y = 2x - 1$.

Example 2

Find the equation of the line shown.

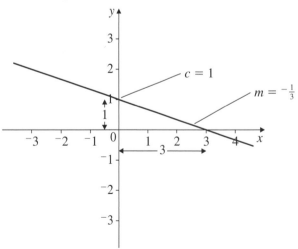

Note:
The gradient is negative because the line is sloping downwards.

The equation of this line is $y = {}^-\frac{1}{3}x + 1$.

You could rearrange this equation to remove the fraction:

$3y = {}^-x + 3 \quad \text{or} \quad 3y + x = 3$

To **sketch** a straight-line graph, you only need to find and plot two points. You can then join them up with a ruler.

Example 3

Sketch the graph of the line $2y + x = {}^-4$.

The easiest points to find are where $x = 0$ and $y = 0$.

When $x = 0$, $2y = 4$

so $y = 2$ the line passes through $(0, 2)$.

When $y = 0$, $x = 4$ the line passes through $(4, 0)$.

Plot these points on a set of axes and draw a straight line through them.

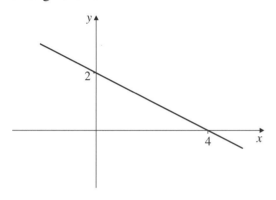

Note:
Sketch graphs do not
need to be accurate.

Exercise 2F

1. Find the equation of each of these lines.

(a)

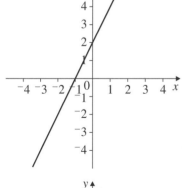

(b)

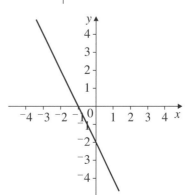

(c)

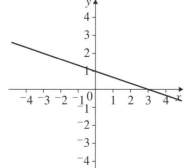

(d)

(e)

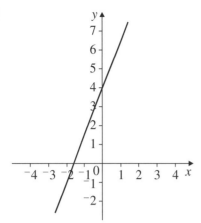

(f)

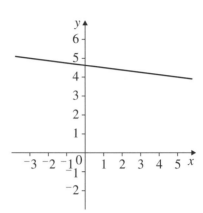

2. Match each of these sketch graphs to one of the equations
below.

(a) $x = 5$ (b) $y + 3x = {}^-3$ (c) $y + 5x = 6$

(d) $y = x + 6$ (e) $y = 3x$ (f) $y = 4$

(i)

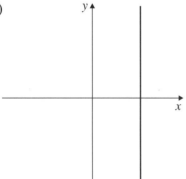

(ii)

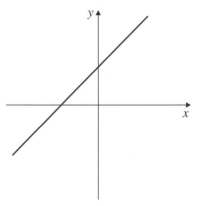

(iii)

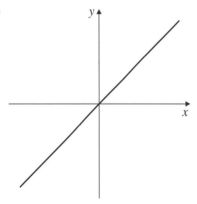

(iv)

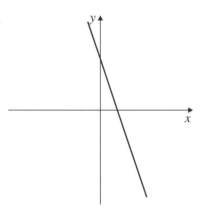

(v)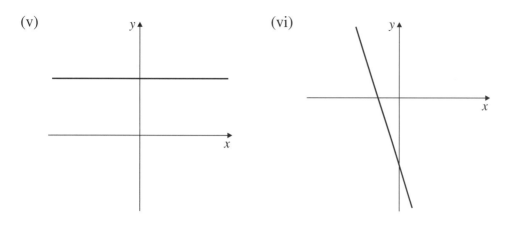

(vi)

3. Sketch these graphs of straight lines, marking and labelling the values where each graph crosses the axes.
Use a new set of axes for each answer.
(a) $y = x$
(b) $y = x + 1$
(c) $x = 4$
(d) $y = 2x$
(e) $y = x - 5$
(f) $2y = x + 1$
(g) $y = ^{-}3$
(h) $y = 3x - 1$
(i) $y + 2x = 6$
(j) $x + y = 9$

2.7 Graphs of quadratic functions

Quadratic functions always have a term in x^2.

An example of a quadratic function is $y = x^2 + 3x + 1$.

In general $y = ax^2 + bx + c$ where a, b and c are numbers.

The graph of a quadratic function always has a characteristic shape:

a, b and c are usually referred to as **constants**.

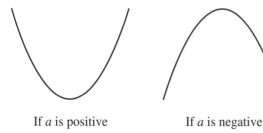

If a is positive   If a is negative

The shape of a quadratic curve is called a **parabola**.

- Quadratic curves always have either a maximum or a minimum value, and they are symmetrical about a vertical line.

MODULE 5

Example 1

Draw the graph of $y = x^2 - 9$ for values of x from $^-5$ to $+5$.

Use your graph to find and state the minimum value of the function.

First work out the y values:

When $x = {}^-5$, $y = ({}^-5)^2 - 9$
$$y = 25 - 9 = 16$$

Now work out the y values for all the other values of x and put these into a table.

x	$^-5$	$^-4$	$^-3$	$^-2$	$^-1$	0	1	2	3	4	5
y	16	7	0	$^-5$	$^-8$	$^-9$	$^-8$	$^-5$	0	7	16

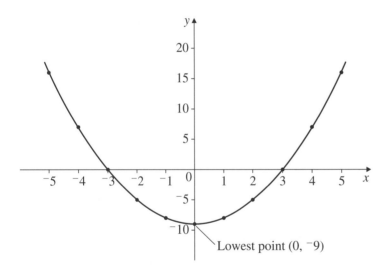

Lowest point (0, $^-9$)

Note:
The lowest or highest point may not be a point that you have plotted.

You can use a quadratic graph to solve quadratic equations.

Example 2

Draw the graph of $y = 2x^2 - 8x + 7$ for values of x between $^-1$ and 5.

(a) Draw in the line of symmetry for this graph and write down its equation.

Use your graph to answer the following.

(b) What is the minimum value of y for the function $y = 2x^2 - 8x + 7$ and what value of x gives this minimum value for y?

(c) Find solutions to the equations
   (i) $2x^2 - 8x + 7 = 0$
   (ii) $2x^2 - 8x + 7 = 10$

First find the y values:

   When $x = -1$ $y = 2 \times (^-1)^2 - 8 \times (^-1) + 7$
                       $= 2 + 8 + 7$
                       $= 17$

Put them in a table.

x	$^-1$	0	1	2	3	4	5
y	17	7	1	$^-1$	1	7	17

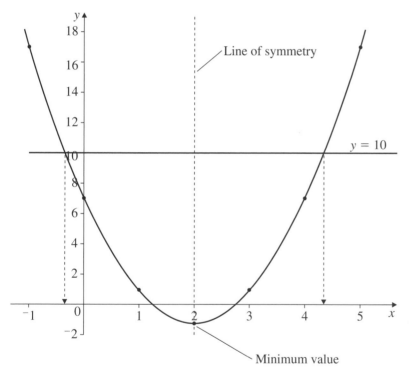

Line of symmetry

$y = 10$

Minimum value

Note:

The axes need to be drawn with x from $^-1$ to 5, and y from 1 to 17.

MODULE 5

(a) The line of symmetry is drawn on the graph and has the equation $x = 2$.
(b) Minimum value of y is $^-1$ and occurs at $x = 2$.
   (i) Look at the curve where $y = 0$. There are two intersection points.
        The two x values are $x = 1 \cdot 29$ and $x = 2 \cdot 71$ (approximately).
   (ii) Look at the curve where $y = 10$.
        The two x values are $x = {}^-0 \cdot 21$ and $x = 4 \cdot 47$ (approximately).

Exercise 2G

1. Draw graphs of the following functions on graph paper. Use values of x from $^-5$ to $+5$ on a new set of axes for each question. On each graph draw in the axis of symmetry and write down its equation.

   (a) $y = 2x^2$ 　　　　　　　　(b) $y = x^2 + 4$

   (c) $y = x^2 - 3x$ 　　　　　　(d) $y = {}^-2x^2 + 5$

   (e) $y = x^2 - 4x + 5$ 　　　　(f) $y = {}^-x^2 + 2x + 4$

   (g) $y = 2x^2 + 4x - 3$

2. (a) Copy and complete the table of values for $y = x^2 - 10x + 24$.

x	0	1	2	3	4	5	6	7	8	9
y	24			3						15

   (b) Draw the graph of $y = x^2 - 10x + 24$ for values of x from 0 to 9.

   (c) Use your graph to solve the equations

   　(i) $x^2 - 10x + 24 = 0$

   　(ii) $x^2 - 10x + 24 = 6$

3. (a) Copy and complete the table of values for $y = 2x^2 - 7x - 3$.

x	$^-2$	$^-1$	0	1	2	3	4	5	6
y		6			$^-9$				27

   (b) Draw the graph of $y = 2x^2 - 7x - 3$ for values of x from $^-2$ to $^+6$.

   (c) Use your graph to solve the equations

   　(i) $2x^2 - 7x - 3 = 0$

   　(ii) $2x^2 - 7x - 3 = {}^-6$

4. Make a table of values to draw each of the graphs given below. The range of values of x to use is given with each question.

   (a) Draw the graph of $y = x^2 - 5x + 6$ for values of x from 0 to 5. Use this graph to solve $x^2 - 5x + 6 = 0$.

   (b) Draw the graph of $y = 2x^2 + 7x - 4$ for values of x from $^-5$ to 2. Use this graph to solve $2x^2 + 7x - 4 = 0$.

   (c) Draw the graph of $y = {}^-2x^2 - 3x + 5$ for values of x from $^-5$ to 3. Use this graph to solve $^-2x^2 - 3x + 5 = 0$.

5. An aircraft was flying at a height of 12 km above ground level. Due to weather conditions the pilot put the aircraft into a dive and then pulled it out of the dive. The height of the aircraft above the ground, in km, is given by the equation $y = \frac{1}{5}x^2 - 3x + 12$, where x is the horizontal distance (in km) that the aircraft travels.

Copy and complete the table of values for $y = \frac{1}{5}x^2 - 3x + 12$ and use the values to draw a graph showing the flight path of the aircraft.

x	0	2	4	6	8	10	12	14
y								

Use your graph to answer the following questions.

(a) How close to ground level did the aircraft become before beginning to climb upwards again?

(b) How far did the plane travel horizontally before beginning to climb upwards again?

6. A boy throws a stone from a cliff top into the sea below. The equation $h = 72 + 12t - 4t^2$ gives the height, h metres, of the stone above sea level t seconds after the boy threw the stone.

Copy and complete the table of values for $h = 72 + 12t - 4t^2$, using the values of t given below.

t	0	1	2	3	4	5	6
h							

(a) Draw the graph for the path of the stone.

(b) Use your graph to answer the following questions.

    (i)   What is the height of the cliff?

    (ii) What is the greatest height of the stone above sea level?

    (iii) How long does the stone take to reach its greatest height?

    (iv) How long does the stone take until it splashes into the sea?

MODULE 5

7. A farmer has 20 metres of chicken wire which he uses to make a rectangular enclosure for his chickens. He uses a brick wall to make one side of the rectangle and the chicken wire to make the other sides of the rectangle.

The area, A m^2, inside the enclosure depends on the width x m of the rectangle and is given by the equation $A = 20x - 2x^2$.

Copy and complete the table of values for $A = 20x - 2x^2$, using the values of x given.

x	0	1	2	3	4	5	6	7	8	9	10
A											

(a) Draw the graph showing the area enclosed within the rectangle as x increases.

(b) Use your graph to answer the following questions.

(i) What is the largest possible area that the rectangle could enclose?

(ii) What is the width of the rectangle which contains the largest area?

(iii) What width of rectangle contains an area of 45 m^2? Is there more than one answer for an area of 45 m^2? Give a brief explanation of your findings.

2.8 Cubic and reciprocal graphs

Cubic functions always have a term in x^3.
The simple cubic functions that you need to know about at GCSE are of the type $y = ax^3$ or $y = x^3 + c$ where a and c are both numbers.
They look like this:

or like this:

if the x^3 term is positive   if the x^3 term is negative

The **reciprocal function** is of the form $y = \dfrac{1}{x}$ with $x \neq 0$.

$y = \dfrac{1}{x}$ looks like this

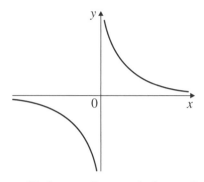

In the next exercise you will draw a few variations of these curves.

Example

Draw the graph of

$$y = \frac{1}{x} - 1.$$

Use values of x from $^-3$ to 3.

First work out the y values.

When $x = ^-3$, $y = \dfrac{1}{^-3} - 1$

$ = ^-1\tfrac{1}{3}$

Now work out the rest of the y values and put them in a table.

x	$^-3$	$^-2$	$^-1$	0	1	2	3
y	$^-1\tfrac{1}{3}$	$^-1\tfrac{1}{2}$	$^-2$	–	0	$^-\tfrac{1}{2}$	$^-\tfrac{1}{2}$

Note:
When $x = 0$, $y = \tfrac{1}{0} - 1$ which is undefined – try it on your calculator.

Now draw a set of axes and plot a graph.

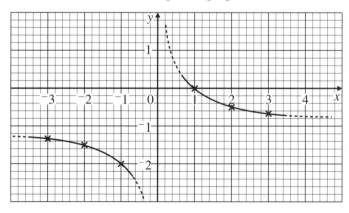

Exercise 2H

1. (a) Draw the graphs of   (i) $y = x^3$
                                 (ii) $y = 2x^3$
                                 (iii) $y = 3x^3$

   Draw them on the same axes, and use values of x from $^-3$ to 3.

   (b) Describe the shape of your graphs.

2. (a) Draw the graphs of   (i) $y = x^3 + 1$
                                 (ii) $y = x^3 + 2$
                                 (iii) $y = x^3 - 1$

   Draw them on the same axes, and use values of x from $^-3$ to 3.

   (b) Describe the shape of your graphs.

3. Draw the graph of $y = \dfrac{^-1}{x}$

   Use values of x from $^-3$ to 3.

4. Draw the graphs of

   (a) $y = \dfrac{1}{x + 1}$ (b) $y = \dfrac{1}{x + 2}$

   Draw the two graphs on the same axes. Use values of x from $^-3$ to 3.

Summary

1. You can plot points on a grid.

2. You can draw a straight line.

3. You can find the gradient and intercept of a graph.

Check out AS2

1. On a grid, plot the points

   $(2, 4), (1, ^-3), (^-3, 2), (^-4, ^-2)$

2. Draw the lines $y = x + 3$, $y = 2x - 1$.

3. Write down the gradient and intercept of the line shown.

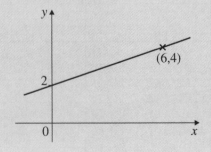

4. You can
   (a) draw the graph of a quadratic function
   (b) use graphs to solve an equation.

4. (a) Draw the graph of $y = x^2 - 3x + 2$ for values of x from $^-1$ to 5.
   (b) Solve the equations
      (i) $x^2 - 3x + 2 = 0$
      (ii) $x^2 = 3x + 1$.

5. You can draw a mapping diagram.

5. Show the mapping $x \rightarrow 3x - 2$ on a mapping diagram.

Revision exercise AS2

1. (a) On a graph draw and label the following lines

$$y = 2x + 3 \quad \text{and} \quad y = {}^-x$$

   (b) Solve the equation $2x + 3 = {}^-x$.

2. (a) Copy and complete the table of values for $y = x^3 + x$.

x	$^-3$	$^-2$	$^-1$	0	1	2	3
y		$^-10$		0	2		30

   (b) Draw the graph of $y = x^3 + x$ for values of x from $^-3$ to 3.
   (c) Use your graph to solve the equation $x^3 + x = 5$.

3. The diagram shows a sketch of the line $y = ax + b$.

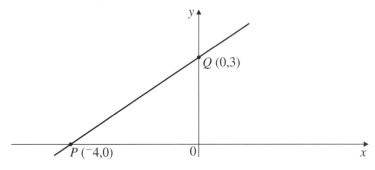

The line $y = ax + b$ goes through the points $P(^-4, 0)$ and $Q(0, 3)$.

   (a) Work out the values of a and b.
   (b) On a copy of the diagram sketch the line $y = 3 - x$.
   (c) A single region is satisfied by all of these inequalities.

$$x \geqslant 0 \qquad y \geqslant 0 \qquad y \leqslant 3 - x$$

   Label this region R.

MODULE 5

4. (a) On a graph draw and label the lines

$$x = 1 \quad \text{and} \quad x + y = 4$$

(b) Show clearly on the graph the single region that is satisfied by all of these inequalities.

$$y \geqslant 0 \qquad x \geqslant 1 \qquad x + y \leqslant 4$$

Label this region R.

5. (a) Copy and complete the table of values for $y = x^2 - 4x + 2$.

x	$^-1$	0	1	2	3	4
y			$^-1$		$^-1$	2

(b) Draw the graph of $y = x^2 - 4x + 2$ for values of x from $^-1$ to 4.

(c) Hence, or otherwise, solve the equation $x^2 - 4x + 2 = 0$.

6. The diagram shows a sketch of the line $2y = x - 2$.

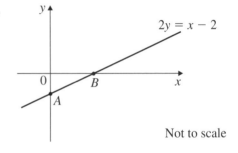

$2y = x - 2$

Not to scale

(a) Find the coordinates of points A and B.

(b) Find the gradient of the line $2y = x - 2$.

(c) Explain why the simultaneous equations $2y = x - 2$ and $2y = x - 3$ have no solution.

(d) Another line passes through B and through the point $(0, 2)$.
Find the equation of this line.

7. (a) Copy and complete the table of values for $y = 5 - x^2$.

x	$^-3$	$^-2$	$^-1$	0	1	2	3
y		1	4	5			$^-4$

(b) Draw the graph of $y = 5 - x^2$ for the values of x from $^-3$ to 3.

(c) Use your graph to solve the equation $5 - x^2 = 0$.

8. (a) Copy and complete the table of values for $y = x^2 - x - 1$.

x	$^-2$	$^-1$	0	1	2	3
y		1	$^-1$			5

(b) Draw the graph of $y = x^2 - x - 1$ for the values of x from $^-2$ to 3.

(c) Use your graph to solve the equation $x^2 - x - 1 = 0$.

AS3 FURTHER ALGEBRA

There are patterns all around us, and many of them can be described using numbers.

Fractal patterns are based on sequences of numbers. They have a wide variety of uses, ranging from computer graphics to meteorology.

This unit will show you how to:

- Describe sequences
- Solve inequalities
- Solve simultaneous equations
- Expand and factorise quadratics
- Solve quadratic equations
- Transform formulae
- Use 'trial and improvement' to solve equations

Before you start:

MODULE 5

You should know how to ...	Check in AS3
1. Expand brackets For example, $3(2x - 4)$ $= 6x - 12$	**1.** Expand (a) $2(x + 3)$ (b) $x(2x + 3)$ (c) $^-5(3x - 2y + 7)$
2. Solve equations For example, $4x - 6 = 22$ $+6 \quad 4x = 28 \quad +6$ $÷4 \quad x = 7 \quad ÷4$	**2.** Find x when (a) $4x + 12 = 0$ (b) $2x + 3 = 8$ (c) $5x + 2 = 7 - 3x$
3. Draw straight lines on a grid	**3.** On a single set of axes, draw the lines $x + y = 5$ and $y = 2x - 3$

3.1 Sequences

A **sequence** is a set of numbers that follow a pattern, or rule.
Each member of the sequence is called a **term**.

For example 2, 5, 8, 11, 14, 17, … is a sequence.

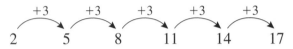

This pattern starts at 2 and increases by 3 each time.
The next two terms in this sequence are 20 and 23.

● A **linear sequence** has a constant difference *d* between the
  terms.

2, 5, 8, 11, 14, 17, … is a linear sequence but 2, 4, 8, 16, 32, …
is not.

Example 1

In each of the sequences write down the next two terms.

(a) 5, 9, 13, 17, …
(b) 3, ⁻2. ⁻7, ⁻12, …

(a) The rule is 'add on 4'.
    The next two terms are 21 and 25.

(b) The rule is 'take away 5'.
    The next two terms are ⁻17 and ⁻22.

Example 2

Find the missing terms in the sequences.

(a) 2, 9, —, 23, —, —,
(b) 5, 7, 10, —, —, 25

(a) The rule is 'add 7'.

    9 + 7 = 16   30 + 7 = 37
    23 + 7 = 30

The missing terms are 16, 30 and 37.

(b) The difference increases by 1 each time.

    5 + 2 = 7   14 + 5 = 19
    7 + 3 = 10   19 + 6 = 25
    10 + 4 = 14

The missing terms are 14 and 19.

Exercise 3A

1. In each of these sequences write down the next two terms.

(a) 1, 3, 5, 7, 9

(b) 4, 6, 8, 10, 12

(c) 7, 11, 15, 19, 23

(d) 11, 9, 7, 5, 3

(e) 100, 99, 97, 94, 90

(f) 7, 4, 1, $^-$2, $^-$5, $^-$8

(g) 10, 10, 9, 7, 4

(h) 6, 8, 11, 15, 20, 26

(i) $^-$1, $^-$2, $^-$4, $^-$7, $^-$11

(j) 15, 13, 10, 6, 1

(k) 1, 2, 4, 8, 16

(l) 9, 15, 23, 33, 45

(m) 1, 4, 9, 16, 25

(n) 1, 3, 6, 10, 15

(o) 0, 3, 8, 15, 24

(p) $\frac{1}{3}, \frac{1}{4}, \frac{1}{6}, \frac{1}{12}, 0$

2. Find the missing terms in these sequences.

(a) 1, 3, __, __, 9, 11

(b) 1, 3, 9, __, 81, __

(c) 1, 10, 100, __, 10 000, ____

(d) $\frac{1}{2}, \frac{1}{4}, \frac{1}{8}$, __, $\frac{1}{32}$, __

(e) 5, __, 13, 17, __

(f) 1, 2, 4, __, __, 32

3. Which of the sequences in questions 1 and 2 are linear?

3.2 The *n*th term of a sequence

If you wanted to find, say, the 100th term of a sequence, it would take too long to write down all the numbers leading up to it. Often you can find an expression for the general term in a sequence, or the **nth term**.

For a linear sequence, the differences will help you find the general term.

Example

A sequence is given as 3, 9, 15, 21, 27, 33, …
Find
(a) the next two terms in the sequence
(b) an expression for the *n*th term of the sequence
(c) the 25th term in the sequence.

(a) 3   9   15   21   27   33   39   45

Add 6 to get the next two terms

(b) First draw a table:

Position number	1	2	3	4	5	6
Term	3	9	15	21	27	33
Difference		+6	+6	+6	+6	+6

The difference between successive terms is $(+)6$, so the expression will be $6n +$ something.
Compare each term with $6n$:

Term	3	9	15	21	27
$6n$	6	12	18	24	30

So the nth term $= 6n - 3$

(c) For the 25th term, $n = 25$

$$6 \times 25 - 3 = 147$$

So the 25th term is 147.

Check: for the 6th term: $6 \times 6 - 3 = 33$, so the expression is correct.

● In a linear sequence with difference d, the expression for the nth term will be:

$$n\text{th term} = dn + \text{a number}$$

Exercise 3B

1. In each of these sequences find
   (i)   the next two terms
   (ii) an expression for the nth term
   (iii) the 23rd term of the sequence.
   (a) 1, 5, 9, 13, 17, …
   (b) 9, 11, 13, 15, 17, …
   (c) 4, 9, 14, 19, 24, …
   (d) 6, 13, 20, 27, 34, …
   (e) 2, $2\frac{1}{2}$, 3, $3\frac{1}{2}$, 4, …
   (f) 20, 18, 16, 14, 12, …
   (g) 15, 11, 7, 3, $^-1$, …
   (h) $^-3$, $^-6$, $^-9$, $^-12$, $^-15$, …
   (i) 17, 13, 9, 5, 1, …
   (j) 3.5, 3.25, 3, 2.75, 2.5, …

Hint:
In question 1(f), the difference d is -2, not 2.

2. An expression for the nth term of a sequence is $5n - 4$.
   Use this nth term expression to write down
   (a) the constant difference between successive terms
   (b) the first five terms of the sequence.

3. An expression for the nth term of a sequence is $7 - \frac{3}{4}n$.
   Use this nth term expression to write down
   (a) the constant difference between successive terms
   (b) the first five terms of the sequence.

3.3 More sequences

Sometimes you can only find the next term in a sequence from the term before.

Example (Investigation)

Here is a sequence: 1, 1, 2, 3, 5, 8, 13, 21, ...
It is called the **Fibonacci sequence**.
Each term is the sum of the previous two terms,
for example $3 = 2 + 1$ and $5 = 3 + 2$.

(a) Find the next two terms of the sequence.

(b) Divide each term by the previous term.
For example,

$$1 \div 1 = 1,$$
$$2 \div 1 = 2,$$
$$3 \div 2 = 1{\cdot}5$$

Write your answers as a sequence. What do you notice?

Note: Give your answers to 3 d.p. where appropriate.

(a) Next two terms: $13 + 21 = 34$, $21 + 34 = 55$

(b) $5 \div 3 = 1{\cdot}667$ $8 \div 5 = 1{\cdot}6$
$13 \div 8 = 1{\cdot}625$ $21 \div 13 = 1{\cdot}615$
$34 \div 21 = 1{\cdot}619$ $55 \div 34 = 1{\cdot}618$

Write the answers as a sequence:

$1, 2, 1{\cdot}5, 1{\cdot}667, 1{\cdot}6, 1{\cdot}625, 1{\cdot}615, 1{\cdot}619, 1{\cdot}618$

After a few divisions, the answers round up to $1{\cdot}62$ to 2 d.p.

Terms of a sequence

Each term in a sequence is labelled with the letter u:

$$u_1, \quad u_2, \quad u_3, \quad \ldots \quad u_n, \quad u_{n+1}, \quad \ldots$$

1st term 2nd term nth term $(n+1)$th term

If the first term of a sequence is known, then you can find the second term by using a formula connecting u_n and u_{n+1}.

Example

Find the first four terms of the sequence given by the term-to-term rule:

$$u_1 = 3, \, u_{n+1} = 2\,u_n - 1$$

Note:
The Fibonacci sequence occurs commonly in nature, such as in the spiral patterns of a sunflower (see the front cover of this book).

Note:
This sequence gets closer, or converges, to a particular value called the **golden ratio**, which was commonly used in classical Greek architecture and in mysticism.
The value of this ratio is aproximately 1.62.

MODULE 5

Insert $u_1 = 3$ into the formula:

$$u_2 = 2u_1 - 1$$
$$= 2 \times 3 - 1$$
$$= 5$$
$$u_3 = 2 \times 5 - 1$$
$$= 9$$
$$u_4 = 2 \times 9 - 1$$
$$= 17$$

Exercise 3C

In each of these questions, find the first four terms of the number patterns given by these term-to-term rules.

1. $u_1 = 2$ and $u_{n+1} = 2u_n$
2. $u_1 = 5$ and $u_{n+1} = u_n - 3$
3. $u_1 = {}^{-}2$ and $u_{n+1} = u_n + 1$
4. $u_1 = 9$ and $u_{n+1} = \dfrac{u_n}{2} + 3$
5. $u_1 = 3$ and $u_{n+1} = 2(u_n - 1)$
6. $u_1 = 4$ and $u_{n+1} = u_n - 9$
7. $u_1 = 24$ and $u_{n+1} = u_1$
8. $u_1 = 5$ and $u_{n+1} = 12 - u_n$
9. $u_1 = \frac{1}{2}$ and $u_{n+1} = u_n - 2$
10. $u_1 = 2$ and $u_{n+1} = u_n + n$
11. $u_1 = 1$ and $u_{n+1} = u_n + n + 1$
12. $u_1 = {}^{-}\frac{1}{4}$ and $u_{n+1} = 2u_n + \frac{1}{2}$

3.4 Sequences for patterns

Here is a sequence of matches made into squares.

  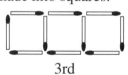 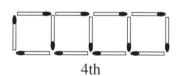

   1st   2nd   3rd   4th

The table records the shape number (n) and the number of matches (m) used to make each shape.

Shape number (n)	1	2	3	4
Number of matches (m)	4	7	10	13
Difference		3	3	3

The difference is +3 so the
rule will include $3n$

The rule is $m = 3n + 1$.

Note:
You can use this rule to find the number of matches for larger shapes.
For the 30th shape,
$$n = 30.$$
So $m = 3 \times 30 + 1$
$$= 91$$

Exercise 3D

1. The following shapes are constructed from matchsticks.

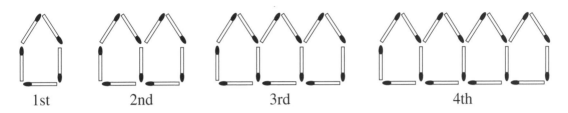

1st   2nd   3rd   4th

(a) Draw the next matchstick pattern for this sequence.

(b) Copy the table for your results and use the diagrams to complete the table.

Shape number (n)	1	2	3	4	5
Number of matches (m)					
Difference					

(c) Find a rule connecting m and n.

(d) How many matchsticks will be in the 25th shape?

2. The following triangle shapes are constructed from matchsticks.

   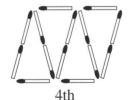

1st   2nd   3rd   4th

(a) Draw the next matchstick pattern for this sequence.

(b) Let the triangle shape be t and the number of matchsticks used be m. Draw a table for the result connecting t to m.

(c) Find a rule connecting t and m.

(d) Use your rule to find how many matchsticks are needed to make the 20th shape.

MODULE 5

3. The following shapes are constructed from matchsticks.

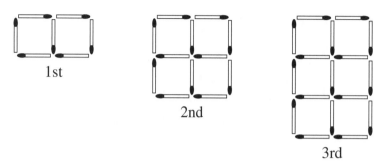

(a) Draw the next matchstick pattern for this sequence.

(b) Let the number of rows be *r* and the number of matchsticks used be *m* for each shape.
Draw a table for the result connecting *r* to *m*.

(c) Find the rule connecting *r* and *m*.

(d) Use your rule to find how many matchsticks are used for a shape with 15 rows.

4. A pattern of squares are placed on a table and the length of the line of squares increases as shown.

(a) How many squares will there be in the 5th and 6th lines of squares?

(b) Let the number of squares in a row be represented by *s* and the pattern position be represented by *p*.
Draw a table for the result connecting *s* and *p*.

(c) Find the rule connecting *s* and *p*.

(d) Use your rule to find how many squares make up the line in the 26th position.

5. A pattern is made using crosses and lines joining the crosses as shown.

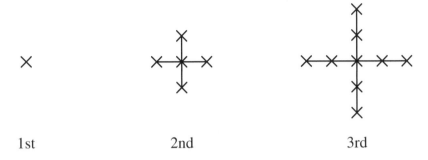

1st   2nd   3rd

(a) Draw the next two shapes using crosses and lines.

(b) Let the pattern number be represented by p, the number of crosses in a pattern be represented by c and the number of lines in a pattern be represented by l.
Draw a table for the result connecting p, c and l.

(c) Find the rule connecting

   (i) p and c (ii) p and l (iii) c and l.

(d) Use your rules to find the numbers of lines and crosses that make up the 19th pattern.

6. These shapes are made using crosses and lines joining the crosses.

  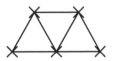

(a) Draw the next two shapes using crosses and lines to form the triangles.

(b) Let the number of triangles, crosses and lines in each shape be represented by t, c and l respectively.
Draw a table of results connecting t, c and l for each shape.

(c) Find the rule connecting

   (i) t and c (ii) t and l (iii) c and l.

(d) Use your rules to find the numbers of crosses and lines that make up the 24th pattern.

(e) If a pattern is made up of 17 triangles, use your rules to find out how many crosses and lines make up this pattern.

MODULE 5

3.5 Inequalities

In an equation, the left-hand side equals the right-hand side.
In an **inequality**, the two sides are not necessarily equal to each other.
You need to know these symbols:

$>$ means 'is greater than' $\qquad$ $<$ means 'is less than'

$\geqslant$ means 'is greater than or equal to' $\quad$ $\leqslant$ means 'is less than or equal to'

If x is the number of people on a bus and the bus can carry
52 people, then you can write

$x \leqslant 52$

This means that the number of people on the bus (x) is less than
or equal to 52.

Inequalities can be represented by a number line.

Example 1

Represent $x \geqslant 2$ on a number line.

The ● indicates that the point $x = 2$ is included in the solution on
the number line.

Example 2

Represent $-1 < x \leqslant 4$ on a number line.

Here the ○ indicates that $x = {}^-1$ is **not** included in the solution.

Exercise 3E

1. Represent each of these inequalities on a number line.
   (a) $x > 5$ $\qquad$ (b) $x < {}^-1$
   (c) $x \geqslant 2$ $\qquad$ (d) $x \leqslant 3$
   (e) $2 < x < 3$ $\qquad$ (f) $^-1 \leqslant x \leqslant 4$
   (g) $1 \leqslant x < 5$ $\qquad$ (h) $2 > x > {}^-3$

2. If x in an integer, write down all of the values of x which satisfy each of these inequalities.

(a) $2 \leqslant x \leqslant 4$ (b) $^-1 \leqslant x \leqslant 3$

(c) $2 < x < 7$ (d) $4 > x > ^-1$

(e) $3 \leqslant x < 5$ (f) $2 \leqslant x \leqslant 7$

3.6 Solving inequalities

Solving inequalities is very similar to solving equations, with one important difference.

To solve an inequality, you can

● Add or subtract any number or term to both sides.

● Multiply or divide both sides by a positive amount.

However,

● If you multiply or divide both sides by a negative amount, you must change the direction of the inequality, or change sides in the inequality.

> This is the important difference between equations and inequalities.

Example

Solve the inequality $3(x + 5) - 6 > 5x - 7$.

Expand out the left-hand side:	$3x + 15 - 6 > 5x - 7$
Simplify:	$3x + 9 \quad\quad > 5x - 7$
Collect the x terms on the LHS:	$^-2x \quad\quad\quad > ^-16$
Divide by $^-2$:	$x \quad\quad\quad\quad < 8$

> **Remember:**
> Change the direction of the inequality because you are dividing by a negative amount.

Exercise 3F

Solve these inequalities.

1. $3x > 12$ **2.** $2x \leqslant 16$

3. $2x + 1 \geqslant 11$ **4.** $3x - 7 \geqslant 2x + 5$

5. $\dfrac{x}{3} - \dfrac{2}{5} > x$ **6.** $\dfrac{x}{5} - \dfrac{2x}{7} > 5$

7. $2(x + 7) > 3x - 1$ **8.** $3(x - 5) + 6 > 2 - 4(x - 3)$

9. $8(1 - 3x) > 4 - 7(x + 2)$ **10.** $7 - 2x > 13$

MODULE 5

3.7 Graphs of inequalities

When you plot an equation on a graph, you obtain a straight line or a curve.
When you plot an inequality on a graph, you obtain a **region**.

Example

Show, by shading, the region satisfied by the inequality $y + x \geqslant 5$.

First, draw the line $y + x = 5$.
Choose three points for x: say $^-3, 0, 3$. Find the y values.
When $x = {}^-3$, $y + {}^-3 = 5$ so $y = 8$.

x	$^-3$	0	3
y	8	5	2

Plot the points on a graph and join them up with a straight line:

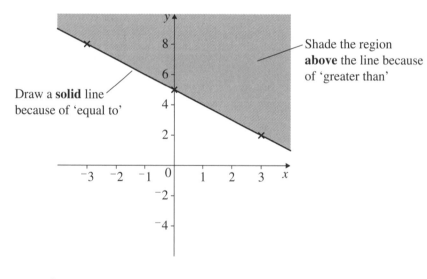

Draw a **solid** line because of 'equal to'

Shade the region **above** the line because of 'greater than'

Note:
Take care to see whether the question asks you to shade the region required, or the region **not** required.

Exercise 3G

Draw a graph to show the region satisfied by these inequalities.
In questions 1–3, shade the region required.
In questions 4–6, shade the region **not** required.

1. (a) $x \geqslant 2$ (b) $y \geqslant 3$
   (c) $x + 2y \leqslant 6$ (d) $2x + y > 4$

2. (a) $^-1 < x < 3$
   (b) $2 < y \leqslant 5$
   (c) $x > 1$ and $x < {}^-1$

3. $2x + 3y \leqslant 6$

4. $y > 2x - 7$ and $2y < 3x - 6$

5. $2y \leqslant 3x + 12$ and $y + 3x < 9$

6. $5y + 2x \leqslant 10,\ x < 4$ and $3x + y > 6$

3.8 Simultaneous equations

To solve problems with two unknown amounts, you need two equations that can be solved at the same time. These are called **simultaneous equations**.

John uses his mobile phone for 6 minutes at peak rate, and 9 minutes at the weekend rate. He notices that his prepaid phone has charged him £2·58.

John's friend Claire uses her mobile phone for 6 minutes at peak rate and 4 minutes at the weekend rate. She is charged £1·98.

Assume that the two friends are charged the same rate.

Let p = peak rate cost per minute (in pence)

and w = weekend rate cost per minute (in pence)

So from John's information: $6p + 9w = 258$

From Claire's information: $6p + 4w = 198$

Now you have two simultaneous equations involving p and w.

Solving simultaneous equations by the elimination method

These are the two equations describing John and Claire's phone usage:

$$6p + 9w = 258$$

$$6p + 4w = 198$$

The difference in the left-hand side is $5w$ and the difference on the right-hand side is 60.

MODULE 5

So $\qquad 5w = 60$

and $\qquad w = 12$

The weekend rate is 12p per minute.

Substituting the value of w into either of the original equations will give you p.

$$6p + 4 \times 12 = 198$$
$$6p + 48 = 198$$
$$6p = 150$$
$$p = 25$$

The peak rate is 25p per minute.

Note:
You are **subtracting** one equation from the other.

Note:
It is slightly easier to choose the second equation because the numbers are smaller.

Example 1

Solve the equations $\qquad\qquad\qquad 3x + 7y = 24 \quad$ (1)

and $\qquad\qquad\qquad\qquad\qquad x + 2y = 7 \quad$ (2)

Write down equation (1): $\qquad\qquad 3x + 7y = 24$

Multiply equation (2) by 3: $\qquad 3x + 6y = 21$

The coefficients of x match up

Subtract these equations: $\qquad\qquad\qquad\qquad y = 3$

Substitute into (2): $\qquad\qquad\qquad 3x + 18 = 21$

$$3x = 3$$
$$x = 1$$

Therefore, the solution is $x = 1$, $y = 3$.

Sometimes you need to **add** the equations.

Note:
It is a good idea to number the equations.

Remember:
A **coefficient** is just the number in front of a letter.

Example 2

Solve the equations $\qquad\qquad\qquad 2x - 3y = {}^-11 \quad$ (1)

and $\qquad\qquad\qquad\qquad\qquad 3x + y = 11 \quad$ (2)

Write down equation (1): $\qquad\qquad 2x - 3y = {}^-11$

Multiply equation (2) by 3 to match up y: $\quad 9x + 3y = 33$

Add the two equations to cancel out y: $\qquad 11x = 22$

$$\therefore x = 2$$

Substitute $x = 2$ into (2): $\qquad\qquad 6 + y = 11$

$$y = 5$$

Therefore, the solution is $x = 2$, $y = 5$.

Graphical solution of simultaneous equations

Simultaneous equations can be solved graphically. You can represent each equation as a line on a graph and see where the lines intersect.

Example

Using a graphical method, solve the equations:

$$4y = 3x - 2$$

$$y + x = 3$$

First you need to draw the two lines on a graph.

A quick way to draw the lines is to find out where they cross the x and y axes.

The graph of $4y = 3x - 2$ …

… crosses the x-axis where $y = 0$

  so $3x - 2 = 0$

  and $x = \frac{2}{3}$

… crosses the y-axis where $x = 0$

  so $4y = {}^-2$

  and $y = -\frac{1}{2}$

So $4y = 3x - 2$ passes through the points $(\frac{2}{3}, 0)$ and $(0, {}^-\frac{1}{2})$

The graph of $y + x = 3$ …

… crosses the x-axis where $y = 0$

  so $x = 3$

… crosses the y-axis where $x = 0$

  so $y = 3$

So $y + x = 3$ passes through the points $(3, 0)$ and $(0, 3)$.

Now draw the two lines on the same axes:

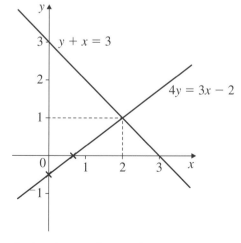

Hint:

The solution is where the two lines cross.

Therefore the solution is $x = 2$, $y = 1$.

MODULE 5

Exercise 3H

Solve each of the pairs of simultaneous equations in questions
1–12 by the elimination method.

1. $x + 2y = 5$
   $3x + 2y = 11$

2. $x + y = 3$
   $x + 3y = 1$

3. $5x + y = 8$
   $5x + 3y = 4$

4. $7x + 5y = 32$
   $7x - 2y = {}^-3$

5. $x - 3y = 1$
   $2x + 5y = 13$

6. $4x - y = 22$
   $3x + 5y = 5$

7. $2x + 3y = 2$
   $3x - y = 14$

8. $5x + 2y = 5$
   $3x - 4y = 29$

9. $3x - 7y = 38$
   $4x + y = {}^-1$

10. $5x + 3y = 19$
    $2x - 5y = {}^-11$

11. $2x + y = 2$
    $5x - 2y = 2$

12. $5x - 3y = 3$
    $3x + 7y = 4$

Hint:

For questions 10 and 12
you will need to
multiply **both** equations
before you can match up
any coefficients.

Use the graphical method to find the solution of the
simultaneous equations in questions 13–18.

13. $x + y = 5$
    $y = x - 1$

14. $x + y = 4$
    $y = 2x - 5$

15. $x + 2y = 7$
    $y = 4x - 1$

16. $2x + 3y = 6$
    $y = 4x + 16$

17. $y = 3x$
    $2y + x + 7 = 0$

18. $y = 2x - 5$
    $2y + 3x = 18$

Hint:

You will need to find out
where each line crosses
the x and y axes before
you can draw them.

3.9 Expanding brackets to give a quadratic expression

To expand a single bracket you multiply the term outside the
bracket by each term inside.

So $\quad 5(2x - 3) = 10x - 15$

and $\quad 2x(3y - 7) = 6xy - 14x$

If you expand two brackets, you often get a quadratic
expression.

- To expand two brackets, you need to multiply each term in
  one bracket by each term in the other bracket.

To remind yourself
about **expanding**, see
page 224.
To remind yourself
about **quadratic
expressions**, see
page 257.

Example 1

Expand $(3x - 5)(2x + 11)$.

$$(3x - 5)(2x + 11) = 3x \times 2x + {}^-5 \times 2x + 3x \times 11 + {}^-5 \times 11$$
$$= 6x^2 - 10x + 33x - 55$$
$$= 6x^2 + 23x - 55$$

> **Note:**
> Because there are two pairs of terms you will have four multiplications to make.

Sometimes brackets contain more than one letter.

Example 2

Expand $(5a + 3b)(2a - b)$

$$(5a + 3b)(2a - b) = 10a^2 - 5ab + 6ab - 3b^2$$
$$= 10a^2 + ab - 3b^2$$

Exercise 3I

Expand each of these expressions.

1. $x(2x + 7)$
2. $y(3y - 5)$
3. $(x + 2)(x + 3)$
4. $(x + 5)(x + 7)$
5. $(x + 3)(x - 5)$
6. $(x + 4)(x - 3)$
7. $(2x + 1)(3x + 7)$
8. $(2x + 3)(5x + 2)$
9. $(2x + 5)(3x - 4)$
10. $(3x - 7)(x - 11)$
11. $(2x + 5)(3x - 8)$
12. $(a + 2b)(2a + 3b)$
13. $(x - 2y)(3x + y)$
14. $(3x - 1)(3x + 1)$
15. $(2x - 5)(2x + 5)$
16. $(2x - 3y)(2x + 3y)$

3.10 Quadratic factors

Imagine you were given the answers to the previous exercise and you had to work out the questions. You would be **factorising a quadratic expression**.

You can factorise a linear expression like this:

$$2x + 8 = 2(x + 4)$$

2 is the common factor

> **Remember:**
> Factorising means inserting brackets. There is more about factorising on page 225.

Factorising quadratic expressions is slightly more difficult.

MODULE 5

Example 1

Factorise $x^2 + 6x + 5$.

- First draw two sets of blank brackets: ( ) ( )
- Then insert x terms: $(x \quad) (x \quad)$

Gives x^2

- Then insert numbers: $(x \quad 5) (x \quad 1)$

Gives 5

- Then insert signs: $(x + 5) \ (x + 1)$

Expand this out to check that you get the $+6x$ term:

$$(x + 5)(x + 1) = x^2 + 5x + x + 5$$
$$= x^2 + 6x + 5$$

So $x^2 + 6x + 5 = (x + 5)(x + 1)$

Hint:
Think about the factors of x^2.

Hint:
Think about the factors of 5.

Hint:
Think about the signs in the original expression.

Hint:
This is what you started with so it is correct.

Example 2

Factorise $x^2 - 2x - 8$.

$$x^2 - 2x - 8 = (x \quad)(x \quad)$$

Leave blank as before

Now think about the factors of $^-8$: 1 and $^-8$, $^-1$ and 8, $^-2$ and 4, or 2 and $^-4$.

Try $(x + 1)(x - 8) = x^2 + x - 8x - 8$
$$= x^2 - 7x - 8$$

This is wrong because it is not what you started with

Try $(x - 4)(x + 2) = x^2 - 4x + 2x - 8$
$$= x^2 - 2x - 8$$

This is correct because it is what you started with

So $x^2 - 2x - 8 = (x - 4)(x + 2)$.

Hint:
Only one pair will give the right answer.

Remember:
Always expand out the brackets at the end to check your answer.

Example 3

Factorise $x^2 - 7x$.

If there is no constant term, just take out the common factor x:

$$x^2 - 7x = x(x - 7)$$

Exercise 3J

Factorise these quadratic expressions.

1. $x^2 + 4x + 3$
2. $x^2 + 8x + 7$
3. $x^2 - 5x + 4$
4. $x^2 - 10x - 11$
5. $x^2 - 3x - 4$
6. $x^2 - 2x - 35$
7. $x^2 - 8x - 9$
8. $x^2 + 4x - 12$
9. $x^2 - 5x - 24$
10. $x^2 + 5x - 24$
11. $y^2 - 3y - 10$
12. $y^2 - y - 12$
13. $x^2 - 2x - 24$
14. $x^2 - 3x - 18$

3.11 Quadratic equations

A quadratic equation is an equation containing a quadratic expression, for example:

$$x^2 + 6x = {}^-5 \qquad \text{is a quadratic equation.}$$

To solve a quadratic equation,

- Make one side of the equation equal zero.
  So the equation becomes: $\qquad\qquad x^2 + 6x + 5 = 0$

- Factorise the quadratic expression.
  So the equation becomes: $\qquad\qquad (x - 5)(x - 1) = 0$

- If the product of two terms is zero, then one of the two terms must be zero.

  $$\therefore \text{ either } x - 5 = 0 \qquad \text{or} \qquad x - 1 = 0$$
  $$\therefore x = 5 \qquad \text{or} \qquad x = 1$$

> **Hint:**
> You cannot get zero from multiplying two non-zero terms.

Example

Solve the equation: $x^2 + 3x = 4$.

(i) Making one side equal zero:
$$x^2 + 3x = 4$$
$$\therefore x^2 + 3x - 4 = 0$$

(ii) Factorising:
$$(x + 4)(x - 1) = 0$$

(iii) One of the factors equals zero:
$$x + 4 = 0 \text{ or } x - 1 = 0$$
$$\therefore x = {}^-4 \text{ or } \qquad x = 1$$

Exercise 3K

Solve these equations.

1. $x^2 + 7x + 10 = 0$ 2. $x^2 - 7x + 10 = 0$

3. $x^2 - 5x - 6 = 0$ 4. $x^2 - 7x - 8 = 0$

5. $x^2 + 2x - 8 = 0$ 6. $x^2 - 2x - 3 = 0$

7. $x^2 - 3x + 2 = 0$ 8. $x^2 + 5x - 6 = 0$

9. $x^2 + 7x - 8 = 0$ 10. $x^2 + x - 12 = 0$

3.12 Transformation of formulae

Here is a formula that converts temperatures in degrees Centigrade, C, to degrees Fahrenheit, F.

$$F = \tfrac{9}{5}C + 32$$

F is the **subject** of the formula.

On a cold day in Oxford the temperature is 2 °C.

On a warm evening in Ibiza the temperature is 79 °F.

You can use the formula to convert the temperature in Oxford into Fahrenheit:

$$\tfrac{9}{5} \times 2 + 32 = 35.6\,°C$$

So 2 °C is the same as 35.6 °F.

It is harder to use the formula to convert the temperature in Ibiza into Centigrade. You need to make C the subject of the formula.

Subtract 32 from both sides: $F - 32 = \tfrac{9}{5}C$

Multiply by 5: $5(F - 32) = 9C$

Divide by 9: $\tfrac{5}{9}(F - 32) = C$

So $C = \tfrac{5}{9}(F - 32)$.

> Now C is the subject of the formula because it is alone on the left-hand side.

When $F = 79$, $C = \frac{5}{9}(79 - 32)$

$$= \frac{5}{9} \times 47$$

$$= 26\cdot1 \text{ (to 1 decimal place)}$$

So 79 °F is the same as 26·1 °C (to 1 d.p.).

You may have to change the subject of a formula involving fractions.

Example 1

Make v the subject of the formula $\dfrac{1}{u} - \dfrac{1}{v} = \dfrac{1}{f}$.

• First remove the fractions by multiplying by the common denominator, which is uvf:

$$uvf \times \frac{1}{u} - uvf \times \frac{1}{v} = uvf \times \frac{1}{f}$$

$$vf - uf = uv$$

• Now, to find v, collect the v terms on one side:

$$vf - uv = uf$$

$$v(f - u) = uf$$

$$\therefore v = \frac{uf}{f - u}$$

You may also have to change the subject of a formula involving powers.

Example 2

Make r the subject of the formula $A = \pi r^2$
and find the value of r when $A = 25\pi$.

$$A = \pi r^2$$

Dividing by π, $\qquad r^2 = \dfrac{A}{\pi}$

$$\therefore r = \sqrt{\frac{A}{\pi}}$$

When $A = 25\pi$, $\qquad r = \sqrt{\dfrac{25\pi}{\pi}}$

$$= \sqrt{25}$$

$$\therefore r = \pm 5$$

MODULE 5

Exercise 3L

1. Find r when $v = 3r + 7$.

2. Find R when $3(r + R) = 2(r + 4)$.

3. Make (a) u (b) t the subject of the formula $v = u + at$.

4. Make (a) I (b) R the subject of the formula $V = IR$.

5. Make (a) u (b) a the subject of the formula $s = ut + \frac{1}{2}at^2$.

6. Make (a) T (b) R the subject of the formula $I = \dfrac{PTR}{100}$.

7. Make (a) P (b) r the subject of the formula $A = P\left(1 + \dfrac{R}{100}\right)^n$.

8. Make (a) l (b) x the subject of the formula $E = \dfrac{\lambda x^2}{2l}$.

9. Make v the subject of the formula $I = m(v - u)$.

10. Make l the subject of the formula $T = 2\pi\sqrt{\dfrac{l}{g}}$.

3.13 Trial and improvement

Cubic equations, like the equation $x^3 - 7x = 32$, can be solved by a 'trial and improvement' method.

Example

Find the solution of $x^3 - 7x = 32$ to 2 decimal places.

Start by guessing values of x that give answers as close to 32 as possible.

Let $x = 3$. Then $f(3) = x^3 - 7x = 3^3 - 7 \times 3 = 27 - 21 = 6$

Now let x = 4. Then $f(4) = 4^3 - 7 \times 4 = 64 - 28 = 36$

Try $x = 3.8$. $f(3.8) = 3.8^3 - 7 \times 3.8 = 28.272$

Try $x = 3.9$. $f(3.9) = 3.9^3 - 7 \times 3.9 = 32.019$

32 lies in between these two values. So x lies between 3 and 4, but closer to 4.

<$32   >32

3·8   3·9   4·0

You now know the solution lies between 3.8 and 4.

<$32   >32   >32

3·8   ↑   3·9   4·0

You now know the solution lies between 3.8 and 3.9.

Try $x = 3.85$. $f(3.85) = 3.85^3 - 7 \times 3.85 = 30.11$

<32   <32   >32

3.8   3.85   3.9

You now know the solution lies between 3.85 and 3.9.

Therefore the solution to $f(x) = 32$ is 3.9 (to 1 decimal place).

Exercise 3M

Use the method of trial and improvement to find one of the solutions of these equations.

Give your answers to 1 decimal place.

1. $x^3 + 5x = 27$

2. $x^3 - 3x = 18.5$

3. $x^3 + 9x = 11$

4. $x^3 - 8x = 1$

5. $x^3 + 4x = 17$

6. $x^3 - 7x = 1$

7. $x^3 - 2x = 5$

8. $x^3 - 9x = 7$

9. $x^3 + 5x^2 = 7$

10. $x^3 - 2x^2 = 2$

Summary

1. You can continue a sequence of numbers

2. You can find and use the nth term of a sequence

3. You can identify a sequence where each term is given in terms of a previous term

4. You can solve inequalities

5. You can show inequalities by means of a graph

6. You can solve simultaneous equations algebraically

7. You can solve simultaneous equations graphically

Check out AS3

1. Write down the next two terms in the sequence 7, 10, 13, 16.

2. (a) Find the nth term of the sequence 7, 10, 13, 16.

(b) Write down the first 4 terms of the sequence given by $u_n = 18 - 2n$.

3. Write down the first 4 terms of the sequence given by $u_1 = 2$, $u_{n+1} = 2u_n - 1$.

4. Solve (a) $5x - 14 > 2x + 7$
(b) $^-2x \leqslant 4$
(c) $x^2 \leqslant 16$.

5. Show the region satisfied by $x + y \leqslant 7$, $x > 2$ and $y > 3$.

6. Solve $2x + y = 9$ and $3x - 2y = 10$.

7. Draw on the same axes the two lines $2x + y = 9$ and $3x - 2y = 17$ and hence write down the solution of the simultaneous equations.

MODULE 5

8. You can expand brackets	**8.** Expand (a) $x(2x - 7)$ (b) $(x + 5)(x - 3)$
9. You can factorise a quadratic expression	**9.** Factorise (a) $x^2 - 6x - 7$ (b) $x^2 + 11x$ (c) $x^2 + 4x + 3$
10. You can solve a quadratic equation	**10.** Solve (a) $x^2 + 9x - 10$ (b) $x^2 - 7x$ (c) $x^2 - 6x + 5$
11. You can transform an equation	**11.** (a) Find x when $3x - 2y = x + 6y + 8$. (b) Find r when $V = \frac{4}{3}\pi r^3$.
12. You can solve equations numerically by trial and improvement	**12.** Find the solution of $x^3 - 2x = 3$ to 1 decimal place.

Revision exercise AS3

1. (a) A sequence of patterns is shown.

Pattern 1   Pattern 2   Pattern 3

Write an expression, in terms of n, for the number of squares in the nth pattern of the sequence.

(b) A number sequence begins

$$3, \ 6, \ 11, \ 18, \ 27, \ \ldots$$

Write an expression, in terms of n, for the nth term of this sequence.   [SEG]

2. (a) What is the next number in this sequence?

$$3, \ 7, \ 11, \ 15, \ \ldots$$

One number in the sequence is x.

(b) (i) Write, in terms of x, the next number in the sequence.

(ii) Write, in terms of x, the number in the sequence before x.   [SEG]

3. (a) (i) Work out 2^3.

     (ii) Work out $(^-2) \times (^-3)$.

  (b) A sequence begins 2, 1, …

     The rule for continuing the sequence is

> MULTIPLY THE LAST NUMBER BY 2 AND SUBTRACT 3

     Write down the next two numbers in the sequence.

                         [SEG]

4. The first five terms of a sequence are given.

     5, 3, 1, $^-$1, $^-$3, …

  (a) What is the next term in the sequence?

  (b) Write down the nth term of the sequence.   [SEG]

5. (a) Simplify the expression

     $2(x - 3) - x$.

  (b) Solve the equation $4x - 1 = x + 5$.

  (c) A solution to the equation $x^3 + x = 49$ lies between 3 and 4.
     Use a trial and improvement method to find this solution.
     Give your answer correct to one decimal place.
     You must show all your working.   [SEG]

6. (a) Sticks are arranged to form a sequence of patterns as shown.

Pattern 1   Pattern 2   Pattern 3

     Write an expression, in terms of n, for the number of
     sticks needed to form the nth pattern.

  (b) Squares are arranged to form a sequence of rectangular
     patterns as shown.

 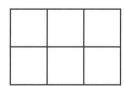 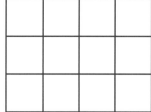

Pattern 1   Pattern 2   Pattern 3

     Write an expression, in terms of n, for the number of
     squares needed to form the nth pattern.   [SEG]

MODULE 5

7. (a) Regular pentagons are used to form patterns, as shown.

  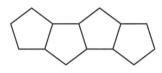

Pattern 1	Pattern 2	Pattern 3	Pattern 4
5 sides	8 sides	11 sides	14 sides

Write, in terms of n, the number of sides in Pattern n.

(b) A number pattern begins

$$0, \ 3, \ 8, \ 15, \ 24, \ \ldots$$

Write, in terms of n, the nth term in this pattern.   [SEG]

8. (a) Solve the equation $x^2 - 8x = 0$.

(b) Solve the inequality $5 \leqslant 2x - 7 < 13$.   [SEG]

9. p and q are positive whole numbers.
p can be an odd number or an even number.
q can be an odd number or an even number.

(a) For each of the following calculations, state whether the answer results in an odd number, an even number or could be either.

   (i) $3p$ (ii) $2q$

(b) For some values of p and q, the sum $p + q$ is even.
    What must be true about the values of p and q?

(c) Work out the values of p and q when

$$p + q = 11 \quad \text{and} \quad p - q = 3.$$ [SEG]

10. (a) Factorise $2x^2 + 4x$.

(b) Solve the quadratic equation $x^2 + 3x - 10 = 0$.

(c) Solve the inequality $3 < 2x + 1 < 5$.   [SEG]

11. (a) Factorise $a^2 + 2a - 8$.

(b) Solve $y^2 + 4y = 0$.

12. (a) Factorise $a^2 + 3a$.

(b) List the values of x, where x is an integer, such that

$$^{-}1 < x - 2 \leqslant 1$$ [SEG]

AS4 SHAPE 1

The most beautiful architecture is often based on simple regular shapes.

This unit will show you how to:

- Calculate with angles and straight lines
- Describe symmetry
- Draw nets of solids
- Calculate angles in polygons and circles
- Describe bearings
- Draw geometrical constructions and loci

Before you start:

You should know how to...	Check in AS4
1. Use BODMAS For example, $180 - 2 \times 41$ $= 180 - 82$ $= 98$	**2.** Find the value of: $180 - (35 + 72)$
2. Divide numbers mentally For example, $360 \div 9$ First ÷ 3 : 120 Then ÷ 3 again: 40	**3.** Without using a calculator, find the value of: (a) $\dfrac{360}{4}$ (b) $\dfrac{360}{15}$ (c) $\dfrac{360}{12}$

4.1 Lines and angles

● On a flat surface, a straight line is the shortest distance between two points.

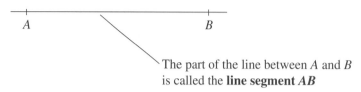

The part of the line between A and B is called the **line segment** AB

When two straight lines meet at a point, they form an **angle**.

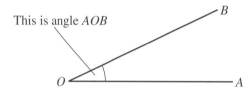

This is angle AOB

An angle is measure of turn.

Angles are measured in **degrees** (denoted by a small circle °).

There are 360° in a complete turn.

360°

A rotation through half a turn is a turn through 180°.

180°

Certain other angles have special names:

● A **right angle** is 90°, and it is one quarter of a turn.

● Two lines that intersect at right angles are called **perpendicular lines**.

Note:
The system of using degrees comes from the ancient Babylonians, who believed that there were 360 days in a yearly cycle.

Note:
The symbol ⌐ is used to denote a right angle

- An **acute angle** is an angle between 0° and 90°.

Note:
Acute means sharp.

- An **obtuse angle** is an angle between 90° and 180°.

Note:
Obtuse means thick or blunt.

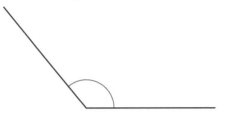

- A **reflex angle** is an angle between 180° and 360°.

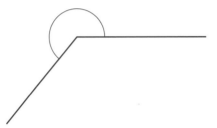

- Two angles which add up to 180° are called **supplementary angles**.

- Two angles which add up to 90° are called **complementary angles**.

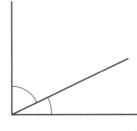

- **Opposite angles** are formed when two straight lines cross.

    Opposite angles are equal.

    The two angles marked x are opposite angles, and are equal in size.

    The two angles marked y are also opposite angles.

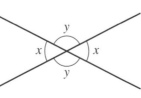

MODULE 5

Example

Find the angles x, y and z.

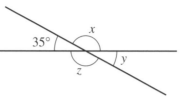

x and 35° lie on a straight line, so

$x + 35° = 180°$

$\therefore x = 145°$

y is opposite to 35°, so $y = 35°$.

z is opposite to x, so $z = x = 145°$.

Note:

When you are working out unknown angles, you should give a reason for each step in your calculation.

Exercise 4A

In questions 1–9 calculate the size of the unknown angles.

1.

40° x

2.

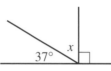

x
37°

3.

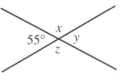

55° x y
z

4.

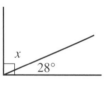

x
28°

5.

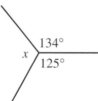

134°
x
125°

6.

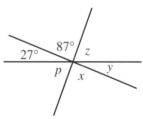

27° 87° z
p x y

7.

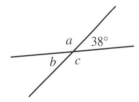

a 38°
b c

8.

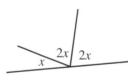

2x 2x
x

9.

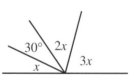

30° 2x
x 3x

In questions 10–17 state whether the angle marked is acute, a right angle, obtuse or reflex.

10.

11.

12.

13.

14.

15.

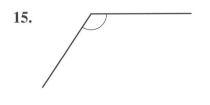

16.

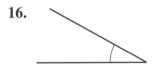

17.

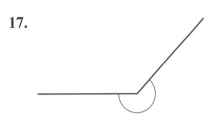

4.2 Parallel lines

● Two straight lines that never meet are called **parallel** lines.

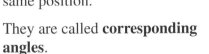

Railway lines are parallel

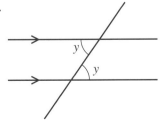

The sides of a door are parallel

In the diagram, *AQB* and *CRD* are parallel lines.

The two angles marked *x* are equal because they are in the same position.

They are called **corresponding angles**.

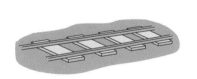

Note:

Arrows is on two lines indicate that they are parallel.

The two angles marked *y* are also equal.

They are called **alternate angles**.

Hint:

Corresponding angles form an F shape; alternate angles form a Z shape.

MODULE 5

Example

In the diagram, find the angles a, b, c and d.

a and $47°$ are on a straight line, so $a + 47° = 180°$

$\therefore$ $a = 133°$

$\qquad b = 47°$ (opposite angles)

$\qquad c = 47°$ (corresponding angles)

c and d are on a straight line, so $c + d = 180°$.

Therefore, $d = 133°$.

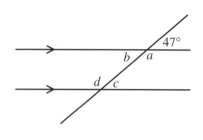

Exercise 4B

Find the size of each lettered angle. You should give a reason to justify each step in your calculation.

1.

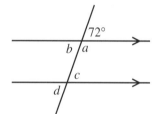

2.

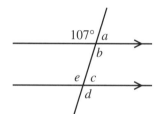

3.

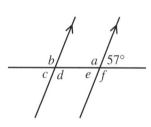

4.

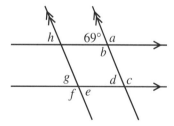

5.

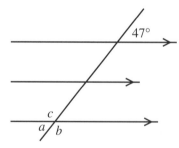

6.

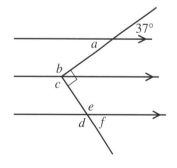

7.

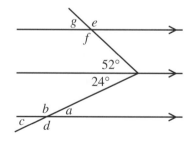

4.3 Reflexive symmetry

This shape can be reflected in the dotted line.

The shape has **reflexive symmetry**.

The dotted line is a **mirror line**, or **line of symmetry**.

Example

Draw all of the lines of symmetry of the shape.

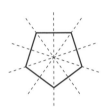

There are five lines of symmetry. These are shown as dotted lines in the diagram.

Exercise 4C

1. State the number of lines of symmetry which can be drawn through each of these shapes.

(a) H   (b) T   (c) X   (d) P

(e) 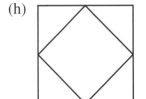   (f) 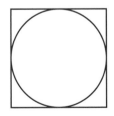   (g)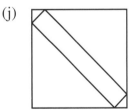

(h)    (i)   (j)

(k) 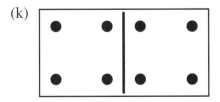   (l)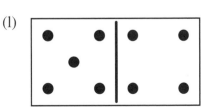

MODULE 5

2. Draw the remainder of each of these shapes so that each complete shape will have the dotted line as a line of symmetry. Use tracing paper to help you.

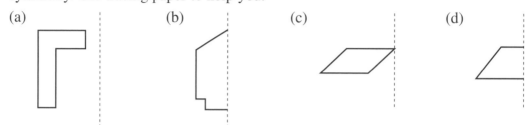

(a)   (b)   (c)   (d)

4.4 Rotational symmetry

This shape can be rotated through 180° and 360° about *O*, and the new shape will be the same as the original.

The shape has **rotational symmetry**.

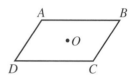

> **Note:**
> There are only **two** positions in which the shape looks identical to how it started.

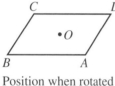

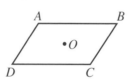

Position when rotated through 180°   Position when rotated through 360°

You can say that the shape has rotational symmetry **of order 2 about point *O*.**

Example

State the order of rotational symmetry of the equilateral triangle ABC.

The triangle can be turned into 3 identical positions about O:

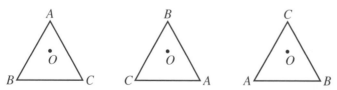

The shape has rotational symmetry of order 3 about point O.

Every shape looks the same when you rotate it about any point through 360°. Therefore, all shapes have rotational symmetry of at least 1.

Exercise 4D

1. State the order of rotational symmetry of each shape in question 1 of Exercise 4C.

2. State the order of rotational symmetry of each of these.

(a)

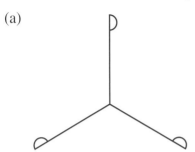

(b)

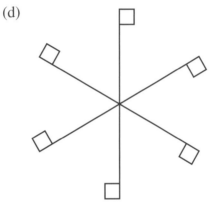

(c)

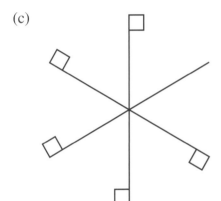

(d)

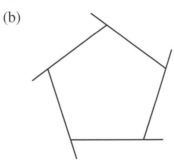

3. Draw the remainder of each shape so that the complete shape has rotational symmetry about *P* of the order stated.

(a) order 3

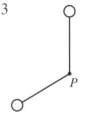

(b) order 4

(c) order 1

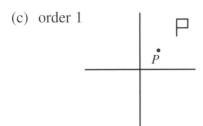

4.5 Planes of symmetry

This is a triangular prism.

It has a **plane of symmetry**, shown as a shaded region.

This plane will cut the prism into two halves, identical to each other.

This cone has an infinite number of planes of symmetry.

Any way you cut it down the middle will give you two identical halves.

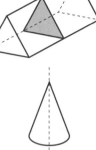

Example

How many planes of symmetry does this cuboid have?

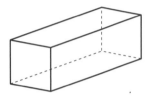 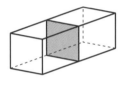 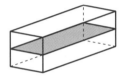 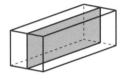

The cuboid has 3 planes of symmetry.

Exercise 4E

State the number of planes of symmetry of

1. a cylinder

2. a triangular prism

3. a square-based pyramid

4. a sphere

5. a cone.

4.6 Nets

This is the **net** of a cube.

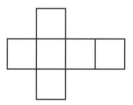

If you fold it up you will get a three-dimensional cube.

Note:
There are many other nets of a cube, but not all shapes with six squares will be a net of a cube.

Example

Which of these is not the net of a cube?

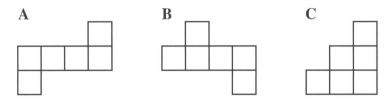

C is not the net of a cube, as it cannot be folded into a cube.

Exercise 4F

1. Draw a net for a cuboid which measures 4 cm by 3 cm by 2 cm.

2. Draw a net for a cuboid which measures 5 cm by 4 cm by 6 cm.

3. Draw a net for a triangular prism of length 6 cm. Each triangular face is an equilateral triangle of side 4 cm.

4. Draw a net for a triangular prism of length 6 cm. Each triangular face is an isosceles triangle of side 5 cm.

5. Draw a net for a pyramid with a square base of side 4 cm. Each slant height of the pyramid is 6 cm.

6. Draw a net for a pyramid with a rectangular base 5 cm by 3 cm. Each slant height of the pyramid is 4 cm.

7. What solid can be constructed using each of these nets?

(a)   (b)

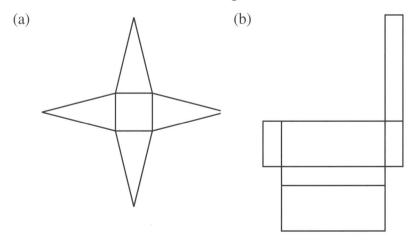

MODULE 5

4.7 Plane figures

Triangles

Here are some different triangles that you should know:

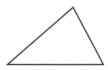  

An **acute-angled triangle**
has all three angles acute

A **right-angled triangle**
has one angle of 90°

An **obtuse-angled triangle**
has one obtuse angle

An **isosceles triangle** has
two sides equal in length.
The two angles opposite
these sides are also equal

An **equilateral triangle** has
all three sides equal in length
and all three angles equal

The sides of a triangle *ABC* are denoted by *a*, *b* and *c*,
where *a* is the side opposite angle *A*, *b* is the side
opposite angle *B*, and *c* is the side opposite angle *C*.

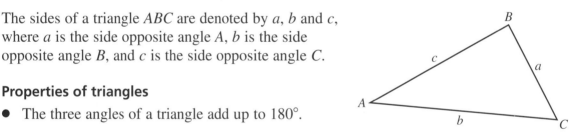

Properties of triangles

● The three angles of a triangle add up to 180°.

Proof

Draw triangle *ABC* with *D* and *E* as shown.

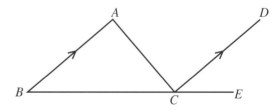

$D\hat{C}A = B\hat{A}C$ (alternate angles)   (1)

$D\hat{C}E = A\hat{B}C$ (corresponding angles)   (2)

The three angles at *C* add up to 180°.   (angles on a straight line)

Using (1) and (2), the three angles $B\hat{A}C$, $A\hat{B}C$ and $A\hat{C}B$ add up
to 180°.

Therefore, the angles of the triangle add up to 180°.

Note:

The three angles of an
equilateral triangle are
all equal, so they must
each be 60°.

Example 1

In triangle PQR, angle $QPR = 74°$. Angle $PQR = 51°$.
Find angle PRQ.

Angle $PRQ + 74° + 51° = 180°$

$\therefore$ Angle $PRQ + 125° = 180°$

$\therefore$ Angle $PRQ = 55°$

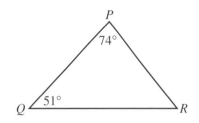

An **exterior angle** of a triangle is the angle formed by extending one side of the triangle.

- The exterior angle of a triangle is equal to the sum of the two opposite interior angles.

Proof

From the proof for the sum of the angles of a triangle:

Angle ACE = angle BAC + angle ABC, as required.

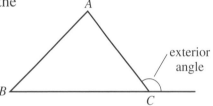

Example 2

In triangle ABC, $AB = AC$, and angle $BAC = 40°$. Find
(a) angle ACB
(b) angle ACD

(a) $A\hat{B}C + A\hat{C}B + B\hat{A}C = 180°$ (angles in a triangle add up to 180°)

$\therefore A\hat{B}C + A\hat{C}B + 40° = 180°$

$\therefore A\hat{B}C + A\hat{C}B = 140°$

Since $AB = AC$, $A\hat{B}C = A\hat{C}B$

$\therefore 2\,A\hat{C}B = 140°$

$\therefore A\hat{C}B = 70°$

(b) $A\hat{C}D = A\hat{B}C + B\hat{A}C$ (exterior angle = sum of opposite interior angles)
$= 70° + 40°$
$= 110°$

Exercise 4G

In questions 1–10 find the lettered angles.

1.

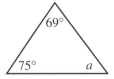

2.

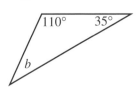

3.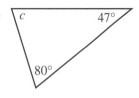

4.

5.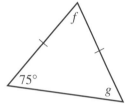

6.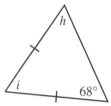

7.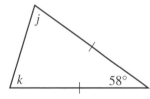

8.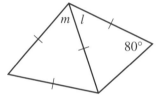

9.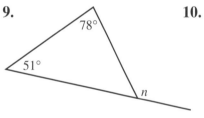

10.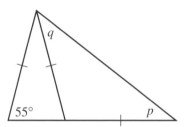

11. In triangle *ABC*, prove that *AB = AC*.

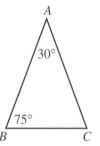

12. Triangle *PQR* is an equilateral triangle. Angle *SPR* = 70°. Find angle *PSQ*.

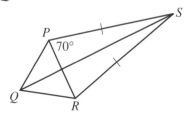

4.8 Quadrilaterals

A **quadrilateral** is a polygon which has four straight lines as its edges.

- The angles in a quadrilateral add up to 360°.

Proof

Draw a quadrilateral *ABCD*.

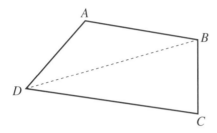

Draw a diagonal *BD* as shown to make two triangles.

The angles in each triangle add up to 180°.

Therefore, the angles in a quadrilateral add up to 360°.

Types of quadrilateral

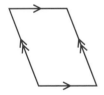

A **parallelogram** is a quadrilateral with both pairs of opposite sides parallel

A **rectangle** is a parallelogram with each internal angle equal to 90°

A **trapezium** is a quadrilateral with **one** pair of opposite sides parallel

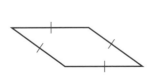

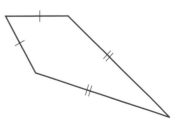

A **square** is rectangle with all sides of equal length

A **rhombus** is a parallelogram with all sides of equal length

A **kite** is quadrilateral with two pairs of adjacent sides equal in length

MODULE 5

Example

In the parallelogram *PQRS*, the angle *PSQ* = 37°,
angle *SPO* = 94° and angle *SRP* = 25°. Find

(a) angle *POS*
(b) angle *SQR*
(c) angle *RSP*

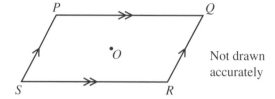

Not drawn
accurately

(a) Angle *POS* = 180° − 94° − 37°   (angles of a triangle add up to 180°)
    = 180° − 131°
    = 49°

(b) Angle *SQR* = angle *PSQ*   (alternate angles, *PS* is parallel to *QR*)
    = 37°

(c) Angle *RSP* + 94° + 25° = 180°   (angles of a triangle add up to 180°)
    ∴ Angle RSP = 180° − 119° = 61°

Exercise 4H

1. *PQRS* is a rectangle. *PQ* = *QT*.

Find angle *TPQ*.

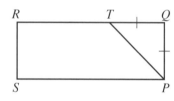

2. *ABCD* is an isosceles trapezium.

Find the angles at *B*, *C* and *D*.

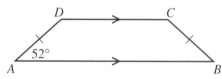

3. *EFGH* is a rhombus.

Find the angles *FĜE*, *GÊH* and *EĤG*.

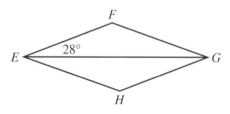

In questions 4–11 find the lettered angles.

4.

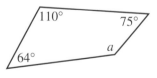

5.

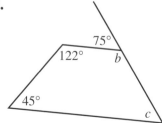

6.

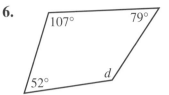

7.

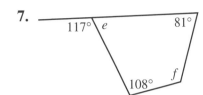

8.

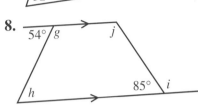

9.

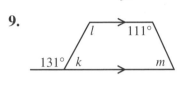

10.

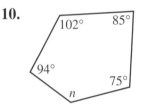

11.

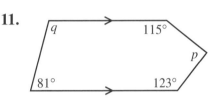

4.9 Polygons

A **polygon** is a plane figure, or two-dimensional shape, which is bounded by straight lines.

A three-sided polygon is called a triangle and a four-sided polygon is called a quadrilateral. Other polygons also have special names, for example:

A **pentagon** is a five-sided polygon

A **hexagon** is a six-sided polygon

A **heptagon** is a seven-sided polygon

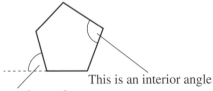

This is an interior angle

This is an exterior angle

- The sum of the exterior angles of a polygon is 360°.

To show this, imagine a pentagonal-shaped field.
You stand at one corner, A, and then walk around the edge of the field, turning through each of the angles shown. When you reach A again, you have turned through a complete circle, or 360°.

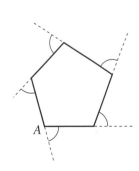

MODULE 5

● A **regular polygon** has all its sides and angles equal.

Note:
Equilateral triangles and
squares are both regular
polygons.

Example 1

A regular polygon has ten sides. Find
(a) the size of each exterior angle
(b) the size of each interior angle.

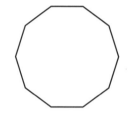

(a) The polygon has 10 exterior angles, all of which are equal.
   They add up to 360°.

   Therefore, one exterior angle is $\dfrac{360°}{10} = 36°$.

(b) Exterior angle + interior angle = 180° (angles on a straight line)
   ∴ The interior angle is 180° − 36° = 144°

Example 2

The interior angle of a regular polygon is 156°.

Find the number of sides of the polygon.

Exterior angle + interior angle = 180°   (angles on a straight line)

∴ The exterior angle is 180° − 156° = 24°

The sum of all the exterior angles is 360°.

∴ The number of exterior angles is $\dfrac{360°}{24°} = 15$

∴ The polygon has 15 sides.

To find the sum of the interior angles of a polygon, you can
divide it up into triangles.

Example 3

Find the sum of the interior angles of a pentagon.

Draw the diagonals *AC* and *AD*.

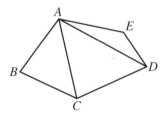

There are three triangles, each with angles adding up to 180°.

∴ The interior angles of a pentagon add up to 3 × 180° = 540°.

Exercise 4I

1. Calculate the number of sides of a regular polygon with exterior angle
   (a) 36°   (b) 30°   (c) 20°   (d) 10°

2. Calculate the exterior angle of a regular polygon which has
   (a) 10 sides   (b) 15 sides   (c) 30 sides

3. Calculate the interior angle of a regular polygon which has
   (a) 8 sides   (b) 16 sides

4. Find the angles marked with a letter.
   (a) 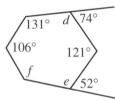   (b)

4.10 Circles

- A circle is a set of points, P, which are at a fixed distance from the centre, O.

You should know certain words that relate to circles:

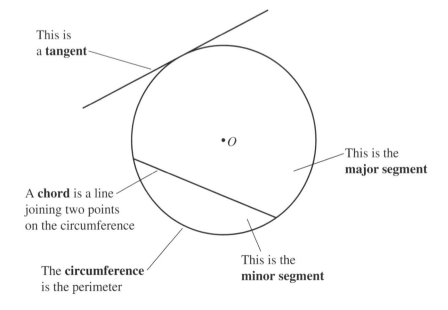

This is
a **tangent**

•*O*

This is the
major segment

A **chord** is a line
joining two points
on the circumference

The **circumference**
is the perimeter

This is the
minor segment

MODULE 5

Angle properties of a circle

There are certain facts relating to circles that you should know.

- Angles in the same segment are equal.

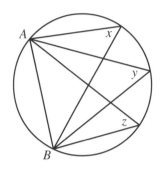

  Angle x = angle y = angle z

- The angle at the centre of a circle is twice the angle subtended by the same chord at any point on the circumference.

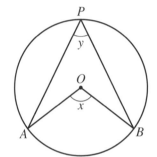

  $x = 2y$

Note:
Subtended means made.

- The angle subtended at the circumference by a semicircle is a right angle.

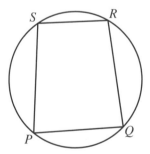

  $\hat{p} = 90°$

Cyclic quadrilaterals

A **cyclic quadrilateral** is a quadrilateral which is drawn inside a circle so that all four vertices lie on the circumference.

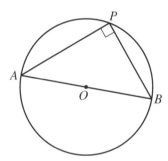

$PQRS$ is a cyclic quadrilateral.

- The opposite angles of a cyclic quadrilateral add up to 180°.
  $\hat{P} + \hat{R} = 180°$
  $\hat{S} + \hat{Q} = 180°$

Note:
The opposite angles of a cyclic quadrilateral are **supplementary**.

Example

Find the missing angles in each of these circles.

(a)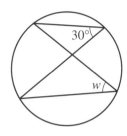

(b)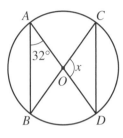

(c)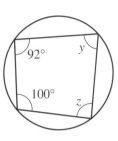

(a) $w = 30°$ Angles in the same segment are equal.

(b) $A\hat{B}O = 32°$ $\triangle ABO$ is isosceles.
    $A\hat{O}B = 180° - (2 \times 32°)$ Angles in a triangle add up to 180°.
        $= 116°$
    $x = 116°$ Opposite angles are equal.

(c) $y = 180° - 100°$ Opposite angles of a cyclic quadrilateral
        $= 80°$ add up to 180°.
    $z = 180° - 92°$ Reasons as above.
        $= 88°$

Exercise 4J

In questions 1–9 find the lettered angles.

1.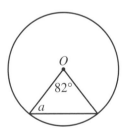

2.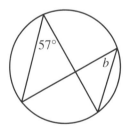

3.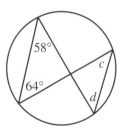

4.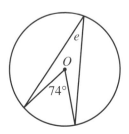

5.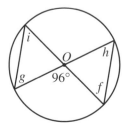

6.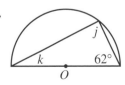

7.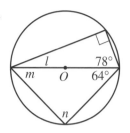

8.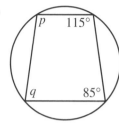

9.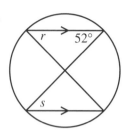

10. Prove that $AX = XB$.

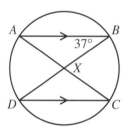

4.11 Tangent properties of a circle

There are certain facts that you need to know about tangents.

- The tangent at any point on a circle is perpendicular to the radius at that point.

  The lines OA and AT are perpendicular.

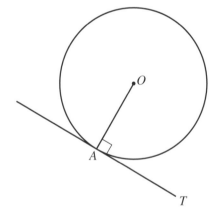

- Tangents from an external point are equal in length.

  $TR = TS$

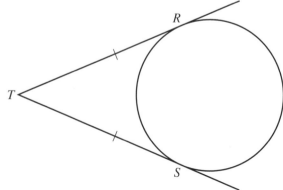

As a consequence of this last fact …

- … the line drawn from the centre of a circle perpendicular to a chord bisects the chord.

  In the circle shown, $AP = PB$.

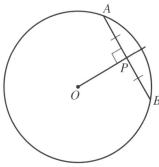

Example

Find the lettered angle.

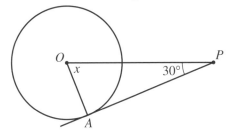

$$O\hat{A}P = 90°$$
$$x = 180° - (90° + 30°)$$
$$= 60°$$

Exercise 4K

Find the lettered angles.

1.

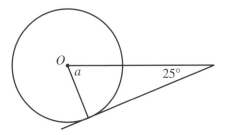

2.

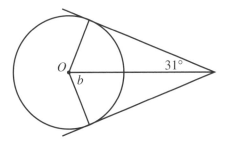

3.

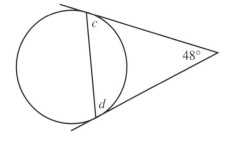

4.

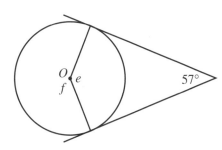

5.

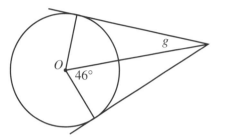

6.

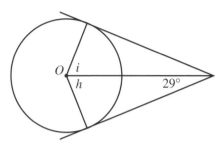

7.

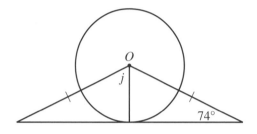

4.12 Inscribed regular polygons

You can use circles to draw regular polygons.

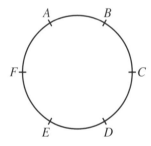

Divide a circle into six equal lengths,
marking off the points *A, B, C, D, E* and *F*.

> **Note:**
>
> You will need to divide
> the circle into six equal
> sectors with angles of
> 60° at the centre.

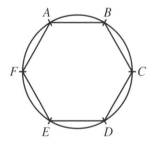

Join neighbouring points with a chord.

You will get an inscribed regular hexagon.

- You can make a regular polygon with any number of sides by equal division of the angle at the centre of a circle.

Exercise 4L

1. Draw a circle of radius 6 cm.
    Draw a regular hexagon inscribed inside this circle.
    Check that each side of your hexagon is within 1 mm of 6 cm.

2. Draw a circle of radius 8 cm.
    Draw a regular decagon (i.e. a ten-sided polygon) inscribed inside this circle.
    Check that each side of your decagon is of equal length.

3. Draw a regular octagon (i.e. an eight-sided polygon) inscribed inside a circle of radius 6 cm.
    Measure the length of each side of the octagon.

4. Draw a regular pentagon inscribed inside a circle of radius 7 cm.
    Measure the length of each side of the pentagon.

4.13 Bearings

You can describe a direction on the ground, either by using a compass or bearings.

A compass

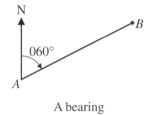

A bearing

- Bearings are measured from North in a clockwise direction, and are always given as a three-digit number.

    For example, a bearing of 4° would be written as 004°.

MODULE 5

Example

The bearing of *A* from *B* is 125°. Find the bearing of *B* from *A*.

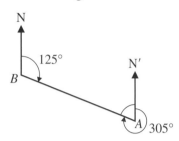

Draw a North line at *B* and at *A*.

Then the angle *NBA* is 125°.

The acute angle at *A* is
180° − 125° = 55°.

The bearing of *B* from *A* is measured **clockwise** from North and so the bearing of *B* from *A* is 360° − 55° = 305°.

Exercise 4M

1. Calculate the angle between
   (a) North and South East   (b) North West and North East
   (c) West and South East   (d) East and South South West
   (e) West and South South West

2. Write each of these compass directions as a bearing.
   (a) North East   (b) South West
   (c) North West   (d) North North East
   (e) West North West

3. The bearing of *C* from *D* is 070°. What is the bearing of *D* from *C*?

4. The bearing of *P* from *Q* is 115°. What is the bearing of *Q* from *P*?

5. The bearing of *R* from *S* is 295°. What is the bearing of S from *R*?

6. The bearing of *T* from *U* is 015°. What is the bearing of *U* from *T*?

4.14 Geometrical constructions

To make a geometrical construction you will need the following equipment:

- a ruler   at least 15 cm long marked in centimetres, to draw straight lines and to measure length
- a protractor   to draw and measure angles
- a pencil   with a **sharp** point
- a pair of compasses to draw circles.

Note:
You should be able to measure a length or draw a line to an accuracy of 1 mm. Angles should be drawn or measured to an accuracy of 1°.

Constructing a triangle

Before you can construct a triangle, you must know at least **three** measurements.

These could be
(a) the lengths of the three sides, or
(b) the lengths of two sides and the angle between them, or
(c) the length of one side and the sizes of two angles.

Each of these cases is shown in these examples.

Hint:
It is helpful to draw a quick sketch of the triangle, marking what you know, before starting the construction.

Example 1   The lengths of the three sides are known

Draw triangle PQR with $PQ = 8$ cm, $QR = 6$ cm, $PR = 7$ cm.

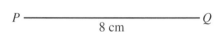

1. Draw the longest side as the base PQ.

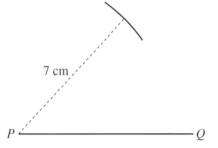

2. With compasses at P, draw an arc of a circle radius 7 cm.

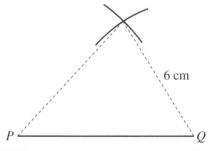

3. With compasses at Q, draw an arc of a circle radius 6 cm.

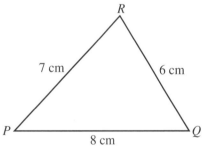

4. Join up the points PR and QR, and label the point R.

Example 2   The lengths of two sides and the angle in between them are known

Draw triangle RST with $RS = 9$ cm, $ST = 7$ cm and angle $RST = 35°$.

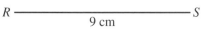

1. Draw the line RS, 9 cm long, as the base.

2. At S, use a protractor to draw an angle of 35°.

MODULE 5

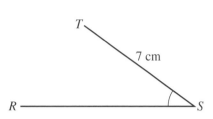

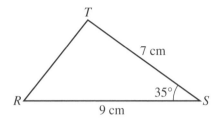

3. Measure *ST* to be 7 cm. Label the point *T*.

4. Join the points *T* and *R* to form the triangle *RST*.

Example 3 The length of one side and the sizes of two angles are known

Draw triangle *ABC* so that *AB* = 6 cm, angle *ABC* = 55° and angle *ACB* = 72°.

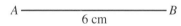

1. Draw the base *AB* of length 6 cm.

Note:

Angle *BAC*
= 180° − (55° + 72°)
= 53°

2. At *A*, use a protractor to draw an angle of 53°.

3. At *B*, use a protractor to draw an angle of 55°.

These lines meet at the point C.

Label the point *C*.

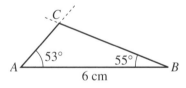

Exercise 4N

Draw these triangles accurately. Measure the length or angle required.

1. Draw triangle *ABC* where *AB* = 6 cm, *BC* = 7 cm, *CA* = 5·5 cm. Measure angle *B*.

2. Draw triangle *PQR* where *PQ* = 7 cm, *QR* = 8·2 cm, *RP* = 6·1 cm. Measure angle *P*.

3. Draw triangle *RST* where *RS* = 8·2 cm, angle *RST* = 75°, angle *SRT* = 39°. Measure *ST*.

4. Draw triangle *ABC* where *AB* = 8 cm, angle *BAC* = 54°, angle *ACB* = 85°. Measure *BC*.

MODULE 5

5. Draw triangle *PQR* where *PQ* = 7·4 cm, *QR* = 11·2 cm,
angle *PQR* = 52°. Measure *PR*.

6. Draw triangle *RST* where *RS* = 6·9 cm, *ST* = 8·2 cm,
angle *RST* = 108°. Measure *RT*.

4.15 More geometrical constructions

You can use your drawing instruments to make these
constructions.

To draw a perpendicular bisector of a line *AB*

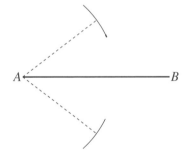

1. Open your compasses to more than half the
   length of the line *AB*.

2. With centre *A* draw arcs above and below the
   line *AB*.

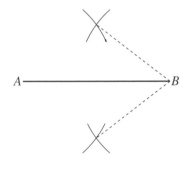

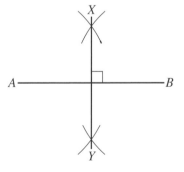

3. With the same radius, but centre *B*, draw arcs
   above and below the line *AB*.

4. Draw a line joining the points where the two arcs
   intersect. Label *X* and *Y*.

The line *XY* is the perpendicular bisector of the line *AB*.

MODULE 5

To bisect an angle *ABC*

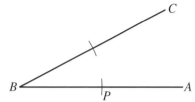

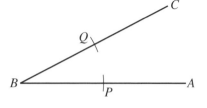

1. With centre *B* draw an arc on the line *BA* to cut the line at the point *P*.

2. With centre *B* and the same radius, draw an arc on the line *BC* to cut the line at the point *Q*.

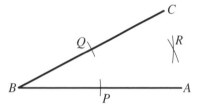

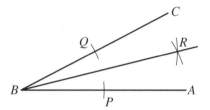

3. With centres at *P* and *Q*, and the same radius, draw arcs which intersect at *R*.

4. Join *BR*.

The line *BR* bisects angle *ABC*.

To draw a perpendicular at a point *P* on the line *AB*

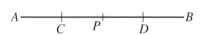

Note:

In an exam, do not rub out arcs after you have finished a construction. They show evidence of your working.

1. With centre *P* draw two arcs crossing the line *AB* at *C* and *D*.

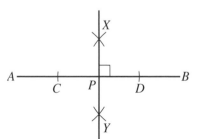

2. Draw the perpendicular bisector of the line *CD*, as described above. Label *X* and *Y*.

The line *XY* is perpendicular to the line *AB* at the point *P*.

Exercise 40

1. (a) Draw an equilateral triangle *PQR* of side 8 cm.
(b) Bisect the angle at *P*.
(c) Draw the perpendicular bisector of side *PQ*.
These two lines meet at point *T*.
(d) Measure *PT*.

2. Draw triangle *PQR* with *PQ* = 9 cm, *QR* = 7·5 cm, and
PR = 8·2 cm. Draw the three perpendicular bisectors of the
sides of the triangle. Show that the three perpendicular
bisectors pass through one point.

3. Draw triangle *ABC* with *AB* = 8 cm, *BC* = 6 cm, and
AC = 9 cm. Bisect the three angles of the triangle.
Show that the three bisectors pass through one point.

4.16 Loci

A **locus** is the path traced out by a point that moves according
to a rule.

Note:
A locus can be a straight
line, a curve or a region.
The plural of locus is
loci.

Example 1

A ship cannot sail within 100 metres of rocks.

Draw the locus of the ship and describe it in words.

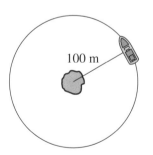

The region in which the ship cannot sail is
the inside of this circle.

The locus is a circle, centre the rocks and radius 100 m.

Example 2

Find the locus of a point *P* which moves so that *P*
(i) is equidistant from the points *A* and *B*, shown in the
diagram, and
(ii) cannot be less than 5 cm from either *A* or *B*.

Note:
Equidistant means
'the same distance'.

A•   •*B*

MODULE 5

P is equidistant from the points *A* and *B*, so

P lies on *RS* (the perpendicular bisector of the line *AB*).

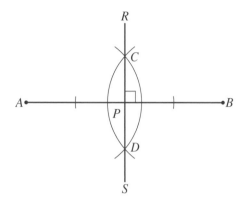

P cannot be less than 5 cm from *A* or *B*, so draw an arc centre *A* and radius 5 cm.

Then draw an arc centre *B* radius 5 cm.

These two arcs cut *RS* at *C* and *D*.

The locus of *P* is those points on the perpendicular bisector which are **not** between points *C* and *D*.

Exercise 4P

1. Draw the locus of a point which moves so that its distance from a given line is 3 cm.

2. Draw the locus of a point *P* which moves so that the point is equidistant from two lines *AB* and *AC*.
    Angle *ABC* is 50°.

3. A point *P* is marked on the circumference of a wheel of a bicycle.
    Using a scale drawing so that the wheel has radius 4 cm, draw the locus of point *P* as the bicycle moves.

4. A house is positioned as shown in a fenced garden of depth 20 m at the back and 8 m at the front. A hosepipe of length 15 m is connected to a tap on the side wall positioned 6 m from the rear corner of the house. The length of the side of the house is 10 m. The side of the house is 2 m from the side fence.

Draw the locus to show the region which the hosepipe can reach.

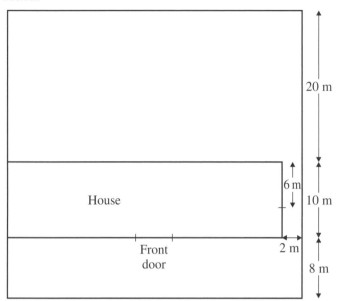

Summary

1. You know the names for special angles and lines and their properties

2. You know the angle properties of parallel lines

3. You can identify lines of reflexive symmetry and the order of rotational symmetry

Check out AS4

1. (a) What is an acute angle?
   (b) What is meant by saying two lines are perpendicular?
   (c) What can you say about two angles being supplementary?

2. Copy the diagram and mark all the angles which are 53°

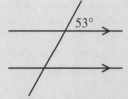

3. Draw the lines of reflexive symmetry for the figure shown. State the order of rotational symmetry.

MODULE 5

4. You can draw a net

4. Draw a net for a cuboid 6 cm by 5 cm by 4 cm.

5. You know the sum of the angles of a triangle and the exterior angle of a triangle

5. Find angles x and y.

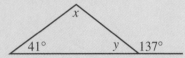

6. You know the properties of specific quadrilaterals

6. (a) What are the properties of a square?
   (b) What are the symmetries, both reflexive and rotational, of a rhombus?

7. You know the relation between the exterior angles, the interior angles and the number of sides of a polygon

7. A regular polygon has 20 sides.
   Find (a) the exterior angle
   (b) the interior angle of the polygon.

8. You know and understand such terms as segment, sector, semicircle

8. (a) Copy the diagram. Draw an angle in the same segment as angle ABC.

(b) What do you know about the size of the angle you have just drawn?

9. You know the angle properties of a circle

9. Angle $ABC = 90°$. What can you say about the line AC?

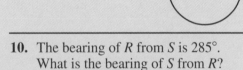

10. You can calculate bearings

10. The bearing of R from S is $285°$. What is the bearing of S from R?

11. You can make geometrical constructions

11. Draw a triangle with sides 3 cm, 4 cm and 5.3 cm. Measure the largest angle.

12. You can find a locus

12. (a) Using only a protractor draw a triangle ABC so that angle $B = 65°$, $AB = 7$ cm and $BC = 9$ cm.
    (b) Point T is such that T is equidistant from both AC and AB. T is also equidistant from points A and B. Use ruler and compasses to draw the locus of point T.

Revision exercise AS4

1. The diagram shows a rectangle which has been partly shaded.

    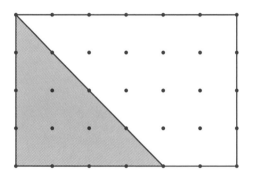

    (a) What fraction of the rectangle is shaded?

    (b) On a copy of the diagram, shade more of the rectangle
         so that the final diagram has rotational symmetry of
         order 2 but no lines of symmetry.   [SEG]

2. (a) The diagram shows a rectangle *ABCD*.
         M is the mid-point of *DC*.
         Angle *AMB* = 80°.
         AM = *MB*.

         Work out the sizes of angles *x* and *y*.

    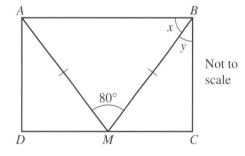

    Not to scale

    (b) The diagram shows a quadrilateral *PQRS*.
         PQ = *QR* and *PS* = *SR*.
         (i)   Which of the following correctly describes the
               quadrilateral *PQRS*?
               Diamond Kite Rhombus Parallelogram Trapezium
         (ii) Angle *PSR* = 42° and angle *QRS* = 100°.
               Work out the sizes of angles *p* and *q*.

         [SEG]

    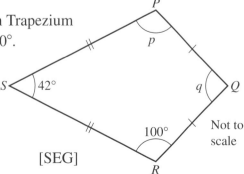

    Not to scale

MODULE 5

3. The diagram shows the positions of three oil rigs, *X*, *Y* and *Z*.

North

Z

North

X

•*Y*

(a) What is the bearing of *X* from *Z*?

A supply boat is moving among the rigs.

At midday it is: (i)   equidistant from *X* and *Y*;
                (ii) equidistant from *XY* and *YZ*.

(b) By drawing the loci of (i) and (ii) find the position of
the boat.
Mark the position of the boat with a cross on a copy of
the diagram.   [SEG]

4. (a) In the diagram $AB = BC = CA = CD$.

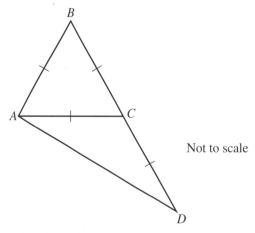

B

A   *C*

Not to scale

D

Work out the size of angle *CDA*.

(b) In the diagram angle $AOB = 90°$.

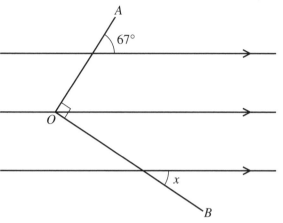

67°

x

Not to scale

Work out the size of angle x.   [SEG]

5. (a) These polygons are similar.

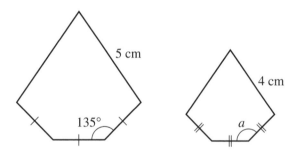

5 cm

4 cm

135°

a

Not to scale

What is the size of angle a?

(b) Part of a regular polygon is shown.

p

q

Not to scale

The complete polygon has n sides, where $n = \dfrac{360}{q}$ and $p + q = 180°$.

(i)   Calculate the value of n, when $p = 168°$.

(ii) Write down a formula for n in terms of p.   [SEG]

MODULE 5

6. The map of an island is shown.

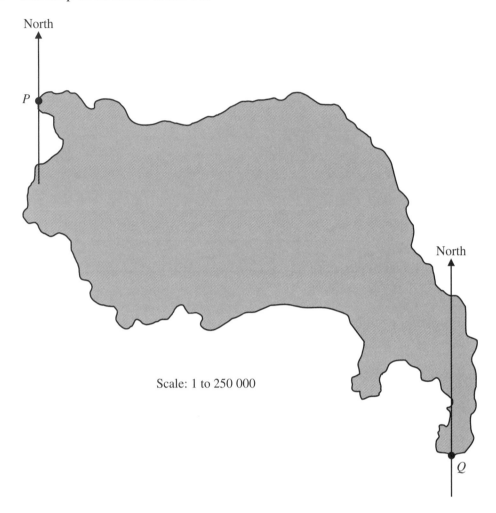

Scale: 1 to 250 000

P and *Q* are the positions of two lighthouses.

(a) What is the bearing of *Q* from *P*?

The map has been drawn to a scale of 1 to 250 000.

(b) Use the map to calculate the actual distance between the lighthouses in kilometres.

AS5 SHAPE 2

When you are reading a map, it is useful to know the scale.

Well, according to the map we should be at the river by now.

Actually the scale is 1 to **fifty** thousand. We've got to walk ten times further than we thought!

This unit will show you how to:

- Understand congruence
- Understand similarity
- Use map scales

Before you start:

You should know how to …	Check in AS5
1. Draw triangles Turn to page 319 to remind yourself how to do this.	**1.** Draw a triangle with sides 5 cm, 6 cm and 7 cm.
2. Use ratios For example, find x such that $3 : 4 = x : 20$ $\times 5 \overset{\frown}{\underset{\smile}{\begin{array}{c} 3 : 4 \\ x : 20 \end{array}}} \times 5$ So $x = 3 \times 5$ $ = 15$	**2.** (a) Find x such that $3 : 7 = 12 : x$ (b) Find y such that $8 : 11 = y : 77$

5.1 Congruence

- Two plane figures are **congruent** if one fits exactly on top of the other.

If two **triangles** are congruent, they will have

- 3 pairs of corresponding equal angles, and
- 3 pairs of corresponding equal sides.

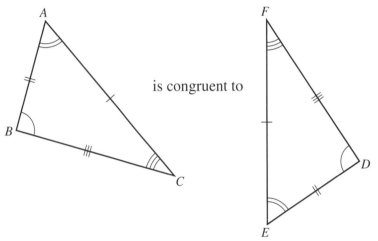

is congruent to

You do not need to check all the sides and angles to ensure that two triangles are congruent.

You can just look for one of these four criteria, known as the **conditions for congruency**:

1. SSS (side, side, side)

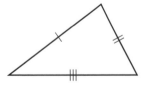   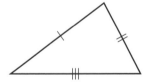

Three sides in the first triangle are equal to three sides in the second triangle.

2. SAS (side, angle, side)

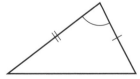   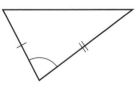

Three sides and the angle between them are the same for both triangles.

3. AAS (angle, angle, side)

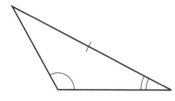
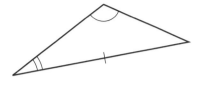

Two angles and a corresponding side are the same for both triangles.

4. RHS (right angle, hypotenuse and side)

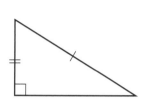
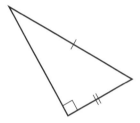

Each triangle contains a right angle. Also, two corresponding sides are equal and one of these is the **hypotenuse**.

> **Note:**
> The **hypotenuse** of a right-angled triangle is the longest side. There is more about the hypotenuse in Unit AS8.

Example

Show that the triangles *ABC* and *XYZ* are congruent.

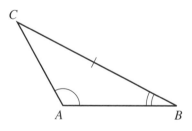
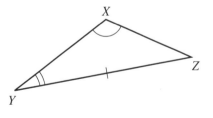

$$BC = YZ \qquad \text{given as equal lengths}$$
$$B\hat{A}C = Z\hat{X}Y \qquad \text{given as equal lengths}$$
$$A\hat{B}C = X\hat{Y}Z \qquad \text{given as equal lengths}$$

These triangles satisfy the AAS condition.

So $\Delta ABC \equiv \Delta XYZ$

> **Note:**
> $\equiv$ means 'is congruent to'.

MODULE 5

Exercise 5A

1. State which pairs of these triangles are congruent.

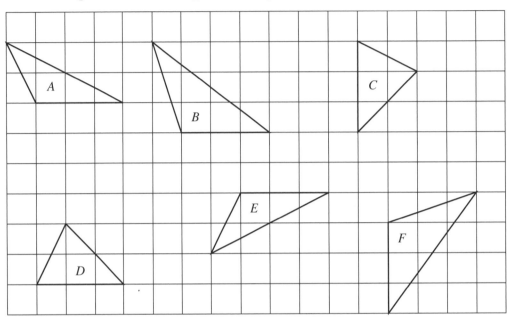

2. Two triangles have the same sized angles.
   Give a reason why they are not necessarily congruent.

3. Look carefully at the following triangles. State which of the
   pairs of triangles are congruent. When a pair of triangles is
   congruent, give a reason for the congruency.

   (a)

   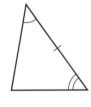

   (b)

   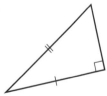
   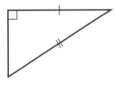

   (c)

   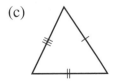

(d)

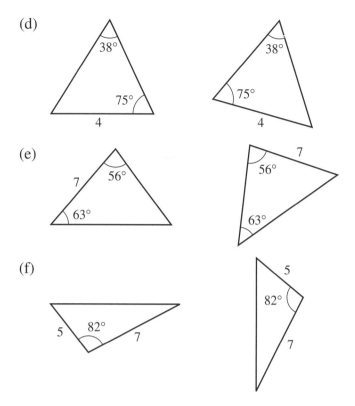

(e)

(f)

4. *ABCD* is a kite. Name a pair of congruent triangles in the figure, giving a reason for the congruency.

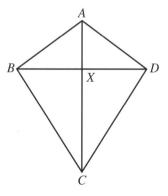

5.2 Similarity

Two plane figures are **similar** if they have the same shape. The following conditions apply for similar shapes:

● all corresponding angles are equal, and

● all corresponding sides are in the same ratio.

Note:

Similar shapes are not necessarily the same size.

Two shapes A and B are drawn on a grid:

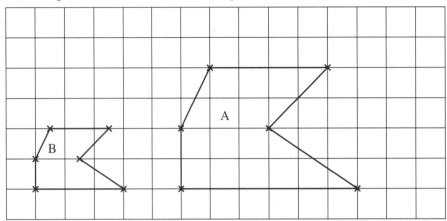

All the angles in shape A are
equal to the corresponding
angles in shape B.

$\Longrightarrow$

So A and B have
the **same shape**.

The sides of shape B are
all half the size of the
corresponding sides of shape A

$\Longrightarrow$

So B is an enlargement
of A with a scale factor
of $\frac{1}{2}$.

$\therefore$ A and B are similar shapes.

When two figures are known to be similar, you can calculate
unknown lengths.

Example

These rectangles are similar. Find the width of the second rectangle.

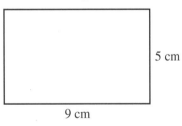

5 cm

9 cm

16·2 cm

The scale factor of the enlargement $= \dfrac{16\cdot2}{9} = 1\cdot8$

So the enlarged width $= 5 \times 1\cdot8 = 9$ cm.

Hint:
You can find the scale
factor by dividing two
corresponding sides with
known lengths.

Exercise 5B

1. Which of the shapes B, C or D is similar to shape A?

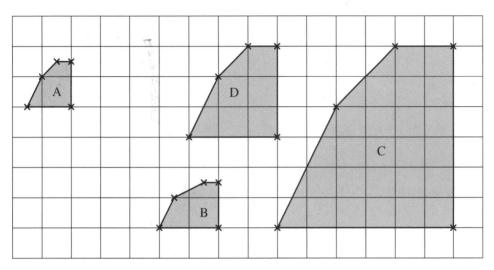

2. Two rectangles are shown below.

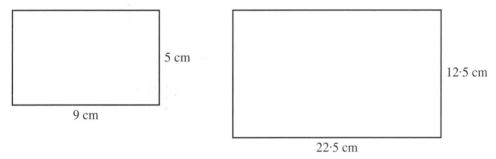

Are the rectangles similar?
Justify your answer with a calculation.

3. The following pairs of shapes are similar. Calculate the lengths and angles marked with letters.

(a)

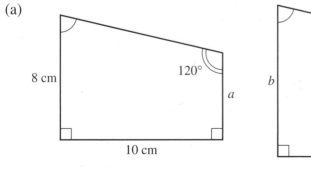
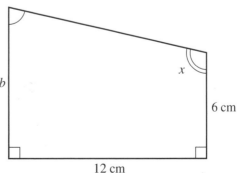

(b)

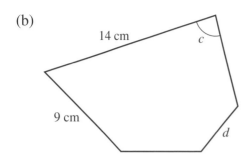

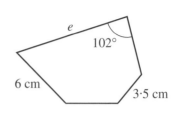

5.3 Similar triangles

Here are two similar triangles:

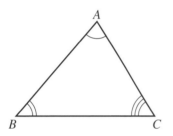

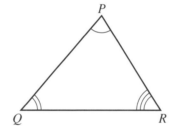

If two triangles are similar, one of the following conditions will be satisfied.

- All corresponding angles are equal.

$$\hat{A} = \hat{P}, \quad \hat{B} = \hat{Q}, \quad \hat{C} = \hat{R}$$

Note:

In a triangle, if two angles correspond, then the third pair must be equal because angles of a triangle add up to 180°.

- All corresponding sides have the same scale factor ratio.

$$\frac{AB}{PQ} = \frac{AC}{PR} = \frac{BC}{QR}$$

Note:

This means that the lengths are in the same **proportion**.

- Two sets of corresponding sides have the same scale factor ratio **and** the angles between these corresponding sides are equal.

For example $\dfrac{AB}{PQ} = \dfrac{AC}{PR}$ and $\hat{A} = \hat{P}$

Example 1

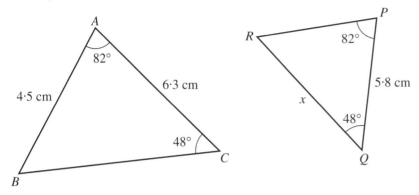

(a) Show that triangles *ABC* and *PQR* are similar.
(b) Find the unknown length marked *x* in triangle *PQR*.

(a) Two pairs of angles are equal, so the third pair of angles must be equal also, and therefore the triangles are similar.

(b) Scale factor of the enlargement $= \dfrac{PQ}{AC} = \dfrac{6{\cdot}3}{4{\cdot}5} = 1{\cdot}4$

So $\dfrac{x}{5{\cdot}8} = 1{\cdot}4$

$\qquad x = 1{\cdot}4 \times 5{\cdot}8$

$\qquad x = 8{\cdot}12 \text{ cm}$

Example 2

In the diagram *DE* is parallel to *BC*. $AC = 12$ cm, $BC = 10$ cm, $DE = 6$ cm and $A\hat{C}B = 109°$.

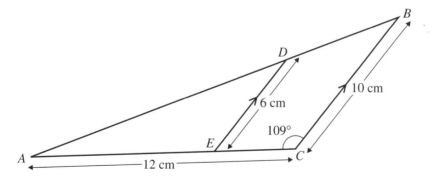

(a) Write down the size of $A\hat{E}D$. Give a reason for your answer.
(b) Show that triangle *ABC* is similar to triangle *ADE*.
(c) (i) Work out the length of *AE*.
    (ii) Hence work out the length of *EC*.

(a) $A\hat{E}D = 109°$ *DE* is parallel to *BC*, so use corresponding angles

(b) In $\triangle ADE$ and $\triangle ABC$, both triangles have:

$A\hat{E}D = A\hat{C}B = 109°$ Corresponding angles since *DE* is parallel to *BC*

$D\hat{A}E = B\hat{A}C$ Common angle

$A\hat{D}E = A\hat{B}C$ Two pairs of angles are equal, so the third pair of angles is equal

(c) (i)   Side *AE* is contained in $\triangle AED$.

Writing the scale factor ratios $\dfrac{\triangle ADE}{\triangle ABC}$: $\dfrac{AD}{AB} = \dfrac{AE}{AC} = \dfrac{DE}{BC}$

Substituting the lengths gives $\dfrac{AD}{AB} = \dfrac{AE}{12} = \dfrac{6}{10}$

so $AE = \dfrac{6}{10} \times 12$

$AE = 7.2\,\text{cm}$

(ii) $EC = AC - AE$

$EC = 12 - 7{\cdot}2$

$EC = 4{\cdot}8\,\text{cm}$

Exercise 5C

1. Each of these pairs of triangles are similar, with all the equal angles marked.
   Without using a calculator, find the size of the unknown lettered lengths.

   (a)

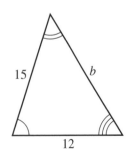
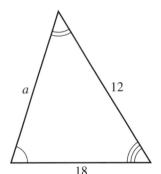

(b)

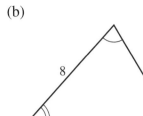

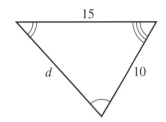

(c)

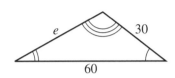

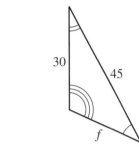

(d)

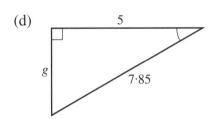

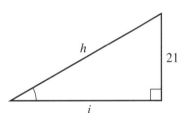

2. Each of these pairs of triangles are similar. Calculate the unknown lengths.

(a)

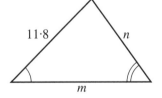

(b)

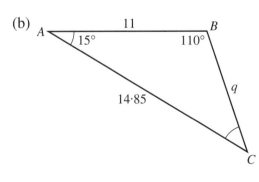

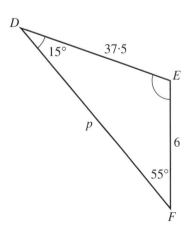

MODULE 5

(c)

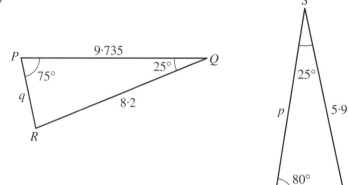

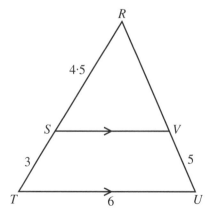

3. Triangles *ABE* and *ACE* are similar, with *BE* parallel to *CD*. *AB* = 6, *BE* = 10, *DE* = 4 and *CD* = 15. Calculate

(a) *AE*

(b) *AC*

(c) *BC*

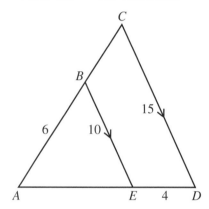

4. Triangles *RSV* and *RTU* are similar, with *SV* parallel to *TU*. *RS* = 4·5, *ST* = 3, *VU* = 5 and *TU* = 6. Calculate

(a) *SV*

(b) *RV*

5. The diagram shows a 4 cm border around a rectangular picture of size 12 cm by 20 cm. Are the two rectangles *ABCD* and *DEFG* similar? Justify your answer.

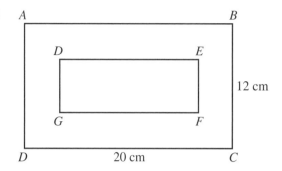

6. In the diagram $Q\hat{P}S = S\hat{Q}R$. $QR = 8$, $QS = 6$ and $SR = 4$.

   (a) Name two similar triangles in this diagram.

   (b) Calculate

      (i) *PQ*

      (ii) *PS*

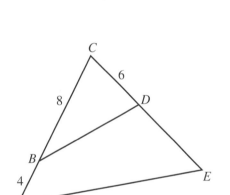

7. Triangles *ACE* and *DCB* are similar. The lines *AE* and *BD* are not parallel. Calculate the length *DE*.

8. In the diagram $A\hat{B}C = C\hat{E}D$ and $AC = 10$ cm, $BC = 8.75$ cm, $CE = 14$ cm, $CD = 16$ cm.

   (a) Explain why triangles *ABE* and *DEC* are similar.

   (b) Calculate the length *DE*.

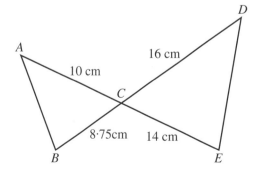

MODULE 5

5.4 Scale

You often need to use a **scale** when
you make a model or draw a diagram
A map is a type of diagram drawn
to scale.

1 : 25 000

This is the scale.
It tells you that
each distance is
drawn $\frac{1}{25\,000}$ of the
original size.

Example 1

The scale of a map is 1 : 25 000.
(a) What distance on the map represents 6·5 km on the ground?
(b) What distance on the ground is represented by 2·9 cm on the map?

(a) 1 cm represents 25 000 cm.

$$\therefore 25\,000\,\text{cm} = \frac{25\,000}{100}\,\text{m} = 250\,\text{m}$$

$$= \frac{250}{1000}\,\text{km} = 0\text{·}25\,\text{km}$$

$$\therefore 0\text{·}25\,\text{km} \longrightarrow 1\,\text{cm}$$
$$1\,\text{km} \longrightarrow 4\,\text{cm}$$
$$6\text{·}5\,\text{km} \longrightarrow 4 \times 6\text{·}5\,\text{cm} = 26\,\text{cm}$$

∴ The distance is 26 cm on the map.

(b) 1 cm represents 25 000 cm.

∴ 2·9 cm represents 2·9 × 25 000 cm

$$= \frac{2\text{·}9 \times 25\,000}{100}\,\text{m}$$

$$= \frac{2\text{·}9 \times 250}{1000}\,\text{km}$$

$$= 0.725\,\text{km or }725\,\text{m}$$

Example 2

A builder's plan is drawn to a scale of 1 cm to 12 m.
How long is a garden which is 3·85 cm on the plan?

1 cm	represents	12 m
∴ 3·85 cm	represents	3·85 × 12 m = 46·2 m

The garden is 46·2 m long.

Exercise 5D

1. The scale of a map is 1 : 20 000. Find the actual length in metres represented on the map by 19·5 cm.

2. Find the actual distance in metres between two points which were 7·9 cm apart on a map whose scale is 1 : 2000.

3. A map is drawn on a scale of 4 cm to 1 km.
   (a) Work out the real length of a lake which is 5·1 cm on the map.
   (b) The distance between two village post offices is 7·9 km. What is the distance between the post offices on the map?

4. The length of a new reservoir is 6·8 km. How long will the reservoir be on a map of scale 1 : 15 000?

5. The scale of a map is 1 cm to 20 m. The length of a field is 168·2 m. What length will the field be on the map?

6. Copy and complete this table.

	Map scale	Actual length on land	Length on map
(a)	1 : 20 000	14·6 km	cm
(b)	1 : 15 000	8·4 km	cm
(c)	1 : 60 000	24·8 km	cm
(d)	1 : 250 000	28 km	cm
(e)	1 : 5000	3·9 km	cm

MODULE 5

MODULE 5

Summary

1. You know the meaning of congruency

2. You know the different cases of congruency

3. You can identify which triangles are congruent

4. You know when two shapes are similar

5. You know when two triangles are similar.

6. You can use a scale

Check out AS5

1. What does congruency mean?

2. State the four different cases of congruency.

3. Which of the these triangles are congruent?

(a)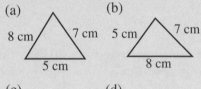

(b)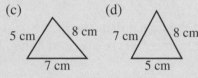

4. Which of these shapes are similar?

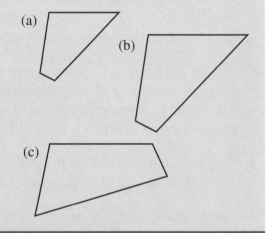

5. These two triangles are similar. Calculate the unknown lengths.

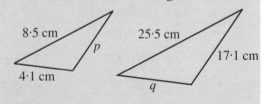

6. A garden has length 2 mm on a map. The scale of the map is 1 : 60 000. What is the length of the actual garden?

Revision exercise AS5

1. The diagram shows a regular hexagon drawn inside a circle with diameter *AD*.

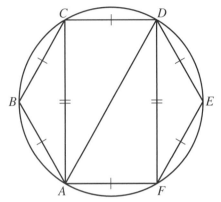

Not to scale

(a) Name a triangle which is congruent to triangle *ACD*.

(b) Calculate the size of angle *DFE*.   [SEG]

2. The diagram shows a kite *PQRS*.

(a) How many lines of symmetry has *PQRS*?

Angle *QRS* = 93° and angle *PQR* = 118°.

(b) Work out the size of angle *PSR*.

(c) *WXYZ* is similar to *PQRS*.
     PQ = 1·8 cm, *SR* = 3·3 cm and *WX* = 2·4 cm.

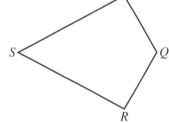

Not to scale

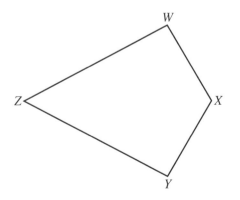

Not to scale

(i)   Find the size of angle *XWZ*.

(ii) Calculate the length of *ZY*.   [SEG]

3. In the diagram, *WA* is a straight line and *ZX* is parallel to *BD*.

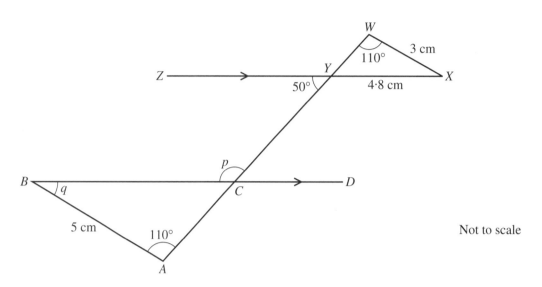

Not to scale

(a) Work out the size of angle *p* and the size of angle *q*.

Triangle *ABC* is similar to triangle *WXY*.

ABC = 5 cm, *WX* = 3 cm and *YX* = 4·8 cm.

(b) Calculate the length of *BC*.   [SEG]

4. These triangles are congruent.

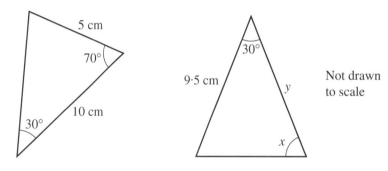

Not drawn to scale

What is the size of

(a) *x*

(b) *y*?   [NEAB]

5. The diagram shows a shape which consists
of two regular polygons.
   (a) Work out the size of angle *x*.

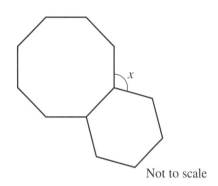

Not to scale

   (b) These irregular polygons are similar.   [SEG]

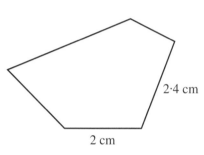

2·4 cm

2 cm

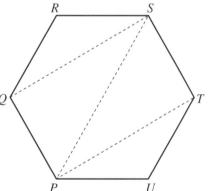

Q

P

3 cm

Not to scale

      Calculate the length of *PQ*.   [SEG]

6. The diagram shows two regular hexagons.

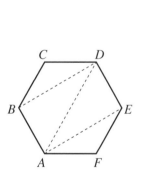

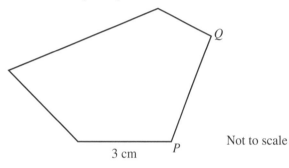

Not to scale

   (a) Name a triangle which is similar but not congruent to
      triangle *BCD*.

   (b) *AB* : *PQ* is 2 : 3.
      (i) Angle *AEF* = 30°. What is the size of angle *PTU*?
      (ii) *AF* = 2·4 cm. Calculate the perimeter of the hexagon
         PQRSTU.   [SEG]

AS6 SHAPE 3

You can see a transformation whenever you look in a mirror.

This unit will show you how to:

- Describe translations, reflections, rotations and enlargements
- Combine transformations
- Find inverse transformations
- Draw tessellations
- Draw 3D objects

Before you start:

You should know how to ...	Check in AS6
1. Plot points on a grid	**1.** On a grid, plot the points (2, 3), (4, 0), (⁻2, 2), (⁻4, ⁻3).
2. Draw a net Look back to page 302 to remind yourself how to do this	**2.** Draw a net for a cuboid 4 cm by 7 cm by 3 cm.

A **transformation** changes the position, or size, of a shape.
There are four main types of transformation:

1. Translation

2. Reflection

3. Rotation

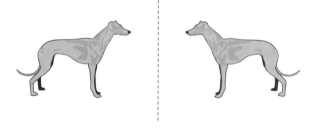

4. Enlargement

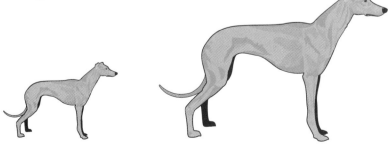

6.1 Translation

A translation moves every point in a shape the same distance and in the same direction.

Every point on this flag is moved by 2 units in the x direction and 1 unit in the y direction.

You can write this translation as a **vector**, $\begin{pmatrix} 2 \\ 1 \end{pmatrix}$.

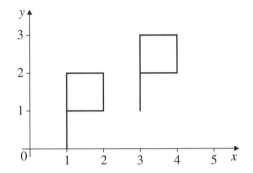

Example 1

In the triangle ABC, the point A is $(3, 5)$, B is $(1, {}^-1)$ and C is $(2, 7)$.

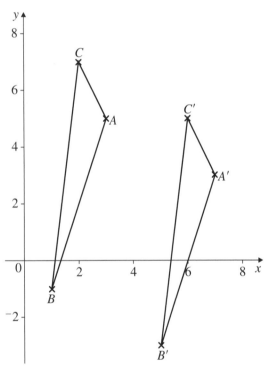

Find the triangle ABC after the translation $\begin{pmatrix} 4 \\ -2 \end{pmatrix}$.

The image is a new triangle $A'B'C'$.

You can find the position of A' by:

    writing the coordinates of A as a vector $\begin{pmatrix} 3 \\ 5 \end{pmatrix}$

    and adding the translation vector $\begin{pmatrix} 4 \\ -2 \end{pmatrix}$

Note:

In the vector, ${}^-2$ in the y direction means 2 units down, just like coordinates.

$$\binom{3}{5} + \binom{4}{-2} = \binom{3+4}{5-2} = \binom{7}{3}$$

$\therefore A'$ is the point $(7, 3)$.

Similarly for B': $\quad \binom{1}{-1} + \binom{4}{-2} = \binom{5}{-3}$ $\qquad \therefore B'$ is the point $(5, -3)$.

And for C': $\quad \binom{2}{7} + \binom{4}{-2} = \binom{6}{5}$ $\qquad \therefore C'$ is the point $(6, 5)$.

Example 2

Find the translation which moves quadrilateral $PQRS$ into its new position $P'Q'R'S'$.

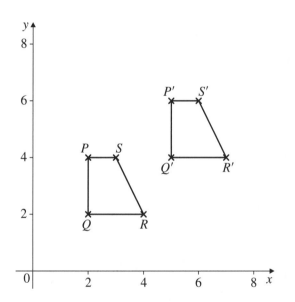

The point P has moved from $(2, 4)$ to $(5, 6)$.

Write these coordinates as vectors and subtract:

$$\binom{5}{6} - \binom{2}{4} = \binom{3}{2}$$

$\therefore$ The translation is $\binom{3}{2}$.

Note:
To **describe** a translation, you only need to look at a single point. All the other points will move similarly.

Exercise 6A

1. Write down the coordinates of the image of each of these points after applying the given translation.

	Original point	Translation
(a)	(3, 5)	$\binom{2}{1}$
(b)	(4, 7)	$\binom{3}{5}$
(c)	($^-$2, 1)	$\binom{4}{1}$
(d)	($^-$2, $^-$3)	$\binom{5}{3}$
(e)	($^-$3, 1)	$\binom{4}{-3}$
(f)	($^-$3, $^-$4)	$\binom{-2}{-5}$
(g)	($^-$1, $^-$8)	$\binom{-3}{-4}$

2. Write down the translation which moves these original points to the image points.

	Original point	Image point
(a)	(4, 5)	(12, 8)
(b)	(3, 1)	(4, 5)
(c)	(2, 4)	($^-$3, 5)
(d)	(1, 5)	($^-$7, $^-$8)
(e)	($^-$3, $^-$4)	($^-$6, $^-$5)

3. Triangle *ABC* is translated into triangle *A'B'C'*. *A* and *B* have coordinates (3, 7) and (5, 8) respectively.
   A' and *C'* have coordinates (5, 10) and (4, 1). Find points *C* and *B'*.

4. Triangle *PQR* is translated into triangle *P'Q'R'*. *P* and *Q* have coordinates (4, 2) and (1, $^-$3) respectively.
   P' and *R'* have coordinates ($^-$2, $^-$5) and ($^-$6, $^-$8).
   Find points *R* and *Q'*.

5. Show the image of this flag after the translation

(a) $\begin{pmatrix} 2 \\ 1 \end{pmatrix}$ (b) $\begin{pmatrix} ^-4 \\ ^-2 \end{pmatrix}$

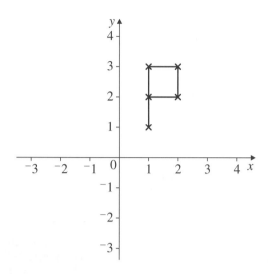

6.2 Reflection

A reflection changes a shape into its mirror image.

P' is the image of P when P is reflected in the line L.

To find the line of reflection, select one point T on P and its image T' on P'.

The perpendicular bisector of the line TT' is the **line of reflection**, or **mirror line**.

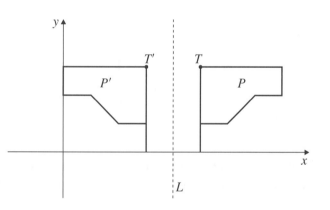

MODULE 5

Example 1

In triangle ABC, point A is $(3, 4)$ B is $(4, 2)$ and C is $(5, 3)$.
Find the image when triangle ABC is reflected in the line $x = 2$.

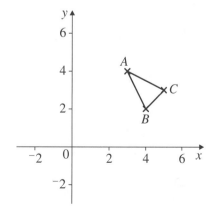

A' is the point $(1, 4)$.
Similarly B' is the point
$(0, 2)$ and C' is $(^-1, 3)$.

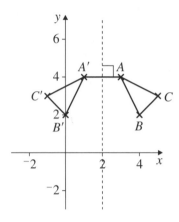

Example 2

The quadrilateral $PQRS$ is reflected into the quadrilateral
$P'Q'R'S'$. Draw the line of reflection.

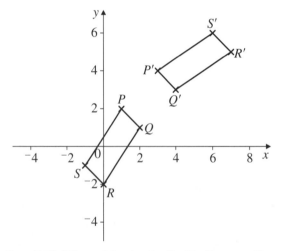

Note:

The mirror line is also
the perpendicular
bisector of the lines
QQ', RR' and SS'.

Draw the line PP'. The midpoint is $(2, 3)$. Draw a line through
$(2, 3)$ perpendicular to PP'. This is the line of reflection.

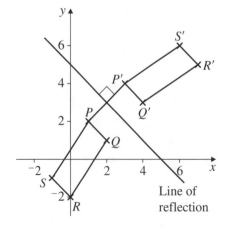

Line of
reflection

Exercise 6B

1. Draw the image of each of these shapes after a reflection in the mirror line, shown dotted.

   (a) 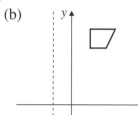 (b) 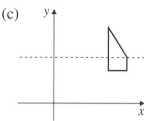 (c)

2. Reflect these shapes
   (a) in the x-axis   (b) in the y-axis   (c) in the line $y = x$

   (i) 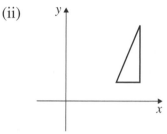   (ii)

3. Find the line of reflection which would reflect each shape S into the shape S'.

   (a) 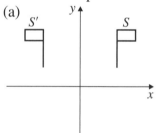   (b) 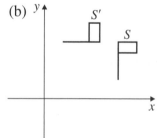   (c)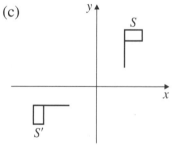

6.3 Rotation

A rotation moves a shape by turning it about a point, which is the **centre of rotation**.

This shape is rotated through 90° anticlockwise about O.

To define a rotation you need to state

(a) the centre of rotation
(b) the angle through which the shape is rotated, and
(c) whether the direction is clockwise or anticlockwise.

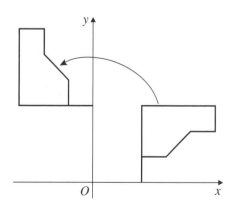

MODULE 5

Example 1

Shape P is rotated about O through $135°$ in an anticlockwise direction.

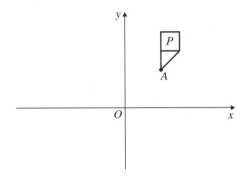

Draw P', the image of P, after this rotation.

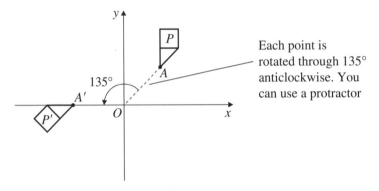

Each point is rotated through $135°$ anticlockwise. You can use a protractor

To find the centre of rotation

You can find the centre of rotation by using the method shown in this example.

Example 2

Describe fully the rotation that maps the shape P onto P'.

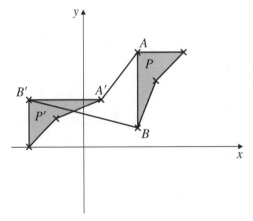

Find two pairs of corresponding points A and A', and B and B'.
Draw the perpendicular bisectors of AA' and BB' and find where
they cross.

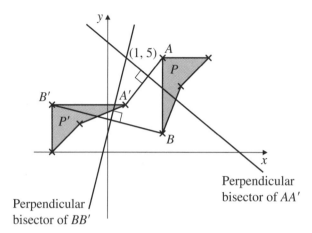

The centre of rotation is $(1, 5)$ and the angle of rotation is $270°$
anticlockwise.

Exercise 6C

1. Give the image of each of these shapes after
   - (i)   a rotation about O through $180°$ anticlockwise
   - (ii) a rotation about O through $90°$ anticlockwise
   - (iii) a rotation about O through $120°$ anticlockwise.

   (a)   (b)

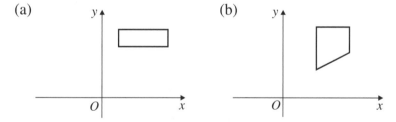

2. Copy these diagrams and draw the image of each shape
   after a rotation about P through the specified angle.

   (a) $180°$ anticlockwise   (b) $90°$ clockwise   (c) $90°$ anticlockwise

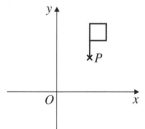
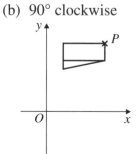
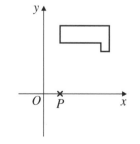

MODULE 5

3. Identify the rotation that will rotate each shape S into shape S'.

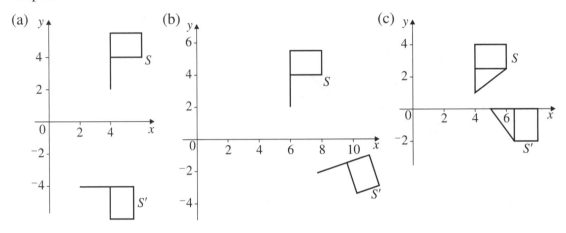

(a)

(b)

(c)

6.4 Enlargement

In an enlargement all corresponding lengths are increased by a **scale factor.**

Shape S' is the image of shape S after an enlargement scale factor 4, centre P. **All** lengths in S' are four times the corresponding length in S.

To identify an enlargement you must state

(a) the centre of enlargement, and
(b) the scale factor of the enlargement.

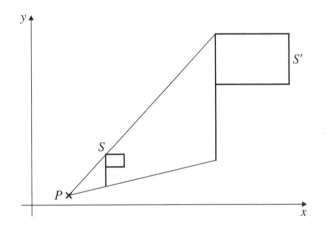

Example 1

Find the image of shape S after an enlargement, centre $C(1, 3)$, of scale factor 2.

Note:
Enlargements change the size of an object. The other three types of transformation do not.

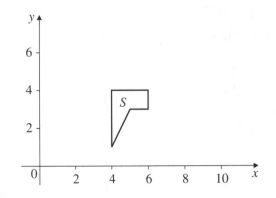

Join C to A. Extend the line so that $CA' = 2CA$.
Repeat for all the other vertices.

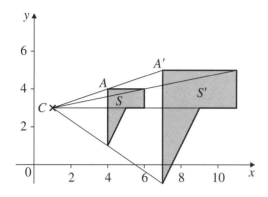

Example 2

Quadrilateral $A'B'C'D'$ is the image of the enlargement of
quadrilateral $ABCD$. Identify the scale factor and the centre of
enlargement.

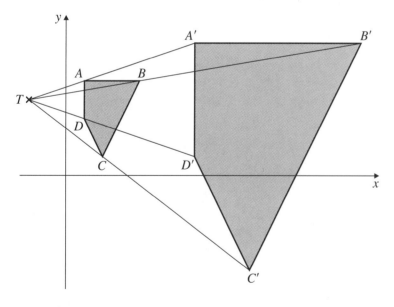

Join A to A', B to B', C to C' and D to D'.
Extend these lines so that they all meet at point T.
Measure TA and TA'.

$$\frac{TA'}{TA} = \frac{4.8}{1.6} = 3$$

$\therefore$ The scale factor of the enlargement is 3, and the centre of
enlargement is at T.

MODULE 5

● If the image diagram is **smaller** than the original, the scale factor is less than 1.

S' is an enlargement of S with a scale factor of $\frac{1}{2}$.

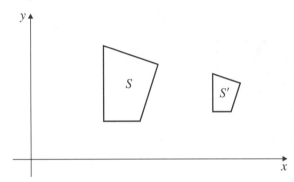

Exercise 6D

1. Trace these shapes and enlarge them by the given scale factor with point P as the centre of enlargement.

    (a) scale factor 2   (b) scale factor $\frac{1}{2}$

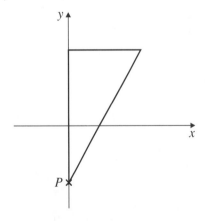

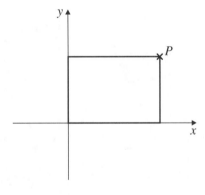

    (c) scale factor 3   (d) scale factor 2

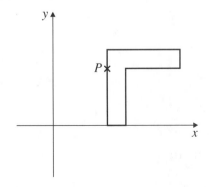
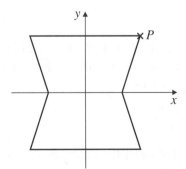

2. Trace this diagram, and draw the enlargement of shape S by a scale factor of 4, centre of enlargement P.

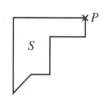

3. Describe fully the transformation which maps each shape A into the shape B.

(a)

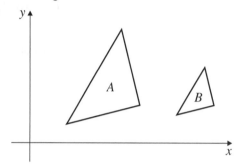

(b)

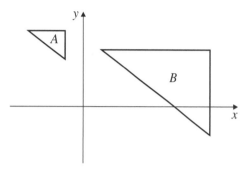

4. Draw a triangle ABC, with $AB = 5$ cm, $BC = 7$ cm and $AC = 8$ cm.
With centre B enlarge this triangle with scale factor
(a) 2   (b) $\frac{1}{3}$.

5. Draw the image of this shape after an enlargement centre A, scale factor
(a) $\frac{1}{2}$ (b) 3

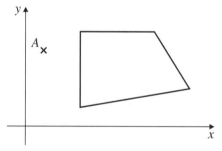

6.5 Combined transformations

You can combine transformations to get a single equivalent transformation.

Example

The shape S is shown on the grid.

T is a translation $\begin{pmatrix} 4 \\ 0 \end{pmatrix}$.

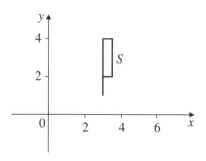

MODULE 5

R is a reflection in the line $x = 2$.
Find the single transformation equivalent to
(a) RT (b) TR (c) T^2

(a) First do transformation T.
    Then do transformation R on the image of S.

Note:

RT and TR give different results. The order in which you combine transformations matters.

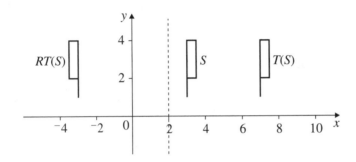

    RT is equivalent to a reflection in the x-axis.

(b) First do transformation R.
    Then do transformation T on the image of S.

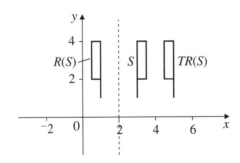

    TR is equivalent to a reflection in the line $x = 4$.

(c)

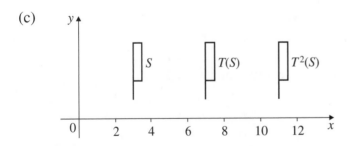

The transformation T^2 is equivalent to a translation of $\begin{pmatrix} 8 \\ 0 \end{pmatrix}$.

Exercise 6E

1. Transformation R is a rotation about the origin
   anticlockwise through 90°.
   Transformation X is a reflection in the x-axis.
   Transformation Y is a reflection in the y-axis.
   Draw the image of this flag after each of these
   transformations.

   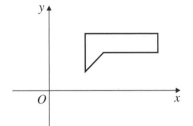

   (a) R followed by X

   (b) X followed by Y

   (c) R followed by R

   Describe fully the single transformation that is equivalent to
   the combined transformations (a), then (b) and then (c).

2. Reflect triangle S in the line $y = x$ to obtain triangle S'.
   Rotate triangle S' about the origin through 90°
   anticlockwise to obtain triangle S''.
   Show the position of S'' on a grid.

   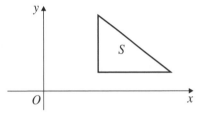

3. Rotate shape A through 180° about O to obtain
   shape A'. Rotate A' through 180° about (5, 2) to
   obtain A''. Describe in full the single transformation
   which maps A onto A''.

   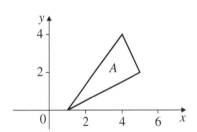

6.6 Inverse transformations

The inverse of a transformation takes the image back to its
original position.

- The inverse of translation $\begin{pmatrix} a \\ b \end{pmatrix}$ is the translation $\begin{pmatrix} -a \\ -b \end{pmatrix}$.

- The inverse of a reflection in a line is a reflection in the same
  line; that is, a reflection is **self-inverse**.

- The inverse of a rotation about a point C through an angle θ
  anticlockwise, is a rotation about the same point C through
  an angle θ clockwise.

- The inverse of an enlargement, centre C, scale factor k, is an
  enlargement, centre C, scale factor $\dfrac{1}{k}$.

Exercise 6F

State the inverse of each of these transformations.

1. A translation of $\begin{pmatrix} 5 \\ 3 \end{pmatrix}$.

2. A translation of $\begin{pmatrix} 2 \\ -4 \end{pmatrix}$.

3. A reflection in the y-axis.

4. A reflection in the line $y = x$.

5. A reflection in the line $2y + x = 7$.

6. A rotation about O through 90° anticlockwise.

7. A rotation about O through 120° anticlockwise.

8. A rotation about O through 150° anticlockwise.

9. A translation of $\begin{pmatrix} 5 \\ 3 \end{pmatrix}$ followed by a reflection in the x-axis.

10. A translation of $\begin{pmatrix} 3 \\ -2 \end{pmatrix}$ followed by a rotation through 90° anticlockwise about (1, 2).

6.7 Tessellation

Certain shapes will slot together on a plane surface without leaving any gaps, such as square tiles completely covering a wall.
Such a pattern is called a **tessellation**.

Many different shapes tessellate:

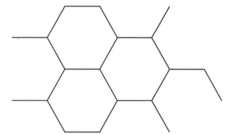

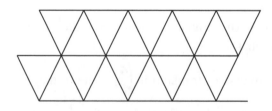

Regular hexagons always tessellate.   **All triangles** tessellate.

Sometimes two shapes are used together to form a tessellation.

In this tessellation, the two shapes are a square and a regular octagon.

However, most shapes do not tessellate.

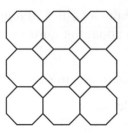

Note:
This pattern is often used in floor tiles.

Example

Does a regular pentagon tessellate?
The interior angle of a pentagon
is 108° (see Unit AS1).

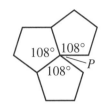

The interior angles at *P* add up
to 108° + 108° + 108° = 324°.

This leaves a gap of 360° − 324° = 36°,
which is unable to be filled with a pentagon.

∴ A regular pentagon does not tessellate.

Exercise 6G

1. Draw a tessellation based upon each of these shapes.

(a) 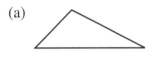   (b) 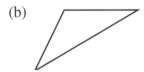   (c)

(d)    (e)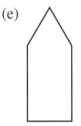

2. To enable a tessellation to be formed using a regular
   octagon, you need an additional shape which is a square.
   If the octagon has side 6 cm, what is the area of each square
   required?

3. To enable a tessellation to be formed using
   this shape, you need an additional shape.
   With dimensions as shown:
   (a) What additional shape is required?
   (b) What is the area of this additional shape?

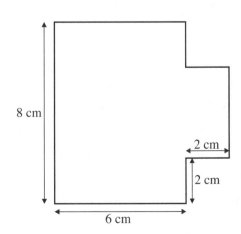

MODULE 5

6.8 2D representation of 3D objects

The diagram shows a cuboid.
The edges that you can see are shown as solid lines, and the
edges that you cannot see are shown as dotted lines.

When representing 3D shapes by 2D diagrams, the
following guidelines apply:

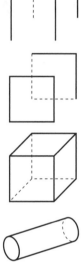

- Vertical lines are always drawn vertically
  up the page.

- Choose a horizontal to be drawn in
  the *x* direction.

- Then you add a second horizontal
  direction at an angle of about 30°
  to the *x* direction.

When drawing cylinders, use an oval for each
of the circular ends.

Isometric paper

Isometric paper uses a tessellation of equilateral triangles.
The lines on isometric paper are in three directions.
The lines going from the top to the bottom of the page
represent the vertical direction, and the other two
directions represent horizontal directions.
The following example uses isometric paper.

Example

Draw a triangular prism which has length 8 cm
and a cross-section which is an isosceles triangle of
base 4 cm and height 5 cm.

Draw the base 4 cm in one horizontal direction.

Draw the height of 5 cm above the midpoint of
this side.

Draw the length 8 cm in the other horizontal
direction.

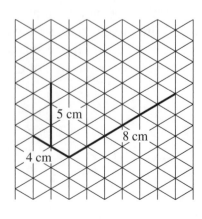

These three lengths form the basis for the complete shape.

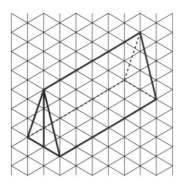

Exercise 6H

Draw a two-dimensional representation of each of these solids.

1. A cube of side 4 units.

2. A cuboid with sides 6, 3 and 5 units.

3. A triangular prism; each triangular end is an equilateral triangle of side 6 units and the length of the prism is 8 units.

4. A triangular prism; each triangular end is an isosceles triangle of side 5, 5 and 8 units and the length of the prism is 7 units.

5. A triangular prism; each triangular end is a triangle with sides 2·5, 6 and 6·5 units. The length of the prism is 9 units.

Summary

1. You can translate a shape

Check out AS6

1. (a) Translate this shape through $\begin{pmatrix} 4 \\ 2 \end{pmatrix}$.

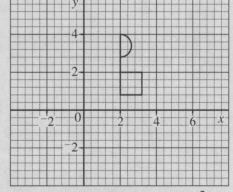

The point (4, 7) is translated by $\begin{pmatrix} 3 \\ -6 \end{pmatrix}$.

What is the image point?

MODULE 5

2. You can reflect a shape

2. Reflect the shape S

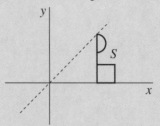

(a) in the x-axis
(b) in the dotted line.

3. You can rotate a shape

3. (a) Rotate the shape S through 90°
anticlockwise about O.

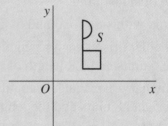

(b) Rotate the shape T through 120°
anticlockwise about P.

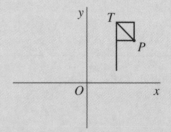

4. You can enlarge a shape

4. Enlarge the shape S by
(a) a scale factor 2
(b) a scale factor $\frac{1}{2}$
about centre of rotation P.

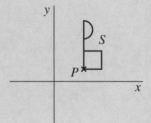

5. You can find the inverse of a transformation

5. Give the inverse of the transformations
  (a) a translation through $\begin{pmatrix} 5 \\ -3 \end{pmatrix}$
  (b) a reflection in the line $y + 2x = 6$
  (c) a rotation about point P through 60° in an anticlockwise sense.

6. You can use isometric paper

6. Draw a triangular prism of length 8 cm. The triangular cross-section is an isosceles triangle with base 4 cm and height 5 cm.

Revision exercise AS6

1. The diagram shows three positions of a shape.

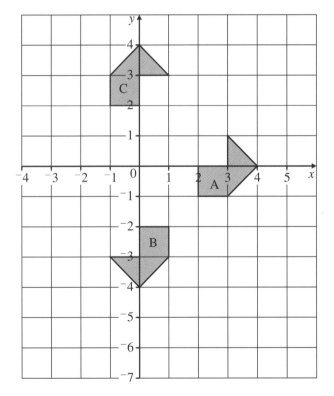

(a) Describe fully the single transformation which takes A onto B.

(b) Describe fully the single transformation which takes B onto C.

(c) A is mapped onto D by a translation $\begin{pmatrix} -2 \\ 3 \end{pmatrix}$.

  Draw the position of D on a copy of the diagram.   [SEG]

2. The diagram shows the positions of two triangles, *P* and *Q*.

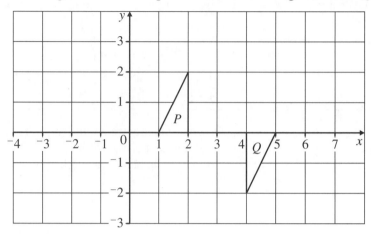

(a) Describe fully the single transformation which takes *P* onto *Q*.

(b) Triangle *P* is reflected in the *x*-axis.
On a copy of the diagram, draw the new position of *P*. Label it *R*.

(c) Describe fully the single transformation which takes *R* onto *Q*.   [SEG]

3. The diagram shows the position of a shape labelled *R*.

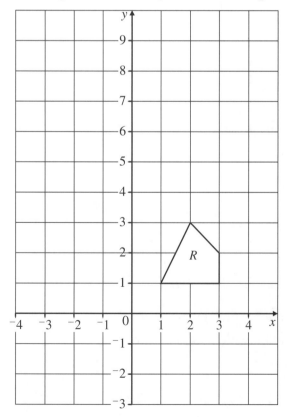

(a) *R* is mapped onto *S* by a reflection in the *y*-axis.
On a copy of the diagram, draw and label *S*.

(b) *S* is mapped onto *T* by a reflection in the line $y = 4$.
Draw and label *T*.

(c) Describe fully the single transformation which maps *T*
onto *R*. [SEG]

4. (a) Which of these regular polygons can be used to form a
regular tessellation? Copy and complete the table for
each polygon by putting a tick in the correct box.

Regular polygons	Will tessellate	Will not tessellate
Equilateral triangle	✓	
Square		
Pentagon		
Hexagon		
Octagon		

(b) The diagram shows a regular octagon *ABCDEFGH*.

(i) Some of the vertices have been joined to form
triangles.
Name the triangle which is congruent to
triangle *CBF*.

(ii) Calculate the size of angle *AHG*. [SEG]

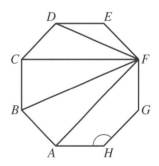

5.

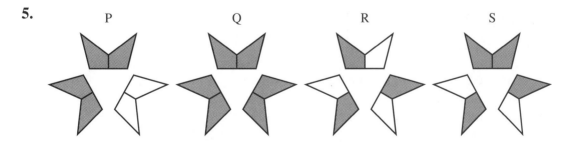

(a) Which of these diagrams has only one line of symmetry?

(b) Which of these diagrams has rotational symmetry but
no lines of symmetry? [SEG]

MODULE 5

6. Shade two more squares on the diagram so that the final pattern has line symmetry **and** rotational symmetry.

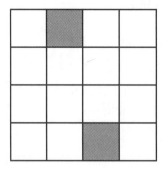

7. The diagram shows three triangles *P*, *Q* and *R*.

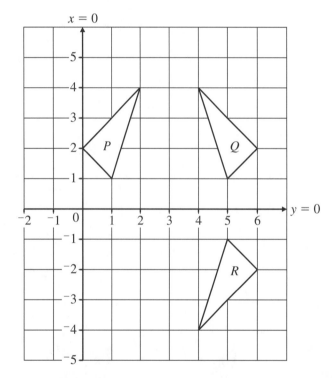

(a) Describe fully the single transformation which takes *P* onto *Q*.

(b) Describe fully the single transformation which takes *P* onto *R*. [SEG]

AS7 SHAPE 4

When you are wrapping presents, it helps to know about volume and surface area.

This unit will show you how to:

- Calculate perimeter and area
- Calculate volume and surface area
- Classify formulae by their dimensions
- Find areas and volumes of similar shapes

Before you start:

You should know how to ...	Check in AS7
1. Identify similar triangles Look back to page 338 to remind yourself how to do this.	**1.** Show that triangles ABC and PQR are similar.

Look back to page 338 to remind yourself how to do this.

1. Show that triangles ABC and PQR are similar.

B   *Q*

4 cm   6·6 cm   6 cm   9·9 cm

A   *P*

6 cm   *C*   9 cm   *R*

2. Substitute in formulae

For example, find the value of

$S = 4\pi r^2$ when $r = 2\cdot5$

$S = 4 \times \pi \times 2\cdot5^2$

$\quad = 78\cdot5$

2. (a) Without using a calculator, find the value of A when $A = \frac{1}{2}(a + b)h$ given that $a = 3$, $b = 7\cdot2$ and $h = 6$.

    (b) Using a calculator, find V when $V = \frac{4}{3}\pi r^3$ given that $r = 2\cdot6$.

7.1 Perimeter of a polygon

● The perimeter of a polygon is the total length of the sides.

Example

Find the perimeter of this shape.

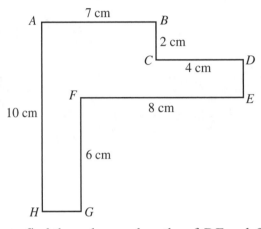

First you have to find the unknown lengths of *DE* and *GH*.

As the shape is regular, $AH = BC + DE + FG$

$$10 = 2 + DE + 6$$

$$\therefore DE = 2 \text{ cm}$$

Similarly, $GH = AB + CD - EF$

$$= 7 + 4 - 8 = 3 \text{ cm}$$

Perimeter $= AB + BC + CD + DE + EF + FG + GH + HA$

$$= 42 \text{ cm}$$

Exercise 7A

1. Find the perimeter of each of these shapes.

(a)

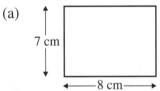

(b)

(c)

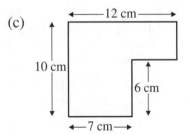

(d)

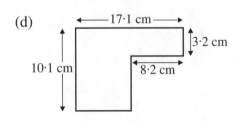

(e)

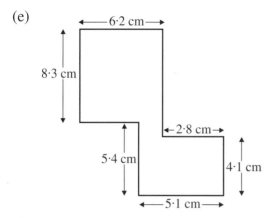

(f)

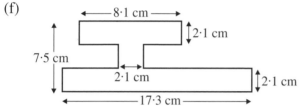

2. A photograph is in a rectangular surround with exterior dimensions 20 cm by 14 cm.
The surround is 2 cm wide. The edges of the surround are covered in gold braid.
What length of gold braid is required?

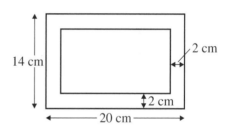

7.2 Area

Area is a measure of the **surface** of a shape.
It is measured in standard sized squares.

This square has an area of 1 mm²

 actual size

It is about the size of a sugar granule.

This square has an area of 1 cm²

actual size

It is smaller than a stamp.

This square has an area of 1 m²

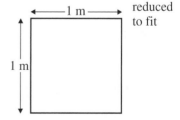 reduced to fit

It is about half the size of a door.

You can find the area of many shapes by using various formulae.

Area of a quadrilateral

The formulae for the areas of quadrilaterals that you need to know are:

Area of a square

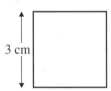

Area = length × length
or $A = l^2$

Area of a rectangle

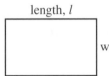

Area = length × width
or $A = lw$

Area of a parallelogram

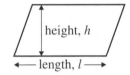

Area = length × height
or $A = lh$

Note:
In the formula for a parallelogram, the **vertical** height is used.

Example 1

Find the area of each of these shapes.

(a)

(b)

(a) The shape is a square.
   $A = l^2 = 3\,\text{cm} \times 3\,\text{cm}$
   $\quad\quad = 9\,\text{cm}^2$

(b) The shape is a parallelogram, so $A = lh$
   Change 35 mm to cm so that the units will mach up.
   $35\,\text{mm} = 35 \div 10\,\text{cm} = 3.5\,\text{cm}$
   $A = 2\,\text{cm} \times 3.5\,\text{cm}$
   $\quad\quad = 7\,\text{cm}$

Area of a triangle

A triangle has half the area of the surrounding rectangle.

Area of triangle $= \frac{1}{2} \times$ area of rectangle

Area of triangle $= \frac{1}{2}$ base × perpendicular height

Algebraically you can write this as:

Area of triangle $= \frac{1}{2}bh$

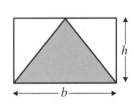

Example 2

Find the area of each of these triangles.

(a) triangle *ABC* (b) triangle *DEF* (c) triangle *PQR*

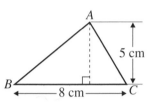 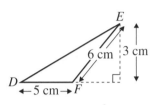 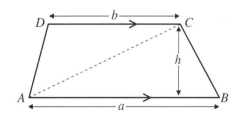

(a) Area of triangle *ABC*
$= \frac{1}{2}bh$
$= \frac{1}{2} \times 5 \times 8 = 20 \text{ cm}^2$

(b) Area of triangle *DEF*
$= \frac{1}{2}bh$
$= \frac{1}{2} \times 5 \times 3 = 7\cdot5 \text{ cm}^2$

(c) Area of triangle *PQR*
$= \frac{1}{2}bh$
PQ is the base, and 7 cm is the perpendicular height.
Area of triangle *PQR*
$= \frac{1}{2} \times 5 \times 7 = 17\cdot5 \text{ cm}^2$

Example 3

Find the base of a triangle which has perpendicular height
8·3 cm and an area of 17·43 cm².

Area of triangle $= \frac{1}{2}bh$

$\therefore 2 \times \text{Area} \quad = bh$

$b \qquad\qquad = \dfrac{2A}{h}$

$\therefore \text{Base} \qquad = \dfrac{2 \times 17\cdot43}{8\cdot3} = 4\cdot2 \text{ cm}$

Area of a trapezium

A trapezium is made up of simpler shapes.
You can use this fact to find the formula for the area of a trapezium.

Area of trapezium $= \frac{1}{2}$ sum of parallel sides $\times$ perpendicular distance between them

Proof

Trapezium *ABCD* can be split into two triangles.

Area of triangle $ABC = \frac{1}{2}ah$

Area of triangle $ACD = \frac{1}{2}bh$

Area of trapezium $= \frac{1}{2}ah + \frac{1}{2}bh$

$\qquad\qquad\qquad = \frac{1}{2}(a + b)h$

MODULE 5

Example 4

Find the area of the trapezium *EFGH*.

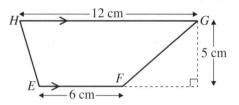

Area of trapezium $= \frac{1}{2}(a + b)h$
$$= \frac{1}{2}(6 + 12) \times 5$$
$$= \frac{1}{2} \times 18 \times 5 = 45 \text{ cm}^2$$

Example 5

Find the perpendicular height of this trapezium, which has an area of 8·2 cm².

$$\text{Area} = \frac{1}{2}(a + b)h$$
$$\therefore 2 \times \text{area} = (a + b)h$$
$$h = \frac{2 \times \text{area}}{(a + b)}$$
$$h = \frac{2 \times 8\cdot2}{3\cdot1 + 4\cdot9} = \frac{2 \times 8\cdot2}{8} = 2\cdot05 \text{ cm}$$

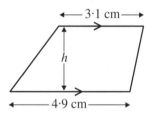

Exercise 7B

1. Find the area of each of these rectangles.

(a)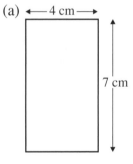

(b)

(c)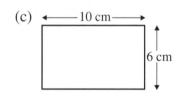

2. Find the length of a rectangle which has
   (a) width 5 cm and area 45 cm²
   (b) width 3 cm and area 25·5 cm²
   (c) width 4 cm and area 31 cm²
   (d) width 6·2 cm and area 31·3 cm².

3. Find the area of each of these parallelograms.

(a)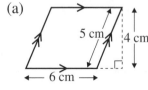

(b)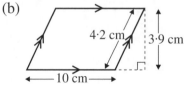

(c)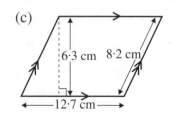

4. Find the area of a square of side

    (a) 7 cm   (b) 0·2 cm   (c) 2·1 cm

5. Find the length of a side of a square which has area

    (a) 36 cm²   (b) 225 cm²   (c) 34·2 cm²

6. Find the area of each of these shapes.

    (a) 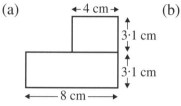   (b) 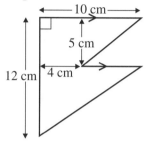   (c)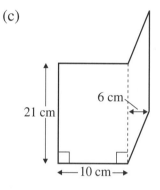

7. Find the area of a triangle with

    (a) base 6 cm and perpendicular height 4 cm

    (b) base 8 cm and perpendicular height 5 cm

    (c) base 10 cm and perpendicular height 7·4 cm

    (d) base 0·6 cm and perpendicular height 0·15 cm.

8. Find the area of each of these triangles.

    (a) 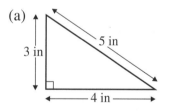   (b)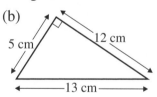

    (c) 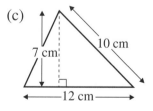   (d)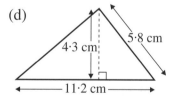

    (e)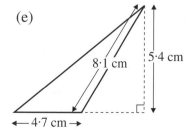

9. Find the area of each of these trapezia.

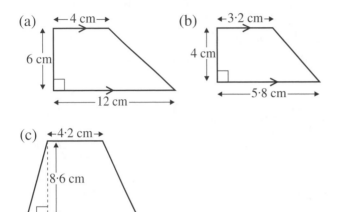

(a) ←4 cm→ 6 cm ←12 cm—

(b) ←3·2 cm→ 4 cm ←5·8 cm—

(c) ←4·2 cm→ 8·6 cm —17·3 cm—

10. (a) Find the height of a triangle which has area 28 cm² and base 7 cm.

   (b) Find the base of a triangle which has area 32 cm² and height 10 cm.

   (c) Find the height of a triangle which has area 41·1 cm² and base 6·2 cm.

   (d) Find the base of a triangle which has area 34·7 cm² and height 11·7 cm.

11. Calculate the area of each of these shapes, giving your answers to 1 decimal place.

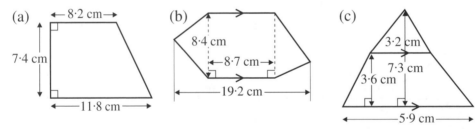

(a) ←8·2 cm→ 7·4 cm —11·8 cm—

(b) 8·4 cm ←8·7 cm→ —19·2 cm—

(c) 3·2 cm 7·3 cm 3·6 cm —5·9 cm—

7.3 Circles

The **circumference** of a circle is the name given to its perimeter.
If you wound a piece of string around the edge of a circle, you would find that its length is just over 3 times the diameter.
The exact multiple is π.

diameter

- For a circle of radius r, the circumference is $2\pi r$, or πd, where d is the diameter of the circle.

By counting squares to work out the area of a circle of radius 1 cm, you will find that its area is just over 3 cm². The exact value of this area is π cm².

For a circle of radius, r cm, the area, A cm², is given by $A = \pi r^2$

Example 1

Find the circumference and area of a circle diameter 7·2 cm.

$$\begin{aligned} \text{Circumference} &= \pi \times d \\ &= \pi \times 7 \cdot 2 \\ &= 22 \cdot 6 \text{ cm} \end{aligned}$$

$$\begin{aligned} \text{Radius} &= \tfrac{1}{2} \times \text{diameter} \\ &= \tfrac{1}{2} \times 7 \cdot 2 \\ &= 3 \cdot 6 \text{ cm} \end{aligned}$$

$$\begin{aligned} \text{Area} &= \pi \times 3 \cdot 6^2 \\ &= 44 \cdot 5 \text{ cm}^2 \end{aligned}$$

Example 2

The area of a circle is 70 cm². Calculate its radius.

Using $A = \pi r^2$,
$$\begin{aligned} r &= \sqrt{\frac{A}{\pi}} \\ &= \sqrt{\frac{70}{\pi}} \\ &= \sqrt{22 \cdot 28 \dots} \\ &= 4 \cdot 72 \text{ cm} \end{aligned}$$

MODULE 5

Exercise 7C

Use the π button on your calculator or take π to be 3·14.

1. Calculate the circumference of a circle which has
   (a) diameter 8·2 cm
   (b) diameter 12·7 cm
   (c) radius 3·2 cm
   (d) radius 6·8 cm

2. The radius of a £1 coin is 11·5 cm.
   What is the length of its circumference?
   Give your answer to 3 significant figures.

3. Find the radius of a circle which has circumference
   (a) 28·4 cm
   (b) 17·2 cm
   (c) 8·64 cm
   (d) 24·3 cm

4. Find the areas of the circles in question 1.

5. Calculate the radius of a circle which has area
   (a) 36π cm^2
   (b) 169π cm^2
   (c) 27·4 cm^2
   (d) 18·2 in^2

6. A washer has outside diameter 2·8 cm and the radius of the inside hole is 2·4 cm. Find the area of the washer.

7.4 Composite areas

To find more complicated areas, split the shapes into parts so that you can find the area of each part.

Example

A running track is shown.

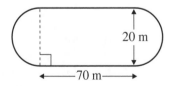

Each straight is of length 70 m and the two curved ends are semicircles of diameter 20 m.

Find (a) the distance around the track
     (b) the area enclosed by the track.

(a) The perimeter of each semicircle is $\frac{1}{2} \times 2\pi r = 10\pi$ metres.

∴ Distance around the running track is

$70 + 70 + 10\pi + 10\pi$ metres

$= 140 + 20\pi$ metres

$= 203$ metres

(b) Area enclosed by the track $= 2 \times$ area of semicircle $+$ area of rectangle

Area of each semicircle is $\frac{1}{2}\pi r^2 = \frac{1}{2}\pi \times 10^2$

$\qquad\qquad\qquad\qquad = 50\pi\,\text{m}^2$

Area of the rectangle $= lw \quad = 20 \times 70\,\text{m}^2 = 1400\,\text{m}^2$

∴ Area enclosed by the track $\quad = (2 \times 50\pi) + 1400\,\text{m}^2$

$\qquad\qquad\qquad\qquad\qquad = 1710\,\text{m}^2$

Exercise 7D

Find the area of each of these shapes.

1.

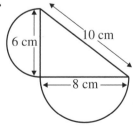

6 cm

11 cm

2.

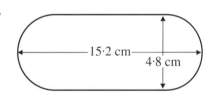

15·2 cm

4·8 cm

3.

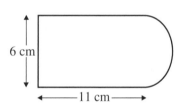

6·8 cm

11·2 cm

4.

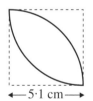

5·1 cm

5.

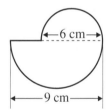

6 cm

9 cm

6.

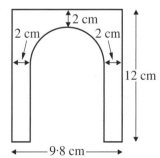

2 cm

2 cm   2 cm

12 cm

9·8 cm

7.

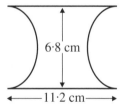

6 cm

10 cm

8 cm

8.

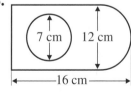

7 cm   12 cm

16 cm

MODULE 5

7.5 Volume

Volume is a measure of the space taken up by a solid shape.

This cube has a volume of 1 cubic millimetre, or 1 mm³.

This cube has a volume of 1 cubic centimetre, or 1 cm³.

This cube has a volume of 1 cubic metre, or 1 m³.

1 m ←1 m→ 1 m

reduced to fit

It is about the size of a grain of sand

It is about the size of a sugar cube

It is about the size of a washing machine.

Volume is measured in standard size cubes.

You can find the volume of many 3D shapes by using formulae.

Volume of a cuboid

- The volume of a cuboid is length × width × height

  $V = lwh$

Example 1

Find the volume of a cuboid with dimensions 4·1 cm, 5·2 cm and 1·9 cm.

$V = lwh$
$\quad = 4\cdot1 \times 5\cdot2 \times 1\cdot9$
$\quad = 40\cdot5 \text{ cm}^3$

Volume of a cube

In a cube, length = width = height.

- The volume of a cube is length cubed

  $V = l^3$

Example 2

Find the volume of a cube of side 3·7 cm.

$V = l^3$
$\quad = 3\cdot7^3$
$\quad = 50\cdot7 \text{ cm}^3$

Volume of a prism

A **prism** is a solid with a constant cross-section.
You name a prism by its cross-section,
for example triangular, hexagonal or circular.

- Volume of a prism = area of one end × length

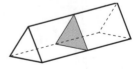

A **cylinder** is a circular prism.

Its volume is $\pi r^2 \times h$

Area × length

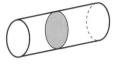

Example 3

The area of one end of a triangular prism is 15 cm² and its length
is 20 cm.
Find its volume.

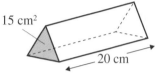

Volume of prism = area of one end × length
$$= 15 \times 20$$
$$= 300 \text{ cm}^3$$

15 cm²

20 cm

Example 4

Find the volume of a cylinder of diameter 8·4 cm and
length 6·1 cm.

Volume $= \pi r^2 l$
$$= \pi \times 4{\cdot}2^2 \times 6{\cdot}1$$
$$= 338 \text{ cm}^3$$

Remember:
Radius $= \frac{1}{2}$ diameter

Exercise 7E

1. Find the volume of each of these cuboids.
    (a) Length 8 cm, width 2 cm and height 6 cm.
    (b) Length 5 cm, width 4 cm and height 6·2 cm.
    (c) Length 12 cm, width 7 cm and height 10 cm.
    (d) Length 8·4 cm, width 2·6 cm and height 6·3 cm.
    (e) Length 15·2 in, width 7·3 in and height 8·2 in.

2. The volume of a cuboid is 80 cm³. Its base area is 16 cm².
    What is its height?

3. Calculate the volume of a cube of side
    (a) 4 cm   (b) 6 cm   (d) 8·3 cm   (d) 9·1 cm

4. Find the side of a cube which has volume
    (a) 125 cm³   (b) 37·4 cm³   (c) 17·26 cm³

5. A water tank, in the shape of a cuboid, has a base 2 m by
    3 m and is 1·8 m high.
    (a) Calculate is volume.
    (b) Paula takes 3·6 m³ of water out of the tank.
         By how much does the level of the water in the tank drop?

MODULE 5

6. A triangular prism is 18 cm in length. Its cross-section is a triangle of sides 5 cm, 5 cm and 8 cm.
   Find the volume of the prism.

7. A triangular prism is 11 cm in length. Its cross-section is a triangle of sides 5 cm, 12 cm and 13 cm.
   Find the volume of the prism.

8. A prism has a cross-section as shown. The prism is 22·1 cm in length. Calculate its volume.

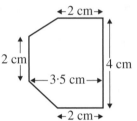

9. A conservatory is 6 m in length. Its cross-section is shown. Find its volume.

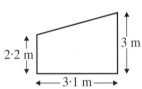

10. A shed is 3 m in length with cross-section as shown. Find the volume of the shed.

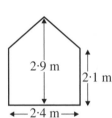

7.6 Surface area

The surface area of a 3D shape is the sum of the areas of its faces.

Surface area of a cuboid

Here is a cuboid …   … open it up …   …to make a net

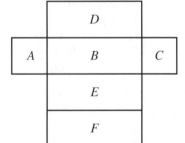

● Find the area of each face, *A* to *F*.

They are all rectangles, so it is just length × width.

● Add together the areas.

Total surface area = area *A* + area *B* + area *C* + area *D* + area *E* + area *F*.

Surface area of a prism

Here is a prism …   … open it up …   …to make a net

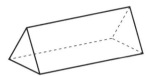   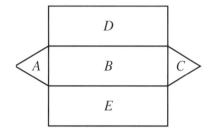

- Find the area of each face, A to E.

    B, D and E are rectangles, so this is just length × width.
    A and C are triangles, so the area is $\frac{1}{2}$(base × height).

- Add together the areas.

    Total surface area = area A + area B + area C + area D + area E.

Example

An open cylinder is 36 cm in length with a radius of 2·8 cm.
Find its total surface area

The cylinder is open, so it only has **one** end.

$$\begin{aligned}
\text{Curved surface area} &= 2\pi r l \\
&= 2\pi \times 2\cdot8 \times 3\cdot6 \\
&= 633\cdot3 \text{ cm}^2
\end{aligned}$$

$$\begin{aligned}
\text{Area of one end} &= \pi r^2 \\
&= \pi \times 2\cdot8^2 \\
&= 24\cdot63 \text{ cm}^2
\end{aligned}$$

$$\begin{aligned}
\text{Total surface area} &= 633\cdot3 + 24\cdot63 \\
&= 657\cdot93 \\
&= 658 \text{ cm}^2 \text{ (to 3 sig. figs.)}
\end{aligned}$$

Exercise 7F

1. Find the surface area of a closed cuboid of dimensions
    (a) length 8 cm, width 6 cm, height 5 cm
    (b) length 5 cm, width 7 cm, height 9 cm
    (c) length 6 cm, width 8 cm, height 4 cm
    (d) length 8·9 cm, width 4·1 cm, height 2·8 cm
    (e) length 11·7 cm, width 3·8 cm, height 4·1 cm.

2. The cross-section of each end of an unsharpened
   pencil is a hexagon, each side of which is 3 mm.
   The length of the pencil is 16 cm.
   Find the surface area of the pencil.

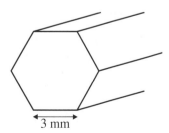

MODULE 5

3. A garden cloche is 5 m in length and has a cross-section with a semicircular top as shown. Find the surface area of the cloche.

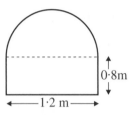

4. A metal pipe is 12 m in length. It has an inner diameter of 18 cm and an outer diameter of 21 cm.
Find (a) the cross-section of the pipe
        (b) the volume of metal in the pipe.

5. Find (a) the curved surface area, and
        (b) the volume of a cylinder of length 10 cm and radius
    (i)   3 cm   (ii) 5 cm   (iii) 7·2 cm   (iv) 0·03 cm

6. A closed cylindrical can is 11 cm high and has a radius of 4 cm. Find the surface area of the can.

7. A cylinder, which has height 9 cm, has a volume of 36π cm^3. Find its radius.

8. The volume of a closed cylinder of radius 4·1 cm is 70·4 cm^3. Find the height of the cylinder.

7.7 Dimensions in formulae

A point has no dimension.

Length has one dimension.

Area has two dimensions.

Volume has three dimensions.

•

————

Area is
a length × a length

Volume is
a length × a length
× a length

The subject of a formula can have any number of dimensions.

For example, $2\pi rh$ is the curved surface area of a cylinder.

In the formula $2\pi rh$, 2 and π are numbers and therefore have no
        dimensions,
        r and h are lengths and have one dimension
        each.

∴ $2\pi rh$ has dimension 2, and this represents an area.

Note:

You cannot add terms in a different number of dimensions.

Example

Which of the following could be the formula for a volume?

$$2\pi r^2, \ \pi r^2, \ \pi r^2 l, \ 2\pi rh, \ \pi(r^2 + l^2)h$$

For the formula to be a volume, it must have dimension 3.

$2\pi r^2$ only has two dimensions, r and r, so it is not a volume.

πr^2 has three dimensions, r, r and r, so it could be a volume.

Similarly, $\pi r^2 l$ has dimension 3.

$2\pi rh$ has dimension two.

$\pi(r^2 + l^2)h$ has dimension 3.

∴ The possible formulae for a volume are: πr^3, $\pi r^3 l$ and $\pi(r^2 + l^2)h$.

> **Note:**
> The total dimension is the number of lengths that are **multiplied**, not added.

Exercise 7G

State, with a reason, whether these could represent the formula for a length, an area, a volume, or none of these.

1. $3\pi r$

2. $2r + 4\pi$

3. $\pi r^2 h$

4. $\pi r^3 + 7r^2 h$

5. $3\pi^2 + 2r^2$

6. $4r^2 + 7rh + h$

7. $\pi r(h + r) + 2r^2$

8. $4\pi r^2 + \frac{2}{3}r^3$

9. $r^2 + h^2 + 3rh$

10. $3r + 7r^2$

MODULE 5

7.8 Areas of similar shapes

When a shape is enlarged, **all** its lengths are enlarged in the same ratio. A square of side 2 cm is enlarged by a scale factor of 3, and by a scale factor of 6.

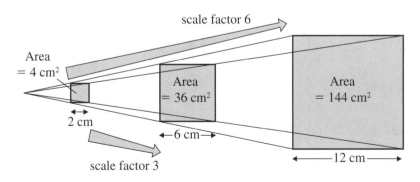

- Area of the new shape = area of the old shape
    × the **square** of the scale factor of the enlargement

- The scale factor of the enlargement =
    a length in the new shape divided by the corresponding length in the original shape

Example 1

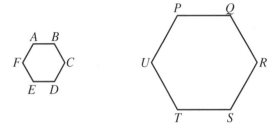

The area of the hexagon *ABCDEF* is 7·4 cm².
The shape *PQRSTU* is obtained by enlarging *ABCDEF*
by a scale factor of 2·5.
Find the area of *PQRSTU*.

Area of the new shape = area of the old shape
    × the square of the scale of enlargement

∴ Area of *PQRSTU* = Area of *ABCDEF* × (scale factor)²
$$= 7{\cdot}4 \times 2{\cdot}5^2$$
$$= 46{\cdot}25 \text{ cm}^2$$

Example 2

The triangles *ABC* and *PQR* are similar.

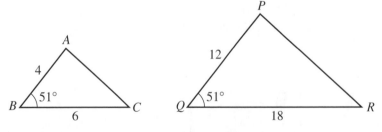

The area of triangle *ABC* is 7·88 cm².
Find the area of triangle *PQR*.

Considering corresponding sides in the two diagrams:

Scale factor of enlargement $= \dfrac{8{\cdot}5}{3{\cdot}4}$

Area of triangle PQR = area of $ABC \times$ (scale factor)^2

$$= \left(\frac{8\cdot5}{3\cdot4}\right)^2 \times 7\cdot88$$

$$= 49\cdot2 \text{ cm}^2$$

- In similar figures, the ratio of the larger area to the smaller area is

  $L^2 : l^2$ where L and l are corresponding lengths in the two figures.

Exercise 7H

1. Triangles ABC and PQR are similar. AB and PQ are corresponding sides, where $AB = 4$ cm and $PQ = 6$cm. The area of triangle ABC is 18 cm^2. Find the area of triangle PQR.

2. Triangles RST and DEF are similar.

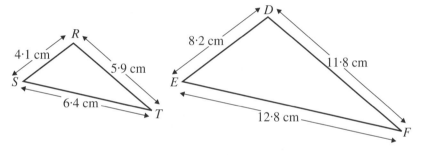

   The area of triangle RST is 27·8 cm^2. Find the area of triangle DEF.

3. Triangle ABC is enlarged by scale factor 3. The area of triangle ABC is 6 cm^2. Find the area of the new triangle.

4. Triangle PQR is enlarged by scale factor 4. The area of triangle PQR is 5·1 cm^2. Find the area of the new triangle.

5. The area of a circle is 37 cm^2. After an enlargement, its area is 148 cm^2. What is the scale factor of the enlargement?

6. The area of a circle is 2 cm^2. After an enlargement, its area is 338 cm^2. What is the scale factor of the enlargement?

7. The area of a quadrilateral $PQRS$ is 31 cm^2. The quadrilateral is enlarged by a scale factor of 2·8. Find the new area of the quadrilateral.

8. The area of a pentagon $PQRST$ is 174 cm^2. The pentagon is enlarged by a scale factor of $\frac{1}{4}$. Find the new area of the pentagon.

MODULE 5

9. The area of a triangle is 37·4 cm². The triangle is enlarged and the new area of the triangle is 284 cm².
Find the scale factor of the enlargement.

10. The area of a triangle is 748 cm². The triangle is enlarged and the new area of the triangle is 32·6 cm².
Find the scale factor of the enlargement.

11. The area of a quadrilateral is 591 cm². The quadrilateral is enlarged and the new area of the quadrilateral is 62·1 cm².
Find the scale factor of the enlargement.

7.9 Volumes of similar solids

A cube of side 3 cm is enlarged by a scale factor of 2 and by a scale factor of 3.

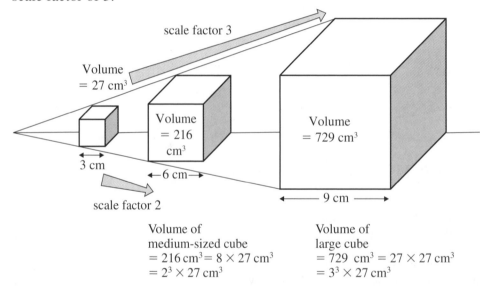

Volume of
medium-sized cube
= 216 cm³ = 8 × 27 cm³
= 2³ × 27 cm³

Volume of
large cube
= 729 cm³ = 27 × 27 cm³
= 3³ × 27 cm³

● Volume of new body = volume of old body × scale factor **cubed**

Example

A Russian doll has a height of 3·2 inches and volume 6·2 cubic inches.
Another doll has a height of 7·2 inches. Find its volume.

New volume = old volume × cube of enlargement

$$= 6 \cdot 2 \times \left(\frac{7 \cdot 2}{3 \cdot 2}\right)^3 \text{ cubic inches}$$

Volume of new doll = 70·6 cubic inches

When you open up a Russian doll, you will find an identical but smaller doll inside, and so on.

As all the dolls are similar to each other, they are scale enlargements.

Exercise 7I

1. The volume of a bottle 8 cm high is 200 ml.
   Find the volume of a similar shape bottle 16 cm high.

2. The volume of a bottle 9 cm high is 250 ml.
   Find the volume of a similar shape bottle 27 cm high.

3. The volume of a sphere is 60 cm³.
   Find its volume after an enlargement of scale factor 4.

4. The volume of a sphere is 120 cm³.
   Find its volume after an enlargement of scale factor $\frac{1}{3}$.

5. Two cylinders are similar in shape. One is 15 cm in length
   and has a volume of 82 cm³. The other is 21 cm in length.
   Find its volume.

6. Two jugs are similar in shape. One jug, 20 cm high, holds
   0·6 litres. The other jug is 30 cm high.
   How much does the larger jug hold?

7. A statue of height 3·8 m weighs 3·4 tonnes. An exact copy
   of it with the same density is made with height 1 m.
   Find the weight of the copy.

8. Two buckets are similar in shape. Their volumes are 23 cm³
   and 395 cm³. What is the ratio of their heights?

9. Two buckets are similar in shape. Their volumes are
   476 cm³ and 37 cm³. What is the ratio of their heights?

Summary

1. You can find the perimeter of a polygon

Check out AS7

1. (a) Find the perimeter of this shape.

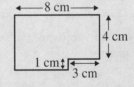

(b) Find the areas of these triangles.

(i)

(ii)

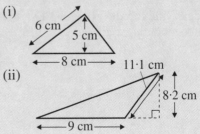

MODULE 5

2. You can find the area of various polygons, including trapeziums

2. (a) Find the area of this trapezium.

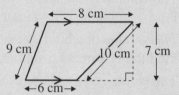

(b) The area of this trapezium is 48 cm. Find the length of the base.

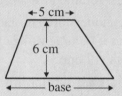

3. You can find the area of a circle

3. (a) A circle has diameter 24 cm. Find its area. Leave your answer as a multiple of π.

(b) The area of a circle is 74·8 cm². Find its radius.

4. You can find the area of a composite shape

4. Find the area of this shape. Give your answer to 3 significant figures.

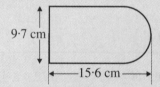

5. You can find the volume of various solids, including prisms

5. Find the volume of a triangular prism of length 100 cm which has a triangular cross-section with sides 13 cm, 13 cm and 10 cm.

6. You can find the surface area of various solids, including cylinders

6. (a) Find the curved surface area of a cylinder of radius 3·7 cm and length 7·9 cm.

(b) Find the surface area of a closed cylindrical can of length 8 cm and radius 7 cm. Leave your answer as a multiple of π.

MODULE 5

7. You can consider dimensions in a formula

7. Which of the following could be
(a) a volume
(b) an area?
$3\pi r, 4r^2 + rh, \pi r^3 + r^2h, \pi rh + 2h^3$

8. You can find areas of similar shapes

8. (a) These two triangles are similar. The area of the smaller triangle is 74 cm^2. Find the area of the larger triangle.

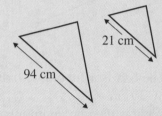

(b) The area of a quadrilateral is 84 cm^2. After an enlargement its area is 525 cm^2. Find the scale factor of the enlargement.

9. You can find the volumes of similar bodies

9. (a) The heights of two similar bottles are 4 cm and 11 cm. The volume of the smaller bottle is 35 cm^3. Find the volume of the larger bottle.
(b) The volume of a prism is 128 cm^3. After an enlargement its volume is 54 cm^3. Find the scale factor of the enlargement.

Revision exercise AS7

1. (a) Which of the following is a net of a cube?

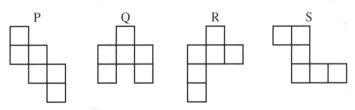

(b) A cube has edges of length 3 cm.
Calculate the surface area of the cube.

(c) Cubes of edge 3 cm are stored in a box, as shown.

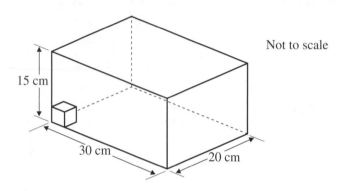

Not to scale

15 cm

30 cm

20 cm

The box is a cuboid with dimensions 15 cm by 20 cm by 30 cm.
What is the maximum number of cubes that can be stored inside the box?   [SEG]

2. The following formulae represent certain quantities connected with containers, where a, b and c are dimensions.

$$\pi a^2 b \quad 2\pi a(a + b) \quad 2a + 2b + 2c \quad \tfrac{1}{2}(a + b)c \quad \sqrt{a^2 + b^2}$$

(a) Which of these formulae represent area?
(b) Which of these formulae represent volume?   [SEG]

3. The diagram shows a prism.

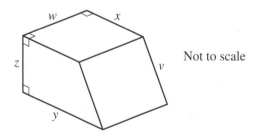

w x

z

v

y

Not to scale

The following formulae represent certain quantities connected with the prism.

$$wx + wy \quad \tfrac{1}{2}z(x + y)w \quad \frac{z(x + y)}{2} \quad 2(v + 2w + x + y + z)$$

(a) Which of these formulae represents length?

(b) Which of these formulae represents volume?   [SEG]

4. The diagram shows a bale of straw.
The bale is a cylinder with radius 70 cm and height 50 cm.

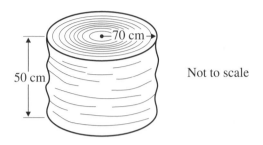

Not to scale

(a) Calculate the circumference of the bale.
Give your answer to an appropriate degree of
accuracy.

(b) Calculate the volume of the bale.
State your units. [SEG]

5. In the diagram *AB* is parallel to *CD*.

$AB = OC = 12$ cm. $OB = 10$ cm.

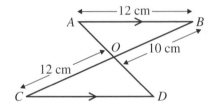

Not drawn
to scale

Use similar triangles to calculate the length of *CD*. [NEAB]

6. The volume of a cube is given by the formula $V = L^3$.

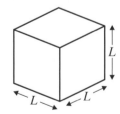

(a) A cube has volume 5832 cm³.
What is the length of each edge?

(b) The area of each face of a different cube is 625 cm².
What is the volume of this cube? [NEAB]

MODULE 5

7. The diagram shows a circular paddling pool with a vertical side.

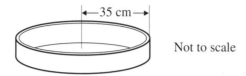

The radius of the pool is 35 cm.

(a) Calculate the circumference of the pool.
(b) The water in the pool is 8 cm deep.
Calculate the volume of the water in the pool.   [SEG]

8. The diagram shows a length of plastic guttering.

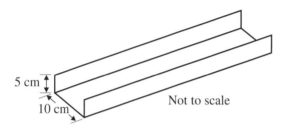

The cross-section of the guttering is a rectangle measuring 10 cm by 5 cm.

(a) Calculate the area of plastic needed to make a 200 cm length of guttering.
(b) Calculate the volume of water a 200 cm length of guttering could contain if the ends were sealed and it was full of water.
State your units.   [SEG]

9. The diagram shows the uniform cross-section of a rubbish skip.

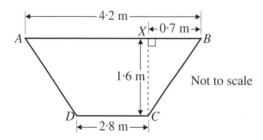

The cross-section is a trapezium.

$AB = 4\cdot2$ m, $CD = 2\cdot8$ m, $XB = 0\cdot7$ m and the height $CX = 1\cdot6$ m.

(a) Calculate the size of angle *XBC*.

A sketch of the rubbish skip is shown.

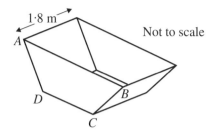

Not to scale

The skip is 1·8 m wide.

(b) Calculate the volume of the skip, stating your units.   [SEG]

10. The diagram shows triangle *PQR*.

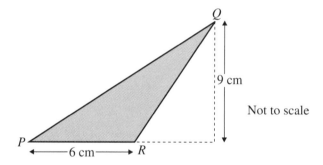

Not to scale

Calculate the area of triangle *PQR*.
State your units.   [SEG]

11. The diagram shows a cuboid which is just big enough to hold six tennis balls.

Not to scale

Each tennis ball has a diameter of 6·8 cm.
Calculate the volume of the cuboid.   [SEG]

MODULE 5

AS8 SHAPE 5

You can often measure lengths and distances using a knowledge of triangles.

This unit will show you how to:

- Use Pythagoras' theorem
- Use the trigonometric ratios
- Calculate angles of elevation and depression

Before you start:

You should know how to …	Check in AS8
1. Calculate bearings	**1.** If P is on a bearing of 143° from Q what is the bearing of Q from P?

For example, find the bearing of A from B.

B

70°

A

Draw a North line at B:

70°

B

180°

A

$70° + 180° = 250°$
The bearing of A from B is 250°.

8.1 Pythagoras' theorem

Pythagoras' theorem connects the lengths in a right-angled triangle.
In any right-angled triangle:

'the area of the square on the
hypotenuse is equal to the sum
of the squares on the other
two sides.'

The equation of Pythagoras'
theorem is $c^2 = a^2 + b^2$.

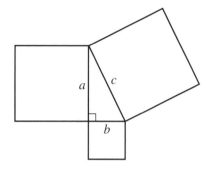

Note:
The hypotenuse of a
right-angled triangle is
the longest side. It is
always opposite the
right angle.

Example 1

Calculate the length a in this triangle.

By Pythagoras' theorem

$$a^2 = 6 \cdot 3^2 + 9 \cdot 5^2$$

$$a^2 = 39 \cdot 69 + 90 \cdot 25$$

$$a^2 = 129 \cdot 94$$

$$a = \sqrt{129 \cdot 94} = 11 \cdot 399\ 112 \ldots$$

$$a = 11 \cdot 4 \text{ cm (to 3 sig. figs.)}$$

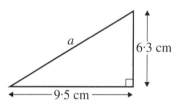

Hint:
Give your final answer
correct to 3 significant
figures.

Example 2

A ship sails due West from a port for 25 miles.
The ship then turns and sails due North for 30 miles.
How far is the ship from the port?

Draw a sketch diagram to represent the distances
from the port.
Let the distance from the port be d miles.
By Pythagoras' theorem

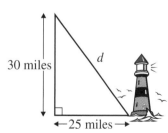

$$d^2 = 30^2 + 25^2$$

$$d^2 = 900 + 625$$

$$d^2 = 1525$$

$$d = \sqrt{1525} = 39 \cdot 1 \text{ miles (to 3 sig. figs.)}$$

The ship is 39·1 miles from the port.

MODULE 5

Exercise 8A

Where necessary give your final answer to 3 significant figures in this exercise.

1. Calculate the unknown lengths.

(a)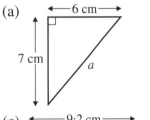

(b)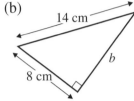

(c)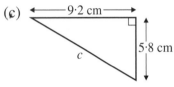

(d)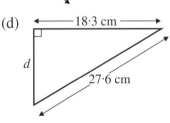

2. (a) Find the length *AB*.

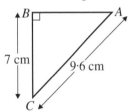

(b) Find the length *DF*.

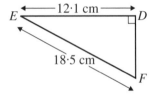

(c) Find the length *HJ*.

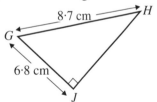

(d) Find the length *KM*.

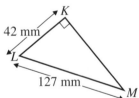

3. Find the length of a diagonal of a rectangle with a length of 12 cm and a width of 8 cm.

4. A square has a diagonal length 15 cm.
   What is the size of the side of the square?

5. Calculate the unknown lengths in these diagrams.

(a)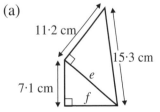

(b)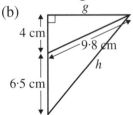

6. A ladder 5·6 m long rests against a vertical wall with the
foot of the ladder 3·2 m from the wall.
How far up the wall does the ladder reach?

7. An isosceles triangle has sides of 8 cm, 8 cm and 5 cm.
Calculate the perpendicular height of the triangle.

8. A thin piece of wire is 30 cm long.
The wire is bent into the shape shown.
Calculate the length from X to Y.

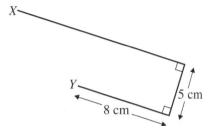

9. O is the centre of a circle of radius 10 cm.
The length of the tangent PT to the circle is 17 cm.
Calculate
(a) length OP
(b) length AP.

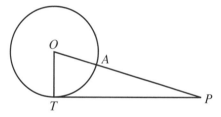

10. A pole 7·5 m high stands on level ground. The pole is
supported in a vertical position by two wires attached to its
top and to points on opposite sides of the foot of the pole, a
distance 16 m apart, as shown in the diagram.

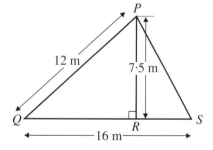

If one wire is 12 m long, find
(a) the distance from the anchor point of each support
to the foot of the pole
(b) the length of the other wire.

8.2 Trigonometry

The word trigonometry means triangle measurement, and you use it to calculate the sides and angles of triangles. Many real-life problems involve similar triangles.

Reminder:
There is more about similar triangles on page 338.

Example 1

On a particularly sunny day the length of the shadow of a tree was measured as 15 m.
The length of the shadow of a nearby pole, 1·4 m high, was 2 m.
Find the height of the tree.

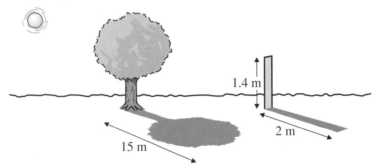

1.4 m

2 m

15 m

The two triangles have the same angles, and so they are similar. Furthermore, the ratio of corresponding sides is the same.

So $\dfrac{\text{height of the tree}}{\text{shadow of the tree}} = \dfrac{\text{length of the pole}}{\text{shadow of the pole}}$

$$\frac{\text{height of tree}}{15} = \frac{1\cdot4}{2}$$

$$\text{height of tree} = \frac{1\cdot4 \times 15}{2}$$

$$= 10\cdot5 \text{ metres}$$

Note:
In ancient times, mathematicians could find the height of a tall building by comparing the length of its shadow with that of a pole of known height.

- If the **angles** of two triangles are the same, they will have the same **proportions**.

Example 2

Draw two triangles labelled ABC with angle $A = 37°$ and angle $B = 90°$.
In each triangle, let side AB be:

(a) 6 cm   (b) 4 cm

Measure the length BC and calculate the ratio $\dfrac{BC}{AB}$ for all three triangles.

What do you notice?

(a)

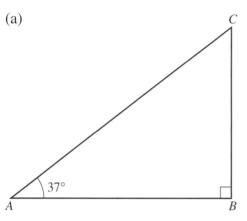

(b)

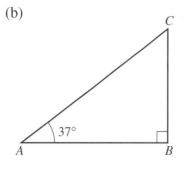

$$BC = 4{\cdot}5 \text{ cm, so } \frac{BC}{AB} = \frac{4{\cdot}5}{6} = 0{\cdot}75 \qquad\qquad BC = 3{\cdot}0 \text{ cm, so } \frac{BC}{AB} = \frac{3{\cdot}0}{4} = 0{\cdot}75$$

The ratio $\dfrac{BC}{AB}$ is the same for both triangles.

In the previous example, if you change the size of angle A then the ratio will change.

For example, if angle A is $50°$ and angle B is $90°$, the ratio $\dfrac{BC}{AB} = 1{\cdot}2$.

If A is the angle involved in a calculation, you can name each side of a right-angled triangle.

The side BC is opposite angle A and is called the **opposite** side.

The side AC is opposite the right angle and is called the **hypotenuse**.

The side AB is next to angle A and is called the **adjacent** side.

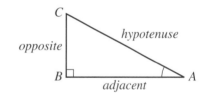

Exercise 8B

1. Draw three triangles ABC with angle $A = 28°$ and angle $B = 90°$.

   In each triangle, let the adjacent side be:

   (a) 8 cm   (b) 5 cm   (c) 6·5 cm

   Measure the opposite side and calculate the ratio $\dfrac{\text{opposite}}{\text{adjacent}}$ for all three triangles (to 2 d.p.). What do you notice?

2. (a) For the triangles that you drew in question 1, measure the hypotenuse and calculate the ratio $\dfrac{\text{opposite}}{\text{hypotenuse}}$ for all three triangles. What do you notice?

   (b) Calculate the ratio $\dfrac{\text{adjacent}}{\text{hypotenuse}}$ for all three triangles. What do you notice?

MODULE 5

8.3 Tangent ratio

The ratio $\dfrac{opposite}{adjacent}$ is called the **tangent** of angle A.

Tangent of angle $A = \dfrac{\text{side opposite to angle } A}{\text{side adjacent to angle } A}$

$$\tan A = \dfrac{opposite}{adjacent} = \dfrac{BC}{AB}$$

Example 1

In triangle ABC, angle $B = 90°$, angle $A = 42°$ and $AB = 7$ cm.
Find BC.

$$\tan A = \dfrac{opposite}{adjacent} = \dfrac{BC}{AB}$$

$$\tan 42° = \dfrac{BC}{7}$$

$$BC = 7 \times \tan 42°$$

$$= 6\cdot30 \text{ cm (3 sig. figs.)}$$

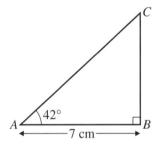

Hint:
To find tan 42° on your calculator, press the keys: tan, 42, =.
If you do not obtain 0·9004... use the keys in the order 42, tan, =.
If neither gives 0·9004... check your calculator is working in degrees mode and if necessary refer to your calculator instruction book.

Example 2

In triangle PQR, angle $Q = 90°$, $PQ = 8\cdot1$ cm and $QR = 3\cdot8$ cm.
Find angle P.

$$\tan P = \dfrac{opposite}{adjacent}$$

$$= \dfrac{RQ}{PQ}$$

$$= \dfrac{3\cdot8}{8\cdot1}$$

$$= 0\cdot469$$

angle $P = 25\cdot1°$ (3 sig. figs.)

Hint:
To find angle P use the keys:
3·8 ÷ 8·1 = inverse tan =.

Example 3

In triangle RST, angle $T = 90°$, angle $R = 38°$ and $ST = 9.2$ cm.
Find RT.

$$\tan R = \frac{opposite}{adjacent}$$

$$= \frac{ST}{RT}$$

$$\tan 38° = \frac{9.2}{RT}$$

$$RT \tan 38° = 9.2$$

$$RT = \frac{9.2}{\tan 38°}$$

$$= 11.775\ldots$$

$$= 11.8 \text{ cm (3 sig. figs.)}$$

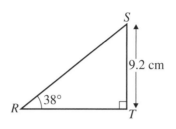

Exercise 8C

1. Find length AB.

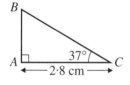

2. Find length PQ.

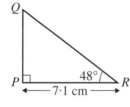

3. Find angle Z.

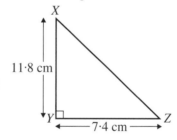

4. Find angle R.

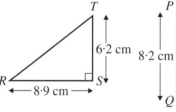

5. Find angle P.

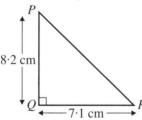

6. Find angle A.

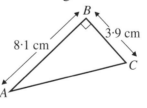

7. Find length DE.

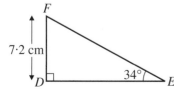

8. Find length PR.

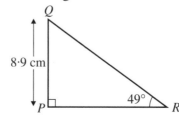

9. Find (a) length *RS*
      (b) length *RT*.

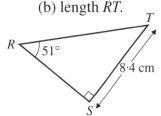

10. Find angle *J*.

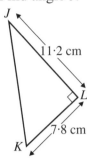

8.4 Sine and cosine ratios

So far you have only considered the opposite and adjacent sides.
You could pair any two sides from a right-angled triangle.

Sine of angle $A = \dfrac{\text{side opposite to angle } A}{\text{hypotenuse}}$

or $\sin A = \dfrac{opposite}{hypotenuse}$

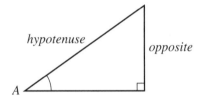

Cosine of angle $A = \dfrac{\text{side adjacent to angle } A}{\text{hypotenuse}}$

or $\cos A = \dfrac{adjacent}{hypotenuse}$

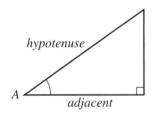

A word to help you remember these ratios is

    SOHCAHTOA

or $\sin = \dfrac{O}{H}$, $\cos = \dfrac{A}{H}$ and $\tan = \dfrac{O}{A}$

Which trigonometrical ratio should you use?

To decide which trigonometrical ratio to use, consider which
two sides you either know or require to find. Use the
trigonometrical ratio which uses those two sides.

Example 1

In this triangle, find *BC*.
BC is the opposite side and *AC* is the hypotenuse.
∴ You use sin *A*.

$$\sin A = \frac{opposite}{hypotenuse}$$

$$= \frac{BC}{AC}$$

$$\sin 37° = \frac{BC}{8·4}$$

$$BC = 8·4 \times \sin 37°$$

$$= 5·055\ldots$$

$$BC = 5·06 \text{ cm (3 sig. figs.)}$$

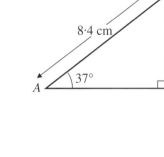

Example 2

In this triangle, find angle *P*.
You know the adjacent side and the hypotenuse.
∴ You use cos *P*.

$$\cos P = \frac{8·2}{11·4}$$

$$= 0·7193\ldots$$

$$\text{angle } P = 44·0° \text{ (3 sig. figs.)}$$

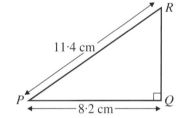

Example 3

Find *RS* in this triangle.
You know the opposite side and you require the hypotenuse.
Hence you use sin 48°.

$$\sin 48° = \frac{opposite}{hypotenuse}$$

$$= \frac{7·1}{RS}$$

$$RS \sin 48° = 7·1$$

$$RS = \frac{7·1}{\sin 48°}$$

$$= 9·5539\ldots$$

$$RS = 9·55 \text{ cm (3 sig. figs.)}$$

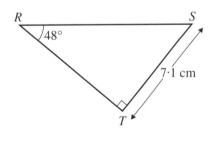

Example 4

A ship leaves a port P and sails 8 miles East and then 7 miles
South to position T.
(a) What is the bearing of T from P?
(b) Find the distance PT.

(a) Using angle P, you know the opposite side and the adjacent side.

$$\tan P = \frac{opposite}{adjacent}$$
$$= \frac{7}{8}$$

∴ angle $P = 41°$

∴ The bearing of T from P is $90° + 41° = 131°$.

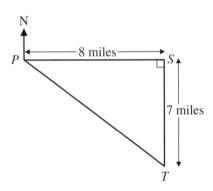

(b) By Pythagoras' theorem, $PT^2 = 8^2 + 7^2$
$$= 131$$
$$PT = 10·6 \text{ miles}$$

Exercise 8D

1. Find length BC.

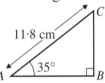

2. Find length DE.

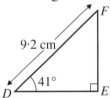

3. Find length GJ.

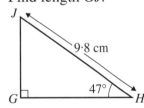

4. Find angle R.

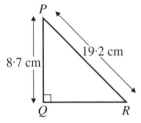

5. Find angle T.

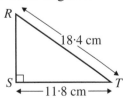

6. Find angle V.

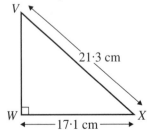

7. Find length *AB*.

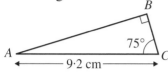

8. Find length *EF*.

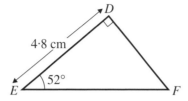

9. Find length *PR*.

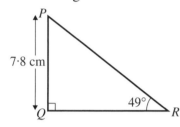

10. Find (a) length *BD*
    (b) length *BC*
    (c) length *CD*.

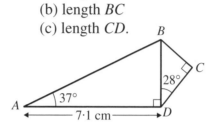

8.5 Angles of elevation and angles of depression

An object is rarely at exactly the same height as your
eyes. Thus when you look at an object you are usually
looking above or below the horizontal.
If the angle is above the horizontal, it is said to be an
angle of elevation and if the angle is below the horizontal,
 it is said to be an **angle of depression**.

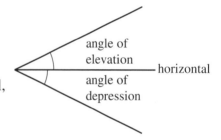

Example 1

Karl and Chloe are in a hot air balloon over a nature reserve.
Chloe looks down on an elephant at an angle of depression of
55·8°. The balloon is at a height of 1200 feet above the ground.
How far horizontally is the elephant from the balloon?

$$\tan 55\cdot 8° = \frac{opposite}{adjacent}$$

$$= \frac{1200}{AB}$$

$$AB \tan 55\cdot 8° = 1200$$

$$AB = \frac{1200}{\tan 55\cdot 8°}$$

$$= 816 \text{ feet (3 sig. figs.)}$$

Example 2

Angela sees a plane at an angle of elevation of 2·7°.
The plane is 3·5 miles horizontally from Angela.
What is the height of the plane?

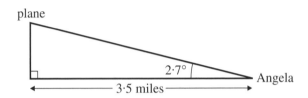

1 mile is 5280 feet.

$$\tan 2\!\cdot\!7° = \frac{opposite}{adjacent}$$

$$= \frac{height}{3\!\cdot\!5 \text{ miles}}$$

height $= 3\!\cdot\!5$ miles $\times \tan 2\!\cdot\!7°$

$\quad\quad = 0\!\cdot\!165...$ miles

$\quad\quad = 0\!\cdot\!165... \times 5280$ feet

$\quad\quad = 871\!\cdot\!49...$

height $= 871$ feet (3 sig. figs.)

Exercise 8E

1. The angle of elevation of the top of a pyramid is 7·8°.
    John is a distance of 560 metres horizontally from the top.
    What is the height of the pyramid?

2. A church tower is 21 m high. Sally is 4·8 m from the tower.
    What is the angle of elevation of the tower?
    You may assume that Sally's eyes are at ground level.

3. Jill is 7 metres from a flagpole which is 5 metres high. Her
    eyes are 1·6 m above the base of the flagpole. What is

    (a) the angle of depression of the foot of the flagpole

    (b) the angle of elevation of the top of the flagpole?

4. Ahmed sees a mountain peak in the distance. The angle of
    elevation of the peak is 2·9°. Ahmed walks away from the
    mountain for 200 yards. He notices that the angle of
    elevation has reduced by 0·4°.
    Calculate

    (a) the height of the mountain peak

    (b) the distance Ahmed now is from
        the peak.

    Give your answer in feet.

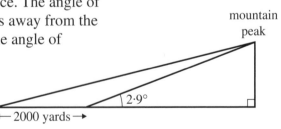

3 feet = 1 yard.

Summary

Check out AS8

1. You know Pythagoras' theorem

1. State Pythagoras' theorem for this triangle.

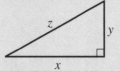

2. You can use Pythagoras' theorem to find the third side in a right-angled triangle

2. (a) Find the length of AB.

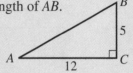

    (b) Find the length of QR.

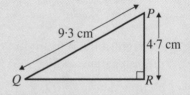

3. You know the trigonometric ratios

3. Which ratio is $\dfrac{AB}{BC}$? (Sine, cosine or tangent?)

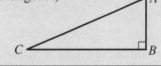

4. You can use trigonometry to find angles and lengths of sides in a right-angled triangle

4. (a) Find angle R

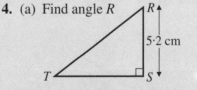

    (b) Find length AB.

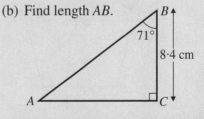

5. You can find angles of depression and elevation

5. Sally is on a hillside. A river is a distance of 2500 feet horizontally away from her. The angle of depression of the river is 6·2°. What is the difference in height between Sally and the river?

MODULE 5

Revision exercise AS8

1. The diagram shows the end view of a building.

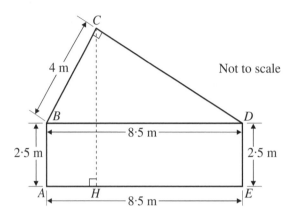

Not to scale

BCD is a right-angled triangle. Angle *BCD* = 90°.
BC = 4 m and *BD* = 8·5 m.

(a) Calculate angle *CBD*.

CH is perpendicular to *AE*.
AB = *ED* = 2·5 m.

(b) Calculate *CH*, the height of the building.   [SEG]

2. The diagram shows a right-angled triangle *ABC* and a trapezium *ACDE*.

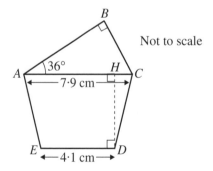

Not to scale

Angle *BAC* = 36° and *AC* = 7·9 cm.

(a) Calculate the length of *AB*.

The area of the trapezium is 52 cm². *ED* = 4·1 cm.

(b) Calculate *DH*, the height of the trapezium.   [SEG]

3. The diagram shows a quadrilateral *ABCD*.

AB = 9 cm and AC = 15 cm.

(a) Calculate the length of *BC*.

(b) Given that cos *x* = 0·7, calculate the
      length of *CD*.   [SEG]

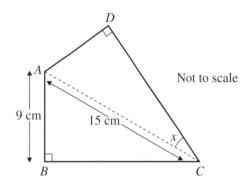

Not to scale

4. The diagram shows a right-angled triangle, *ABC*.
Angle *ABC* = 90°.
Tan *x* = $\frac{3}{4}$.

(a) Calculate sin *x*.

ABC and *PQR* are similar triangles.

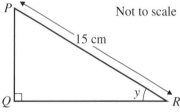

Not to scale

PQ is the shortest side of triangle *PQR*.
Angle *PQR* = 90° and *PR* = 15 cm.

(b) (i)   What is the value of cos *y*?

      (ii) What is the length of *PQ*?   [SEG]

5. A lift at the seaside takes people from sea level to the top of
a cliff, as shown.

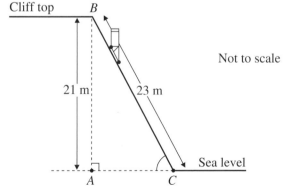

Not to scale

From sea level to the top of the cliff, the lift travels 23 m
and rises a height of 21 m.

(a) Calculate the distance *AC*.

(b) Calculate angle *BCA*.   [SEG]

6. The diagram shows the corner of a tower, *BD*.

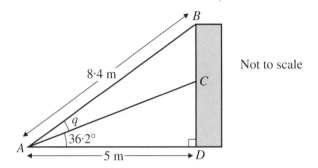

Not to scale

At night, a floodlight, positioned at *A*, lights the upper part of the tower, *BC*.

$AB = 8.4$ m and $AD = 5$ m.

(a) Calculate the height of the tower, *BD*.

Angle $CAD = 36.2°$.

(b) Calculate the size of the angle marked *q*.   [SEG]

7. The diagram shows a kite, at *K*, flying directly above a tree.

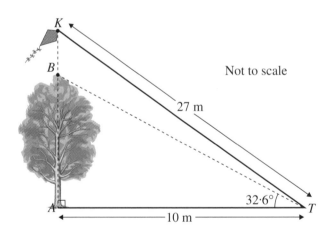

Not to scale

From *T*, the angle of elevation to the top of the tree is $32.6°$ and $AT = 10$ m.

(a) Calculate *AB*, the height of the tree.

When the kite is directly above the tree, the length of the string, *KT*, is 27 m.

(b) Calculate the angle *KTA*.   [SEG]

AS9 ALGEBRA 4

Reading graphs can help you to plan your travel abroad.

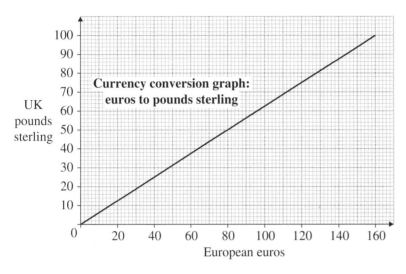

This unit will show you how to:

- Interpret graphs
- Plot graphs from real data
- Use conversion graphs
- Use distance–time graphs

Before you start:

You should know how to ...	Check in AS9

1. Calculate with speed
 	
For example, you travel at an average speed of 40 miles an hour for two and a half hours. How many miles have you covered?
 	
Use the triangle:
 	
Distance = speed × time
           = 40 × 2·5
           = 100
 	
You have covered 100 miles.
	1. You travel 60 miles in 3 hours. What is your average speed?

9.1 Interpreting graphs

You use graphs in real-life situations to see information quickly and easily.

Example

The graph shows the cost of four different types of meat on sale at a supermarket. The different cuts and their prices are labelled A, B, C and D on the graph.

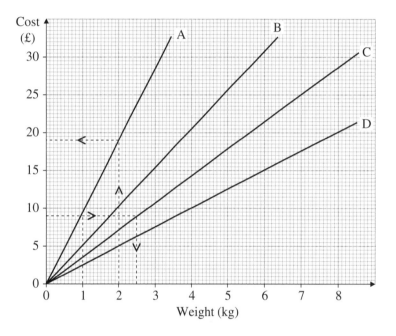

Use the graph to answer these questions.
(a) What is the cost of 2 kg of the most expensive meat?
(b) Samir paid £9 for 2·5 kg of meat.
     Which type of meat did he buy?
(c) How much more expensive per kg is meat B than meat D?

(a) The cost is £19.
(b) Meat C is the only cut of meat with 2·5 kg costing £9.
(c) Meat B costs £5 − £3·50 = £1·50 more per kg.

Exercise 9A

1.

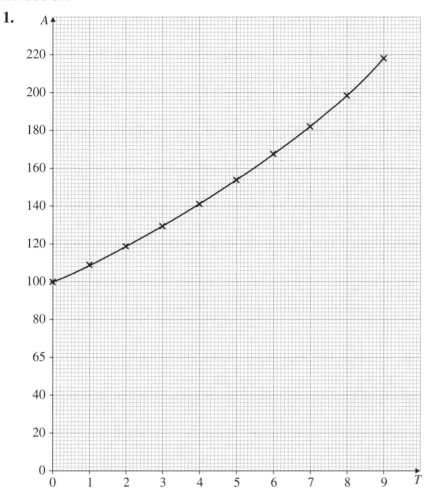

£100 was invested in a bank account that gave 9% interest each year.

The interest was added to the original investment and the money left in the account for 9 years.

The graph shows the amount of investment A (£) over the time T (years).

Use the graph to find

(a) the size of the investment in the account after $4\frac{1}{2}$ years

(b) the time taken to increase the investment to a total of £175.

2.

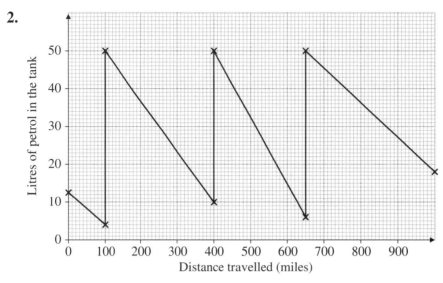

The graph shows the amount of petrol in Jatin's car during a
touring holiday using motorways across Europe.
Use the graph to answer the following questions.

(a) Approximately how much of Jatin's tank was full of petrol
at the beginning of the journey?

(b) How many stops for petrol did he make?

(c) How many miles did Jatin travel on his holiday?

(d) How many litres of petrol did Jatin use during his holiday?

3.

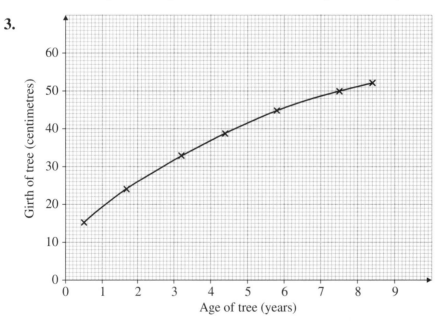

A keen gardener kept a record of the growth for one of the
trees he planted in his garden. He measured the girth

(distance round the trunk) of the tree at the same height from the ground over nine years. The graph shows the girth measurements over the period of time. Use the graph to find

(a) the girth at 2 years old
(b) the age of the tree when the girth was 40 cm
(c) the age of the tree when the girth doubled the size it was at 1 year old.

4.

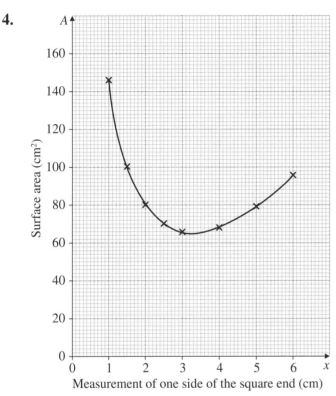

A rectangular box has a square end of size x cm and a constant volume of 36 cm^3. The total outside surface area of the box is A cm^2. The graph shows the connection between the area A cm^2 and the square end side x cm.
Use the graph to find

(a) the length of the side of the square which gives the least surface area
(b) the value of the surface area for a square of side
    (i)   1·7 cm
    (ii) 1·2 cm
    (iii) 4·7 cm
(c) What are the possible sizes of length of the square if the surface area of the box is 75 cm^2?

9.2 Graph plotting from a table of values

Graphs often need to be drawn using information that connects two quantities.

Example

A group of pupils draw circles and estimate the areas of the circles as the radius is increased. The results are given in the table where A cm^2 is the area of the circle and r cm is the radius of the circle.

r (cm)	1	2	3	3·5	4	4·5	5	6	7	8
A (cm^2)	3	12·5	28	38	50	63	78	110	150	200

Draw a graph connecting r and A, then use your graph to estimate

(a) the area of a circle with radius $5\frac{1}{2}$ cm

(b) the radius of a circle of area 170 cm^2.

First draw a graph:

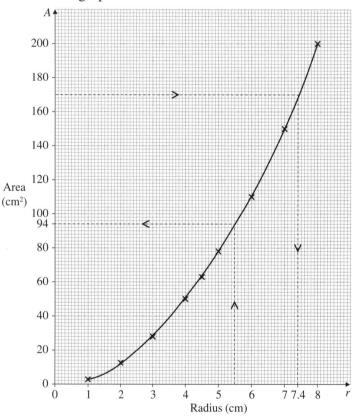

Note:
Always make sure you use a suitable scale.

(a) From the graph, when $r = 5\frac{1}{2}$ cm, $A = 94$ cm^2.

(b) From the graph, when $A = 170$ cm^2, $r = 7·4$ cm.

Exercise 9B

1. A plant is grown from seed and its height is measured at approximately the same time each day over a period of 16 days. The measurements are recorded in the table.

Day	1	2	4	6	8	9	10	11	15	16
Height (cm)	1·5	3	6	9·1	11·8	12·9	14	15	15·9	16·2

Draw a graph to show the data.
Use your graph to answer the following questions.
(a) Find the approximate height of the plant after
    (i)   5 days   (ii) 14 days
(b) Estimate the time (in days) taken for the plant to grow to a height of 14·5 cm.

> **Remember:**
> Time (days in this question) is plotted on the horizontal axis.

2. Water was poured onto a tray and placed in the freezing compartment of a fridge to make some ice cubes. The temperature of the water was taken at various intervals over the next hour. The results are recorded in the table.

Time (mins)	0	5	10	15	20	30	40	50	60
Temperature (°C)	22	16	11	8	6	3	2	1·5	1

Draw a graph to show the data.
Use your graph to estimate
(a) the temperature of the water after
    (i)   8 minutes   (ii) 45 minutes
(b) the time when the temperature of the water was
    (i)   17 °C   (ii) 5 °C

3. A golf ball is hit over level ground and after t seconds its height h metres above the ground is recorded. The results are given in the table.

t	0	1	2	3	4	5	6	7
h	0	24	40	48	48	40	24	0

Draw the graph of t against h.

Use your graph to find
(a) the greatest height reached by the ball
(b) the length of time the ball takes to reach the greatest height
(c) the height of the ball at $4\frac{1}{2}$ seconds
(d) the times when the ball is at a height of 35 metres.

4. A clear glass conical measuring beaker has water poured
into it. The height of the water poured into the cone is
measured after known volumes of water have been poured
into the cone. The results for the volume V ml and the height
h cm are recorded in the table.

V (ml)	10	25	40	50	100	150	200
h (cm)	4·5	6·0	7·1	7·7	9·6	11·0	12·1

Draw a graph connecting V and h.
Use your graph to estimate

(a) the height of water for a volume of 130 ml
(b) the volume of water enclosed when the height is
     9·2 cm.

5. A student uses a motion detector to take measurements of
the distance a ball has fallen when dropped from the top
floor of a tower block. The distance d metres is recorded
t seconds after the ball is dropped, and the measurements
are recorded in the table.

t (secs)	0	0·5	1	1·5	2	2·25	2·5	3
d (m)	0	1·2	4·9	11·0	19·6	24·8	30·6	44·1

Draw a graph connecting d and t.
Use your graph to estimate

(a) how far the ball has fallen after 1·25 seconds
(b) the time elapsed for the ball to travel a distance of
     38 metres.
If the tower block is 52 metres tall,
(c) estimate the time when the ball has travelled half
     way to the ground.

9.3 Conversion graphs

You can use straight-line graphs to convert between different
units or measurements, such as currency exchange rates, or
metric and imperial measures.

Example

Anne-Marie and Julian are going on holiday to Japan. If the
exchange rate is 170 yen to £1, draw a graph to convert values
up to £100 into yen.

Use your graph to find

(a) the cost in £ of a meal costing 5600 yen
(b) how many yen would be equivalent to £64.

You need three points to draw a straight-line graph:

Use 2 points to draw the
line, 1 point to check.

$£1$ $= 170$ yen
$£50$ $= 8500$ yen
$£100 = 17\,000$ yen

Now plot these points on a graph:

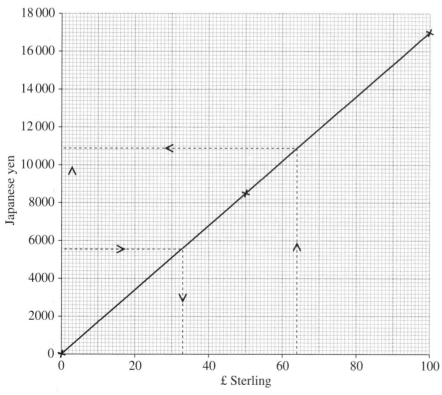

(a) 5600 yen correspond to £32·94.
(b) £64 correspond to 10 880 yen.

MODULE 5

Exercise 9C

1. This graph can be used to convert speed units from miles per hour (mph) to kilometres per hour (km/h).

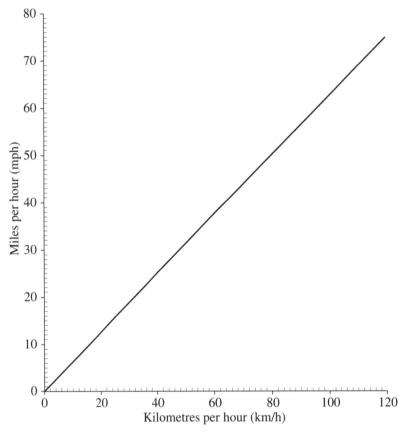

Use the graph to answer the following questions.

(a) (i) How many miles per hour does 1 small division represent on the vertical axis?

   (ii) How many kilometres per hour does one small division represent on the horizontal axis?

(b) Convert
   (i) 42 mph to km/h
   (ii) 95 km/h to mph
   (iii) 14 km/h to mph
   (iv) 74 mph to km/h
   (v) 56 km/h to mph.

2. Draw a graph to convert pounds (lbs) to kilograms (kg). Use the two facts that 0 pounds and 0 kilograms are equal, and that 110 pounds are equivalent to 50 kilograms. Use a scale of 2 cm to represent 10 kg on one axis and 2 cm to represent 20 lbs on

the other axis. Plot points to represent the conversion facts given above and draw a straight line joining these two points.

Use your graph to convert
(a) 15 lbs to kg   (b) 42 kg to lbs   (c) 57 lbs to kg
(d) 19 kg to lbs   (e) 28 lbs to kg   (f) 35·9 kg to lbs

3. A modular examination has a maximum mark of 35. This means 35 marks are equivalent to 100%. Draw a graph which will convert marks to a percentage for this examination. Use a scale of 2 cm to represent 5 marks on one axis and 2 cm to represent 20% on the other axis.

Plot two points converting marks to a percentage using

0 marks $\rightarrow$ 0%
35 marks $\rightarrow$ 100%

Draw a straight line between these values and use your graph to answer the following questions.
(a) Convert the following marks to a percentage
    (i)   12   (ii) 31
(b) What mark did a candidate gain in order to achieve 65% for this examination?
(c) If 75% is needed to avoid re-sitting the paper, what is the pass mark for this examination paper?

4. An electrical repair firm charges a basic call-out fee plus a charge depending on the time spent completing the repair. The firm charges £65 for a 1 hour repair and £185 for a repair taking 5 hours to complete. Use a scale of 2 cm to represent 1 hour horizontally and 2 cm to represent £20 vertically with ranges of 0 to 6 hours on the time axis and £0 to £200 on the charges axis. Plot the values given above and draw a straight line connecting these points.

Use your graph to find
(a) the call-out charge
(b) the cost for a repair taking $1\frac{3}{4}$ hours
(c) the time spent completing a repair, if the bill for the repair was £165.

5. Draw a graph to convert litres to gallons. Use the two facts that 0 litres and 0 gallons are equal, and that 91 litres are equivalent to 20 gallons. Use a scale of 2 cm to represent 4 gallons on one axis and 2 cm to represent 20 litres on the other axis. Plot points to represent the conversion facts given above and draw a straight line joining the two points.

(a) Use your graph to convert
  (i) 8·5 gallons to litres   (ii) 23 litres to gallons
  (iii) 2 gallons to litres   (iv) 86 litres to gallons
  (v) 14·3 gallons to litres   (vi) 57 litres to gallons

(b) The minimum volume of petrol which can be bought
 from a petrol pump at a filling station is 2 litres.
 What is this mimimum volume in gallons?

(c) A large car has a fuel tank which has a maximum capacity
 of 17 gallons. What is this maximum capacity in litres?

9.4 Distance–time graphs

Distance–time graphs give information about journeys.
You calculate speed using the following rule:

● Speed = $\dfrac{\text{distance travelled}}{\text{time taken}}$

Note:
This rule only applies to constant speed.
However, this is all you need to know at GCSE level.

Example 1

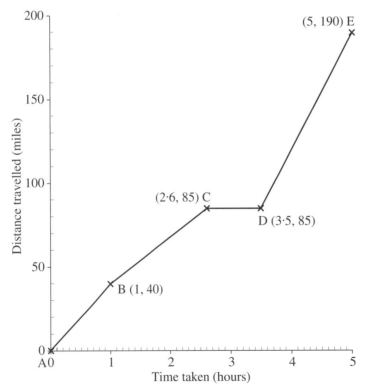

The graph represents a delivery driver's journey on one day,
travelling between two different company offices. He starts at

office A and travels to office E for the final stop of the day.
Use the graph to answer the following questions.

- (a) (i) On the distance axis, what is represented by one small division?
  - (ii) On the time axis, what time unit is represented by one small division?
- (b) The driver travels from A to his first stop at B.
  - (i) How far did he travel?
  - (ii) How long did this journey take?
  - (iii) What was his average speed between A and B?
- (c) At what time did he arrive at point C? Answer in hours and minutes.
- (d) What do you think happened between C and D on the graph? Explain your answer.
- (e) The driver eventually reached his destination office E.
  - (i) How far was the journey from office A to office E?
  - (ii) What was his average speed for the whole journey?

- (a) (i) 10 divisions represent 50 miles on the distance axis, so one division represents $\dfrac{50}{10} = 5$ miles.
  - (ii) 10 divisions represent 1 hour on the time axis, so one division represents $\dfrac{60}{10} = 6$ minutes.
- (b) (i) The driver travels 8 divisions $= 8 \times 5 = 40$ miles from A to B.
  - (ii) The journey takes 1 hour.
  - (iii) The average speed between A and B $= \dfrac{40}{1} = 40$ miles per hour.

- (c) He arrives at C after 2·6 hours $=$ 2 hours $(0·6 \times 60)$ minutes
  $$= 2 \text{ hours } 36 \text{ minutes}$$

- (d) He stopped between C and D for
  (3 hours 30 minutes $-$ 2 hours 36 minutes) $=$ 54 minutes

  The horizontal line between C and D shows that he was stationary here.

- (e) (i) Distance from A to E is 190 miles.
  - (ii) Average speed overall $= \dfrac{190}{5} = 38$ mph

Example 2

Draw a graph to represent a car journey which starts from rest at 10:00 am. The car is driven from the start at a constant speed of 16 miles per hour for 30 minutes. At this point the speed is then increased and the car travels for 32 miles at this new constant speed for 45 minutes. The car is then parked for one hour before the return journey is made at a constant speed of 32 miles per hour.

For the first part of the journey the car travels $16 \times \frac{1}{2} = 8$ miles in 30 minutes.

In the second part the car travels 32 miles in 45 minutes.

The car is then at rest for 1 hour.

The final return journey is 40 miles at 32 miles per hour, so

$$\text{time taken} = \frac{40}{32} = 1 \cdot 25 \text{ hours}$$
$$= 1 \text{ hour } 15 \text{ minutes.}$$

The time axis needs

30 minutes + 45 minutes + 1 hour + 1 hour 15 minutes
= 3 hours 30 minutes.

The distance axis needs

$8 + 32 = 40$ miles.

Draw the distance axis from 0 to 40 miles and the time axis from 10:00 am to 1:30 pm.

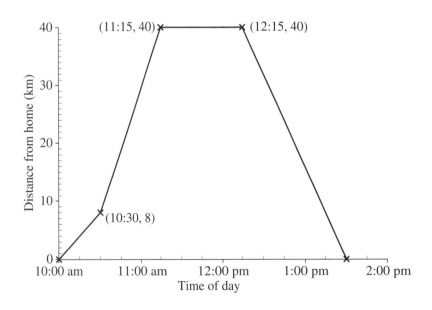

Exercise 9D

1. This is a distance–time graph for Mr Day taking his dog for a walk.

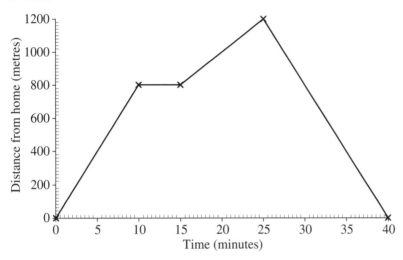

He leaves home and walks to a local park where he meets a friend and spends a while talking, while sitting on a park bench. He then continues the walk to a post box to post a birthday card before immediately returning home by the same route.

(a) (i)   How far is the local park from Mr Day's home?
    (ii) How long does he take to walk to the park?
(b) What is Mr Day's average speed when he travels from home to the park?
(c) How long does Mr Day spend talking to his friend?
(d) How far is the post box
    (i)   from Mr Day's house
    (ii) from the park?
(e) (i)   How long does Mr Day take to return home from posting the birthday card?
    (ii) What is his average speed for this return journey?

2. Peter sets off for school. He walks 500 metres down a lane to the bus stop and takes 10 minutes to do this. He waits at the bus stop for 6 minutes then catches a bus to travel the remaining 2250 metres. He arrives at the bus stop outside the school 31 minutes after he set off from home.

(a) Draw a distance–time graph to show this journey to school.
(b) Work out the average speed of the bus, in metres per minute.

3. A seaside resort has a narrow gauge railway that operates along the coast between two stations which are a total of 2800 metres apart. The outward journey takes 8 minutes travelling at a steady speed. The train timetable then allows 12 minutes to change the passengers before completing the return journey in 7 minutes.

(a) Draw a distance–time graph to show the information using a scale of 2 cm to represent 4 minutes along the horizontal axis and 2 cm to represent 500 m on the vertical axis.

(b) Use your graph to find
   (i)   the speed of the train over the outward journey
   (ii) the speed of the train over the return journey.

4. The distance–time graph shows the journey made by two coaches from the same firm. The first, coach A, travels from town P to town S, passing through towns Q and R, whilst the second, coach B, travels in the opposite direction from town S to town P.

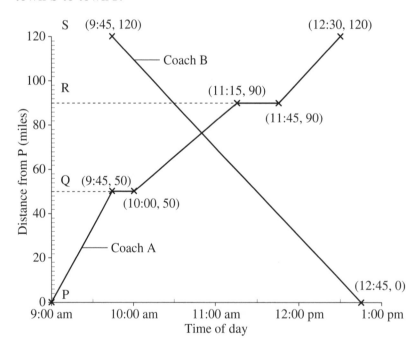

Use the graph to find
(a) the average speed of coach A
   (i)   between P and Q
   (ii)   between Q and R
   (iii) between R and S

(b) the average speed of coach A over the whole journey

(c) the average speed of coach B travelling from town S to town P

(d) where the two coaches pass each other and the time when this happens

(e) the distance between the two coaches at 12:00 pm.

5. Ahmed and his sister Inder both travel to visit a friend who lives 55 km from their house. Ahmed leaves the house at 9:00 am and cycles to the friend's house. He travels the first 30 km at a speed of 24 km per hour and then rests for 30 minutes. He then completes the journey at a speed of 20 km per hour.

Inder leaves her home at 10:30 am and travels by car along the same road at an average speed of 60 km per hour.

(a) Draw the distance–time graph to show these journeys, using a scale of 2 cm to represent $\frac{1}{2}$ hour on the horizontal axis and 2 cm to represent 10 km on the vertical axis.

(b) Use your graph to find

    (i)   the time when Inder overtakes Ahmed

    (ii)   the distance from their friend's house where she overtakes her brother.

6. A lorry is driven a total of 180 miles during one day, travelling between two factories. The lorry travels 50 miles at a speed of 50 miles per hour and then takes $1\frac{1}{2}$ hours travelling the next 60 miles before the driver has a break for 45 minutes. He then drives to the second factory taking a total of 5 hours to complete the journey.

(a) Draw the distance–time graph to show this journey using a scale of 2 cm to represent 1 hour on the horizontal axis and 2 cm to represent 40 miles on the vertical axis.

(b) Use your graph to find

    (i)   the time when the lorry was 35 miles from the second factory

    (ii)   the average speed for the whole journey.

MODULE 5

Summary

1. You can use a conversion graph

2. You can use a distance–time graph

Check out AS9

1. The graph shows a conversion graph of degrees Celsius to degrees Fahrenheit. What is the temperature equivalent to
(a) 20 °C (b) 52 °F?

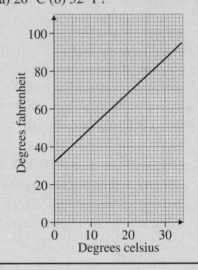

2. The graph shows a journey made by John and Mary.
(a) Find the speed from point A to point B.
(b) How long was the stop at point B?

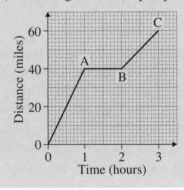

Revision exercise AS9

1. The graph shows how the monthly pay of a salesperson depends on sales.

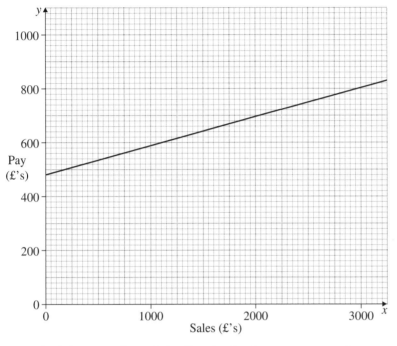

(a) Find the equation of the line in the form $y = ax + b$.
(b) Calculate the pay of a salesperson when sales are £5400.   [SEG]

2. The travel graph shows the journey of a cyclist from the town of Selby.

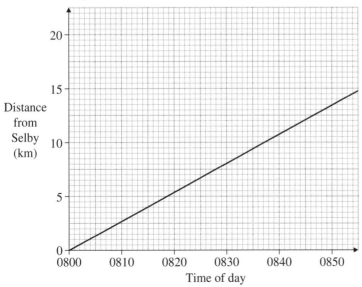

(a) What is the average speed of the cyclist in kilometres per hour?

A motorist is driving towards Selby along the same road as the cyclist. At 0820 the motorist is 20 km from Selby and travelling at a uniform speed of 60 km/h.

(b) (i) On a copy of the graph on page 437, draw a graph to show the journey of the motorist to Selby.

    (ii) At what time does the motorist pass the cyclist?　　　[SEG]

3. The graph shows the cost of printing wedding invitation cards.

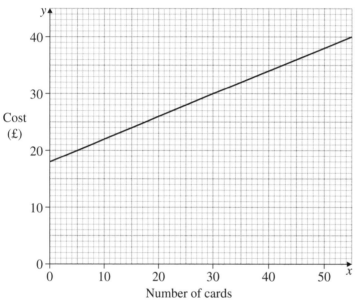

(a) Find the equation of the line in the form $y = mx + c$.

(b) For her wedding, Charlotte needs 100 cards to be printed.　　[SEG]
How much will they cost?

4. In an experiment, different weights are attached to a spring and the length of the spring is measured each time.
The graph shows the results obtained.

(a) Estimate the length of the spring when no weight is attached.

(b) Calculate the gradient of the line.

(c) Estimate the weight needed to stretch the spring by 20 cm.　　[SEG]

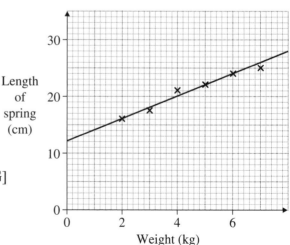

5. Aisha takes part in a race.
The graph shows her distance from the starting line during
the race.

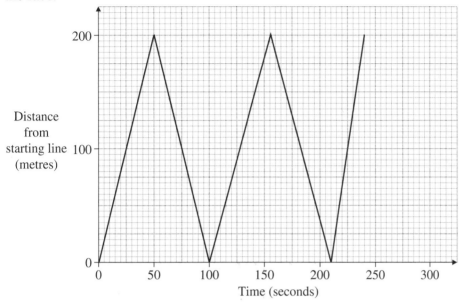

(a) (i)   What was the length of the race?

(ii) The race started at 1458.
At what time did Aisha finish?

(iii) What was her average speed, in metres per second, for the race?

(b) Another runner, Jayne, runs the race at a constant speed of 5 m/s.
On a copy of the same diagram draw a graph for Jayne's run.   [SEG]

6. A shop in Dover sells gifts.
The gifts can be bought in either English or French currency.
A box of fudge costs £5 or 48 francs.
A watch costs £15 or 144 francs.

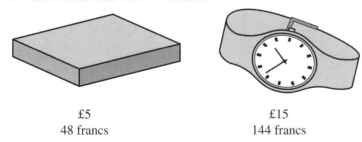

£5   £15
48 francs   144 francs

(a) Use this information to draw a conversion graph for pounds (£) and francs.

(b) A clock costs 120 francs.
How much is the clock in pounds (£)?

(c) A camera costs £60.
How much is the camera in francs?   [SEG]

Module 5 Practice Calculator Test

1. Anna and Julie go to the same college.
   The scale drawing shows the positions of their homes and
   the college.

   Anna's home is 4 kilometres from the college.

   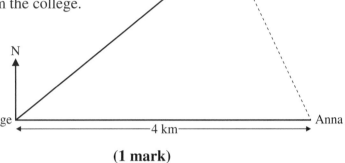

   (a) Measure the distance on the
       scale drawing from Anna's
       home to the college and
       hence copy and complete
       the statement:
       'On the scale
       drawing, 1 km
       is represented by … cm.'   **(1 mark)**

   (b) What is the actual distance from Julie's
       home to the college?   **(2 marks)**

   (c) What is the three-figure bearing of Julie's
       home from the college?   **(1 mark)**   [SEG]

2. (a) Andy is making a pattern that is symmetrical
       about both diagonals of this large square.
       Copy Andy's pattern and shade in 2 more
       small squares to complete it.

       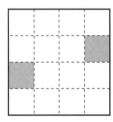

                                               (2 marks)

   (b) Tara is making a pattern with rotational symmetry of
       order 2.
       Copy Tara's pattern and shade in 3 more small squares
       to complete it.

       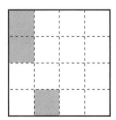

                                   (2 marks)   [SEG]

3. Ayesha and Zoe buy some flowers.
Ayesha buys a rose and a lily. These cost her £5·35.
Zoe buys a rose and 3 lilies. These cost her £7·25.
What is the cost of a lily?   **(3 marks)**   [SEG]

4. (a) Write down the next two terms in the sequence

3, 5, 9, 15, 23   **(2 marks)**

(b) (i) Write down the next term in the sequence

3, 5, 9, 17, 33   **(1 mark)**

(ii) Explain how you got your answer.   **(1 mark)**

(c) Write down the *n*th term for the sequence

3, 5, 7, 9, 11   **(2 marks)** [NEAB]

5. Part of a number grid is shown below.

1	2	3	4	5	6	7	8	9	10
11	12	13	14	15	16	17	18	19	20
21	22	23	24	25	26	27	28	29	30
31	32	33	34	35	36	37	38	39	40
41	42	43	44	45	46	47	48	49	50

The shaded shape is called P_2 because it has the
number 2 in the top left-hand corner.
The sum of the numbers in P_2 is 17.

(a) Calculate the sum of the numbers in P_{14}.   **(1 mark)**

(b) Copy this diagram and fill in the empty
squares of P_n.

(2 marks)

(c) Write down an expression, in terms of *n*, for
the sum of the numbers in P_n.
Simplify your expression.   **(2 marks)**

(d) If the sum of the numbers in P_n is 149, find
the value of *n*.   **(2 marks)**   [SEG]

6. (a) Calculate the circumference of a circle of diameter 6·5 cm.
   Leave your answer in terms of π. **(2 marks)**

   (b) Calculate the area of a circle of diameter 6·2 cm. **(3 marks)** [AQA]

7. In triangle *ABC*, the length of side *AB* is 6·2 cm and the length of side *BC* is 8·4 cm. Angle *BAC* is 90°.

   (a) Find the length of side *AC*. **(3 marks)**

   (b) Find angle *ABC*. **(3 marks)** [AQA]

8. In the diagram shown, find

   (a) the length of *BC* **(2 marks)**

   (b) the length of *BD*. **(3 marks)** [AQA]

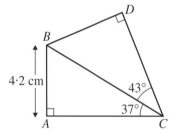

9. (a) Triangle *PQR* is mapped onto triangle $P_1Q_1R_1$, by an enlargement, centre *O*, scale factor 3.
   Copy this diagram and draw $P_1Q_1R_1$.

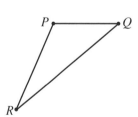

   (3 marks)

   (b) Describe fully the single transformation which maps $P_1Q_1R_1$ onto *PQR*. **(2 marks)** [SEG]

10. The radius of Paul's bike wheel is 33 cm.

    (a) Calculate the circumference of the wheel. **(2 marks)**

    (b) How many revolutions does the wheel make when travelling a distance of 500 m? **(3 marks)**

Paul rides his bike to school, a distance of 3 km.
On Monday he left home at 0820 and cycled to school at a
steady speed of 15 km/hour.

(c) At what time did he arrive at school? **(3 marks)** [SEG]

11. (a) Factorise $3a + 6b$. **(1 mark)**

(b) A solution of the equation

$$x^3 - x^2 = 7$$

lies between $x = 2$ and $x = 3$.
Use trial and improvement to find this solution.
Give your answer correct to one decimal place.
You must show all your working. **(4 marks)**

(c) Solve the equations $2x + 3y = 3$
$5x - 2y = 17$ **(3 marks)** [SEG]

12. (a) Copy and complete the table of values, and
use it to draw the graph of

$$y = 3x^2 + 2x - 5$$

x	$^-3$	$^-2$	$^-1$	0	1	2
y	16	3	$^-4$	$^-5$	0	11

(4 marks)

(b) Use your graph to find the values of x
when $y = 5$. **(2 marks)**

13. Noel (N) can just see the top of the church tower (C)
appearing over the tree (T).

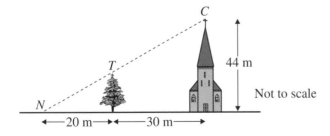

Noel is 20 metres from the tree.
The tree is 30 metres from the tower.
The tower is 44 metres high.
Calculate the height of the tree. **(4 marks)** [SEG]

Module 5 Practice Non-calculator Test

1. (a) Triangle *PQR* has a right angle at *R*.
   Angle *PQR* = 50°.

   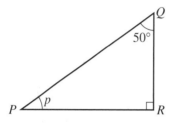

   Not to scale

   Work out the size of angle *p*.   **(1 mark)**

   (b) *ABCD* is a quadrilateral and *DCE* is a
       straight line.

   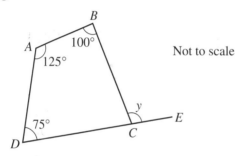

   Not to scale

   Work out the size of angle *y*.   **(3 marks)**   [SEG]

2. (a) Simplify these expressions.
   (i) $2p + p = 5p$ **(1 mark)**
   (ii) $t \times t \times t \times t$ **(1 mark)**
   (b) Simplify as much as possible
       $4a + 7b - 3a + 2b$ **(2 marks)**
   (c) Solve this equation.
       $$\frac{x - 4}{2} = 3$$ **(2 marks)**   [SEG]

3. In triangle *ABC*, *AB* = 80 cm, *BC* = 70 cm
   and *AC* = 50 cm.

   Make a scale drawing of the triangle, using
   a scale of 1 : 10.   **(3 marks)**   [SEG]

4. Serena measures the height of door **A** as 2 metres.
   Tom measures the height of door **B** as 70 inches.
   Which door is the higher, **A** or **B**?
   You must show all your working.   **(3 marks)**   [SEG]

5. (a) A cuboid has volume 60 cm². Its base is a
rectangle 5 cm by 3 cm.
Calculate the height of the cuboid. **(2 marks)**

(b) Find the area of this triangle.

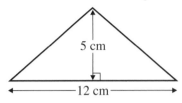

(2 marks)

(c) Find angle x in the diagram.
Explain each step in your working.

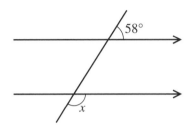

(2 marks)

6. (a) Work out the value of $\dfrac{1}{(0 \cdot 2)^2}$ **(2 marks)**

(b) If $x = 7$ and $y = 5$, find the value of
 (i) $3x - 2y$ **(2 marks)**
 (ii) $2xy$ **(2 marks)**
 (iii) $\dfrac{x + y}{2x - y}$ giving your answer as a
    fraction in its lowest terms. **(2 marks)**

(c) Find all the integer values of p which
satisfy the inequality:
 $5 < 3p \leqslant 18$ **(3 marks)** [AQA]

7. (a) Solve the equation $9x + 7 = 4(x + 2)$ **(3 marks)**

(b) Simplify
 (i) $2x - 3(x - 4)$ **(2 marks)**
 (ii) $t^7 \times t^4$ **(1 mark)**
 (iii) $\dfrac{p^2}{p^5}$ **(1 mark)**
 (iv) $x(x^2 - 2)$ **(2 marks)** [AQA]

8. Ryan is making gingerbread men for the
   Christmas fair.
   Each gingerbread man needs five chocolate
   drops for his eyes and his buttons.

(a) How many chocolate drops does Ryan
    need for *n* gingerbread men?   **(1 mark)**

The gingerbread men are sold in boxes of three.

Ryan's *n* gingerbread men fit exactly into *k* boxes.

(b) Write an equation which shows the
    relationship between *n* and *k*.   **(2 marks)**   [SEG]

9.

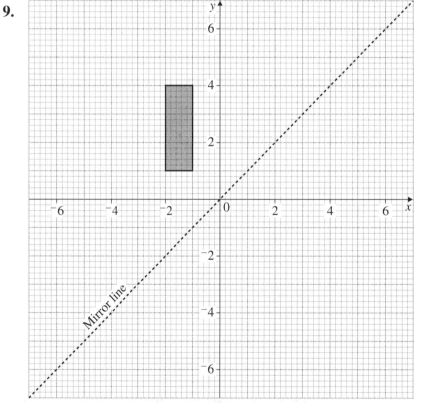

(a) On a copy of the diagram draw the reflection
    of the rectangle in the mirror line.   **(2 marks)**

(b) Write down the equation of the mirror line.   **(1 mark)**   [SEG]

10. (a) Calculate the size of an exterior angle of a
regular octagon.
You must show all your working. **(2 marks)**

(b) What is the size of an interior angle of a
regular octagon? **(1 mark)**

(c) Explain why a regular polygon cannot have
an interior angle equal to 110°. **(2 marks)** [SEG]

11. (a) Find the equation of the line shown on the
graph in the form $y = mx + c$. **(4 marks)**

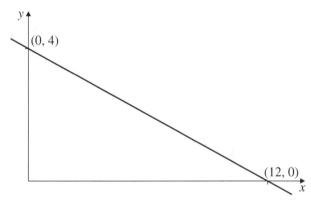

(b) Rearrange the formula $t = \dfrac{p}{s} + q$ to find p. **(2 marks)**

(c) Factorise the expression $x^2 - 5x + 6$,
and hence solve the equation $x^2 - 5x + 6 = 0$. **(3 marks)**

12. The letters a, b, h and r represent lengths.
Which of the following formulae could represent
volume?

$\pi r(a^2 + b^2) \quad \pi r h \quad \pi r \sqrt{a^2 + h^2} \quad \dfrac{\pi r^2}{3}(h + 2r)$ **(2 marks)** [SEG]

13. For each of these three different quadrilaterals, choose the
correct name from this list.
kite rectangle rhombus square trapezium

(a) One pair of sides are parallel but they are not
equal in length.

(b) The diagonals are of different lengths and cross
at 90°. Each diagonal is a line of symmetry of
the quadrilateral.

(c) The diagonals are equal in length. They bisect
each other, but they do not cross at right
angles. **(3 marks)** [SEG]

MODULE 5

14.

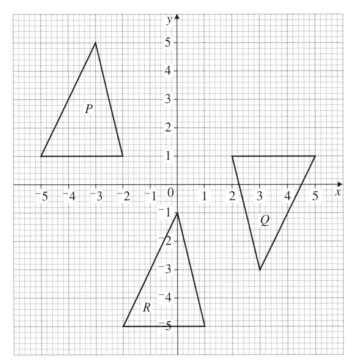

(a) Triangle *P* can be moved onto triangle *Q* using a rotation through 180°.
Write down the coordinates of the centre of this rotation. **(1 mark)**

(b) Write down the vector for the translation which moves triangle *P* onto triangle *R*. **(2 marks)** [SEG]

COURSEWORK GUIDANCE

For your GCSE Maths you will need to produce two pieces of coursework:

1. Investigative – module 4
2. Statistical – module 2

Each piece is worth 10% of your exam mark.

This unit gives you guidance on approaching your coursework and will tell you how to get good marks for each piece.

Module 4: Investigative coursework

In your investigative coursework you will need to:

- Say how you are going to carry out the task and provide a plan of action
- Collect results for the task and consider an appropriate way to represent your results
- Write down observations you make from your diagrams or calculations
- Look at your results and write down any observations, rules or patterns – try to make a general statement
- Check out your general statements by testing further data – say if your test works or not
- Develop the task by posing your own questions and provide a conclusion to the questions posed
- Extend the task by using techniques and calculations from the content of the intermediate tier
- Make your conclusions clear and link them to the original task giving comments on your methods.

Assessing the task

Before you start, it is helpful for you to know how your work will be marked. This way you can make sure you are familiar with the sort of things which examiners are looking for.

Investigative work is marked under three headings;

1. **Making and monitoring decisions to solve problems**
2. **Communicating mathematically**
3. **Developing skills of mathematical reasoning**

Each strand assesses a different aspect of your coursework. The criteria are:

1. Making and monitoring decisions to solve problems

This strand is about deciding what needs to be done then doing it. The strand requires you to select an appropriate approach, obtain information and introduce your own questions which develop the task further.

For the higher marks you need to analyse alternative mathematical approaches and, possibly, develop the task using work from the higher GCSE syllabus content.

For this strand you need to:

- solve the task by collecting information
- break down the task by solving it in a systematic way
- extend the task by introducing your own *relevant* questions
- extend the task by following through alternative approaches
- develop the task by including a number of mathematical features
- explore the task extensively using higher level mathematics.

2. Communicating mathematically

This strand is about communicating what you are doing using words, tables, diagrams and symbols. You should make sure your chosen presentation is accurate and relevant.

For the higher marks you need to use mathematical symbols accurately, concisely and efficiently in presenting a reasoned argument.

For this strand you need to:

- illustrate your information using diagrams and calculations
- interpret and explain your diagrams and calculations
- begin to use mathematical symbols to explain your work
- use mathematical symbols consistently to explain your work
- use mathematical symbols accurately to argue your case
- use mathematical symbols concisely and efficiently to argue your case.

3. Developing skills of mathematical reasoning

This strand is about testing, explaining and justifying what you have done. It requires you to search for patterns and provide generalisations. You should test, justify and explain any generalisations.

For the higher marks you will need to provide a sophisticated and rigorous justification, argument or proof which demonstrates a mathematical insight into the problem.

For this strand you need to:

- make a general statement from your results
- confirm your general statement by further testing
- make a justification for your general statement
- develop your justification further
- provide a sophisticated justification
- provide a rigorous justification, argument or proof.

This unit uses a series of investigative tasks to demonstrate how each of these strands can be achieved.

Task 1

TRIANGLES

Patterns of triangles are made as shown in the following diagrams:

  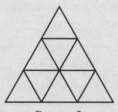

Pattern 1   Pattern 2   Pattern 3

What do you notice about the pattern number and the number of small triangles?

Investigate further.

Planning your work

A straightforward approach to this task is to continue the pattern further. You can record your results in a table and then see if you can make any generalisations.

MODULES 2 and 4

Collecting information

A good starting point for any investigation is to collect information about the task.

You can see that:

- Pattern 1 shows 1 small triangle
- Pattern 2 shows 4 small triangles
- Pattern 3 shows 9 small triangles

You can then extend this by considering further patterns.

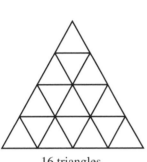
16 triangles

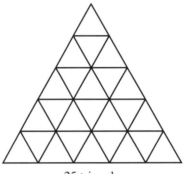
25 triangles

> **Moderator comment:**
> It is a good idea not to collect too much data as this is time consuming ... aim to collect 4 or 5 items of data to start with.

Drawing up tables

The information is not easy to follow so it is **always** a good idea to illustrate it in a table.

A table to show the relationship between the pattern number and the number of triangles.

pattern number	1	2	3	4	5
no of triangles	1	4	9	16	25

> It is important to give your table a title and to make it quite clear what the table is showing.

Now you try ...

Using the table:

- Can you see anything special about the number of triangles?
- Ask yourself: are they odd numbers, even numbers, square numbers, triangle numbers, are they multiples, do they get bigger, do they get smaller ...
- What other relationships might you look for?

Being systematic

Another important aspect to your work is to be systematic.

This task shows you what that means.

Task 2

ARRANGE A LETTER
How many different ways can you arrange the letters ABCD?

Investigate further.

You could haphazardly try out some different possibilities:

ABCD
BCDA
CDAB etc

You may or may not find all the arrangements this way. To be sure of finding them all you should list the arrangements systematically. To be systematic you group letters starting with A:

ABCD
ABDC
ACBD
ACDB
ADBC
ADCB

Notice the system here:
A followed by B,
then A followed by C,
then A followed by D
and so on.

Now you try ...
Now see if you can systematically produce all of the arrangements starting with B (you should find six of them) then complete the other arrangements.

You should also be systematic about the way you collect your data. In Task 2, you were asked to find the arrangements of 4 letters: A, B, C and D.

To approach the whole task systematically, you should start by finding the arrangements for:

- 1 letter: A
- 2 letters: A and B
- 3 letters: A, B and C

This will give you more information about the task.

MODULES 2 and 4

For different numbers of letters you should find:

Arrangement of different numbers of letters

number of letters	1	3	3	4
number of arrangements	1	2	6	24

You should now try and explain what your table tells you:

> *From my table I can ...*

Finding a relationship – making a generalisation

To make a generalisation, you need to find a relationship from your table of results. A useful method is to look at the differences between terms in the table.

Here is the table of results from Task 1:

A table to show the relationship between
the pattern number and the number of triangles.

pattern number	1	2	3	4	5
no of triangles	1	4	9	16	25

$$+3 \quad +5 \quad +7 \quad +9 \quad +11$$
$$+2 \quad +2 \quad +2 \quad +2$$

In this table the 'first differences' are going up in two's.

The 'second differences' are all the same ... this tells you that the relationship is quadratic, so you should compare the numbers with the square numbers.

Here are some generalisations you could make:

> *From my table I notice that the number of triangles are all square numbers*

> *From my table I notice that the number of triangles are the pattern numbers squared*

A graph may help you see the relationship:

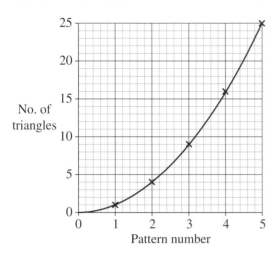

From my graph I notice that there is a quadratic relationship between the number of triangles and the pattern number

Using algebra

You will gain marks if you can express your generalisation or rule using algebra.

The rule:

I notice that the number of triangles are the pattern numbers squared

can be written in algebra:

$t = p^2$ where t is the number of triangles and p is the pattern number

Remember that you must explain what t and p stand for.

Testing generalisations

You need to confirm your generalisation by further testing.

From my table I notice that the number of triangles are the pattern numbers squared so that the sixth pattern will have $6^2 = 36$ triangles

MODULES 2 and 4

You can confirm this with
a diagram:

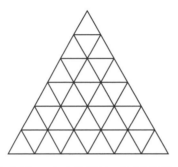

My diagram confirms the generalisation for the sixth pattern

Now try to use all of these ideas by following Task 3.

> Always confirm your testing by providing some comment, even if your test has not worked!

Now you try …

For Task 3: 'Perfect Tiles' given below:
- Collect the information for different arrangements
- Make sure you are systematic
- Draw up a table of your results.

Task 3

PERFECT TILES

Floor spacers are used to give a perfect finish when laying tiles on the kitchen floor.

Three different spacers are not used including

    L spacer
    T spacer
    + spacer

Here is a 3 × 3 arrangement of tiles

This uses   4 **L** spacers
             8 **T** spacers and
             4 **+** spacers

Investigate different arrangements of tiles.

> **Note:**
> You are reminded that any coursework submitted for your GCSE examination must be your own. If you copy from someone else then you may be disqualified from the examination.

You should be able to produce this table:

Number of spacers for different arrangement of tiles

size of square	1 × 1	2 × 2	3 × 3	4 × 4
number of L spacers	4	4	4	4
number of T spacers	0	4	8	12
number of + spacers	0	1	4	9

Now you try …

What patterns do you notice from the table?

What general statements can you make?

Now test your general statements.

Generalisations for the 'Perfect Tiles' task might include:

$L = 4$ where L is the number of L spacers

$T = 4(n - 1)$ where T is the number of T spacers and
                 n is the size of the arrangement ($n × n$)

The formula $T = 4(n - 1)$ can also be written as $T = 4n - 4$.

Test:

For a 5 × 5 arrangement (ie $n = 5$)

$T = 4(n - 1)$
$T = 4(5 - 1)$
$T = 4 × 4$
$T = 16$

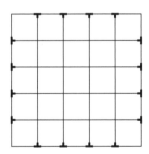

The number of T spacers is 16 so the formula works for a
5 × 5 arrangement.

$+ = (n - 1)^2$ where $+$ is the number of $+$ spacers and
                  n is the size of the arrangement ($n × n$)

Test:

For a 6 × 6 arrangement (ie $n = 6$)

$+ = (n - 1)$
$+ = (6 - 1)$
$+ = (5)^2$
$+ = 25$

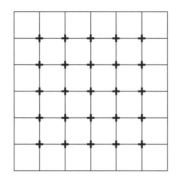

The number of + spacers is 25 so the formula works for a
6 × 6 arrangement.

Making justifications

Once you have found the general statement and tested it then you
need to justify it. You justify the statement by explaining WHY it
works.

For example, here are possible justifications for the rules in task 3:

WHY is the number of L spacers always 4?

The number of L spacers is always 4 because there are 4

corners to each arrangement.

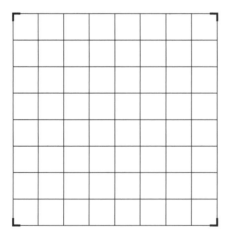

WHY are all of the T spacers multiples of 4?

The number of T spacers are multiples of 4 because each time

you add another tile to the side then you add another T spacer.

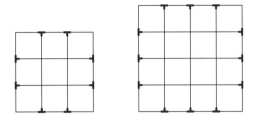

As there are 4 sides to the arrangement then the number of

T spacers will go up by 4.

WHY are all of the + spacers square numbers?

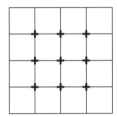

Now you try ...
Explain why the number of + spacers are **always** square numbers.

Extending the problem – investigating further

Once you have understood and explained the basic task, you should extend your work to get better marks.

To extend a task you need to pose your own questions.
This means that you must think of different ways to extend the original task.

Extending task 1: The triangle problem
You could ask and investigate:

What about different patterns?

For example, triangles:

What about patterns of different shapes?

For example, squares:

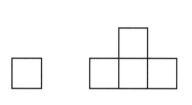 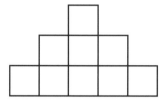

What about three dimensional patterns?

For example, cubes:

 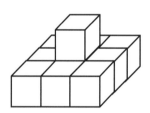 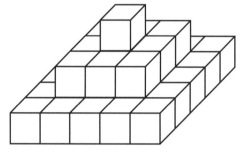

Extending task 2: 'Arrange a letter'

What about different numbers of letters?   For example, ABCDE

What happens when:
- a letter is repeated?   For example, AABCD
- a letter is repeated more than once?   For example, AAABC
- more than one letter is repeated?   For example, AAABB

Of course, you will have to do more than just pose a question – you will have to carry out the investigation and come to a conclusion.

Extending task 3: 'Perfect Tiles'

You could ask:

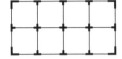

What about rectangular arrangements of tiles?

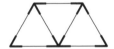

What about different shaped tiles?

For example, triangles:

Consider rectangular arrangements of tiles:

Remember to work systematically.

Number of spacers for different arrangement of tiles

size of arrangement	2 × 1	2 × 2	2 × 3	2 × 4	2 × 5
number of L spacers	4	4	4	4	4
number of T spacers	2	4	6	8	10
number of + spacers	0	1	2	3	4
number of spacers	6	9	12	15	18

Number of spacers for different arrangement of tiles

size of arrangement	3 × 1	3 × 2	3 × 3	3 × 4	3 × 5
number of L spacers	4	4	4	4	4
number of T spacers	4	6	8	10	12
number of + spacers	0	2	4	6	8
number of spacers	8	12	16	20	24

MODULES 2 and 4

Rules for the 'Perfect Tiles' task extension might include:

$L = 4$ where L is the number of L spacers

$T = 2(x - 1) + 2(y - 1)$ where T is the number of T spacers and

       x is the length of the arrangement and

       y is the width of the arrangement

$P = (x - 1)(y - 1)$ where P is the number of + spacers and

       x is the length of the arrangement and

       y is the width of the arrangement

$N = (x + 1)(y + 1)$ where N is the number of + spacers and

       x is the length of the arrangement and

       y is the width of the arrangement

> Note that the formula
> $T = 2(x - 1) + 2(y - 1)$
> can also be written
> $$T = 2(x - 1) + 2(y - 1)$$
> $$= 2x + 2y - 4$$

> It is sensible to replace + by P so that P stands for the number of + spacers.

The total number of spacers should equal the number of L spacers plus the number of T spacers plus the number of + spacers

Proof: $N = L + T + P$

$$= 4 + [2(x - 1) + 2(y - 1)] + [(x - 1)(y - 1)]$$

$$= 4 + 2x - 2 + 2y - 2 + xy - y - x + 1$$

$$= xy + x + y + 1$$

$$= (x + 1)(y + 1)$$

Since $N = (x + 1)(y + 1)$ is true, then my theory is proved

> **Moderator comment:**
> The use of a higher order algebra can result in high marks awarded on the middle strand as well as an opportunity to provide a sophisticated justification.

Task 4:

SQUARE SEA SHELLS

Square sea shells are formed from squares whose pattern of growth is shown as follows:

Day 1

Day 2

The length of the new square is half that of the previous day

Day 3

The length of the new square is half that of the previous day

Day 4

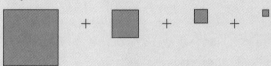

The length of the new square is half that of the previous day

This pattern of growth continues

Investigate the area covered by square sea shells on different days.

Investigate further.

For a square of side a

$$\text{Day 1} \qquad \text{Area} = a^2$$

$$\text{Day 2} \qquad \text{Area} = a^2 + \frac{a^2}{4}$$

$$\text{Day 3} \qquad \text{Area} = a^2 + \frac{a^2}{4} + \frac{a^2}{16}$$

$$\text{Day 4} \qquad \text{Area} = a^2 + \frac{a^2}{4} + \frac{a^2}{16} + \frac{a^2}{64}$$

The proof of the formula is beyond GCSE and the rest of the work is left as a challenge for the reader.

MODULES 2 and 4

In this unit we have tried to give you some hints on approaching investigative coursework to gain your best possible mark.

This mathematics is often useful in investigative tasks:

- Creating tables
- Drawing and interpreting graphs
- Recognising square numbers
- Recognising triangular numbers
- Finding the nth term of a linear sequence

Summary

These are the grade criteria your coursework will be marked by:

Identifying information and making statements (grade E/F)

To achieve this level you must:

- solve the task by collecting information
- illustrate your information using diagrams and calculations
- make a general statement from your results

Testing general statements (grade D)

To achieve this level you must:

- break down the task by solving it in an orderly manner
- interpret and explain your diagrams and calculations
- confirm your general statement by further testing

Posing questions and justifying (grade C)

To achieve this level you must:

- extend the task by introducing your own *relevant* questions
- begin to use mathematical symbols to explain your work
- make a justification for your general statement
- provide a sophisticated justification

Making further progress (grade B)

To achieve this level you must:

- extend the task by following through alternate approaches
- use mathematical symbols consistently to explain your work
- develop your justification further

Justifying a number of mathematical features (grade A)

To achieve this level you must:

- develop the task by including a number of mathematical features
- use mathematical symbols accurately to argue your case
- provide a sophisticated justification

Module 2: Statistical coursework

In your statistical coursework you will need to:

- Provide a well considered hypothesis and provide a plan of action to carry out the task
- Decide what data is needed and collect results for the task using an appropriate sample size and sampling method
- Consider the most appropriate way to represent your results and write down any observations you make
- Consider the most appropriate statistical calculations to use and interpret your findings in terms of the original hypothesis
- Develop the task by posing your own questions – you may need to collect further data to move the task on
- Extend the task by using techniques and calculations from the content of the intermediate tier
- Make your conclusions clear – always link them to the original hypothesis recognising limitations and suggesting improvements.

Assessing the task

It may be helpful for you to know how the work is marked. This way, you can make sure you are familiar with the sort of things that examiners are looking for.

Statistical work is marked under three headings:

1. **Specifying the problem and planning**
2. **Collecting, processing and representing the data**
3. **Interpreting and discussing the results**

Each strand assesses a different aspect of your coursework as follows:

1. Specifying the problem and planning
This strand is about choosing a problem and deciding what needs to be done then doing it. The strand requires you to provide clear

aims, consider the collection of data, identify practical problems and explain how you might overcome them.

For the higher marks you need to decide upon a suitable sampling method, explain what steps were taken to avoid possible bias and provide a well structured report.

2. Collecting, processing and representing the data

This strand is about collecting data and using appropriate statistical techniques and calculations to process and represent the data. Diagrams should be appropriate and calculations mostly correct.

For the higher marks you will need to accurately use higher level statistical techniques and calculations from the higher tier GCSE syllabus content.

3. Interpreting and discussing the results

This strand is about commenting, summarising and interpreting your data. Your discussion should link back to the original problem and provide an evaluation of the work undertaken.

For the higher marks you will need to provide sophisticated and rigorous interpretations of your data and provide an analysis of how significant your findings are.

This unit uses a series of statistical tasks to demonstrate how each of these strands can be achieved.

Planning your work

Statistical coursework requires careful planning if you are to gain good marks. Before undertaking any statistical investigation, it is important that you plan your work and decide exactly what you are going to investigate – do not be too ambitious!

Before you start you should:

- decide what your investigation is about and why you have chosen it
- decide how you are going to collect the information
- explain how you intend to ensure that your data is representative
- detail any presumptions which you are making.

Getting started – setting up your hypothesis

A good starting point for any statistical task is to consider the best way to collect the data and then to write a clear hypothesis you can test.

Moderator comment:
Your statistical task must always start with a 'hypothesis' where you state exactly what you are investigating and what you expect to find.

Task 1

WHAT THE PAPERS SAY

Choose a passage from two different newspapers and investigate the similarities and differences between them.

Write down a hypothesis to test.

Design and carry out a statistical experiment to test the hypothesis.

Investigate further.

Note:

Your are reminded that any coursework submitted for your GCSE examination must be your own. If you copy from someone else then you may be disqualified from the examination.

First consider different ways to compare the newspapers:

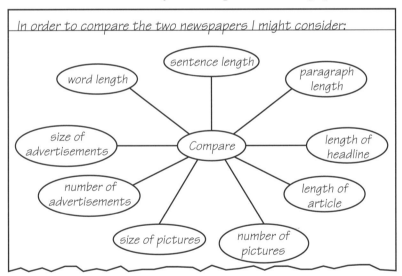

In order to compare the two newspapers I might consider:

- word length
- sentence length
- paragraph length
- size of advertisements
- Compare
- length of headline
- number of advertisements
- length of article
- size of pictures
- number of pictures

Now formulate your hypothesis.
Here are some possible hypotheses:

For my statistics coursework I am going to investigate the hypothesis that 'tabloid' papers use shorter words than 'broadsheet' newspapers.

My hypothesis is that word lengths in the tabloid newspaper will be shorter than word lengths in the broadsheet newspaper.

MODULES 2 and 4

My hypothesis is that sentence lengths in the tabloid newspaper will be shorter than sentence lengths in the broadsheet newspaper.

My hypothesis is that the number of advertisements in the tabloid newspaper will be greater than the number of advertisements in the broadsheet newspaper.

Remember:
It does not matter whether your hypotheses are true or false and you will still gain marks if your hypothesis turns out to be false.

Now you try ...
See if you can add some hypotheses of your own.
Explain how you would proceed with the task.

Choosing the right sample

Once you have decided your aims and set up a hypothesis then it is important to consider how you will test your hypothesis.

Sampling techniques include;

- **Random sampling** is where each member of the population has an equally likely chance of being selected. An easy way to do this would be to give each person a number and then choose the numbers randomly, out of a hat say.

- **Systematic sampling** is the same as random sampling except that there is some system involved such as numbering each person and then choosing every 20th number.

- **Stratified sampling** is where each person is divided into some particular group or category (strata) and the sample size is proportional to the size of the group or category in the population as a whole.

- **Convenience sampling** or opportunity sampling is one which involves simply choosing the first person to come along ... although this method is not particularly random!

Moderator comment:
It is important to choose an appropriate sample, give reasons for your choice and explain what steps you will take to avoid bias.

Moderator comment:
You should **always** say why you choose your sampling method.

MODULES 2 and 4

Here are some ways you could test the hypotheses for task 1:

Sampling method

Reason

> *To investigate my hypothesis I am going to choose a similar article from each type of newspaper and count the lengths of the first 100 words.*

> *I decided to choose similar articles because the words will be describing similar information and so will be better to make comparisons.*

> *To investigate my hypothesis I will choose every tenth page from each type of newspaper and calculate the percentage area covered by pictures.*

> *I decided to choose every tenth page from each type of newspaper because the types of articles vary throughout the newspaper (for example news headlines at the front and sports at the back of the paper).*

Collecting primary data

If you are collecting primary data then remember:

- **Observation** involves collecting information by observation and might involve participant observation (where the observer takes part in the activity), or systematic observation (where the observation happens without anyone knowing).
- **Interviewing** involves a conversation between two or more people. Interviewing can be formal (where the questions follow a strict format) or informal (where they follow a general format but can be changed around to suit the questioning).
- **Questionnaires** are the most popular way of undertaking surveys. Good questionnaires are
  - simple, short, clear and precise,
  - attractively laid and quick to complete

  and the questions are
  - not biased or offensive

Moderator comment:
It is important to carefully consider the collection of reliable data. Appropriate methods of collecting primary data might include observation, interviewing, questionnaires or experiments.

Moderator comment:
It is always a good idea to undertake a small scale 'dry run' to check for problems. This 'dry run' is called a pilot survey and can be used to impove your questionnaire or survey before it is undertaken.

MODULES 2 and 4

- written in a language which is easy to understand
- relevant to the hypothesis being investigated
- accompanied by clear instructions on how to answer the questions.

Avoiding bias

You must be very careful to avoid any possibility of bias in your work. For example, in making comparisons it is important to ensure that you are comparing like with like.

Jean undertook task 1: 'What the papers say'.
She collected this data from two newspapers by measuring (observation).

	Tabloid	Broadsheet
Number of advertisements	3	3
Number of pages	5	3
Area of each page	100 cm^2	200 cm^2

Her hypothesis is:

> The tabloid newspaper has more advertisements than the
> broadsheet newspaper.

A quick glance at the table may make her claim look true:
the broadsheet has 30 adverts but the tabloid has 35, which
is more.

However, the sizes of the newspapers are different so Jean is not really comparing like with like.

To ensure Jean compares like with like she should take account of:

- the area of the pages
- the number of pages

and so on.

Percentage coverage per page:
Tabloid $= 35 \div 50 \times 100\% = 70\%$
Broadsheet $= 30 \div 30 \times 100\% = 100\%$

This shows that:

> *The broadsheet newspaper has more advertisements per page than the tabloid newspaper.*

The total area of the pages is:

Tabloid	$= 50 \times 1000 \text{ cm}^2 = 50\,000 \text{ cm}^2$
Broadsheet	$= 30 \times 2000 \text{ cm}^2 = 60\,000 \text{ cm}^2$

So the percentage coverage is:

Tabloid	$= 35 \div 50\,000 \times 100\% = 0.07\%$
Broadsheet	$= 30 \div 60\,000 \times 100\% = 0.05\%$

This shows that:

> *The tabloid newspaper has more advertisements per area of coverage than the broadsheet newspaper.*

Note:
This still doesn't take account of the size of the adverts!

Methods and calculations

Once you have collected your data, you need to use appropriate statistical methods and calculations to process and represent your data.

You can represent the data using statistical calculations such as the mean, median, mode, range and standard deviation.

Task 2

GUESSING GAME

Dinesh asked a sample of people to estimate the length of a line and weight of a packet.

Write down a hypothesis about estimating lengths and weights and carry out your own experiment to test your hypothesis.

Investigate further.

Note:
You are reminded that any coursework submitted for your GCSE examination must be your own. If you copy from someone else then you may be disqualified from the examination.

Maurice and Angela decide to explore the hypothesis that:

> *Students are better at estimating the length of a line than the weight of a package.*

To test the hypothesis they collect data from 50 children, detailing their estimations of the length of a line and the weight of a parcel.

Here are their findings:

A table to show the estimations for the
length of a line and the weight of a parcel

	Length (cm)	Weight (g)
Mean	15.9	105.2
Median	15.5	100
Mode	14	100
Range	8.6	28
SD	1.2	2.1

Moderator comment:
It is important to consider whether information on all of these statistical calculations is essential.

Note: the actual length of the line is 10 cm and the weight of the parcel is 100 g.

Now you try ...
Using the table:

- What do you notice about the average of the length and weight?
- What do you notice about the spread of the length and weight?
- Does the information suppose the hypothesis?

Graphical representation

The data for task 2 was sorted into different categories and represented as a table.

It may be useful to show your results using graphs and diagrams as sometimes it is easier to see trends.

Graphical representations might include stem and leaf diagrams and cumulative frequency graphs.

Other statistical representations might include pie charts, bar charts, scattergraphs and histograms.

Moderator comment:
You should only use appropriate diagrams and graphs.

Once you have drawn a graph you should say what you notice from the graph:

> From my representation, I can see that the estimations for the line are generally more accurate than the estimations for the weight because:
> - the mean is closer to the actual value for the lengths and
> - the standard deviation is smaller for the lengths
>
> However, on closer inspection:
> - the percentage error on the mean is smaller for the weights
> - so the median and mode value are better averages to use for the weights

Remember to consider the possibility of bias in your data:

The percentage error for the lengths is
$$\frac{0.9}{15} \times 100 = 6\%$$
The percentage error for the weights is
$$\frac{5.2}{100} \times 100 = 5.2\%$$

Using secondary data

You may use secondary data in your coursework.

Secondary data is data that is already collected for you.

Moderator comment:
If you use secondary data there must be enough 'to allow sampling to take place' – about 50 pieces of data.

Task 3

GENDER DIFFERENCES IN EXAMINATIONS

The following information gives the GCSE examination results for Year 11 students at a local comprehensive school.

		%A*–C	%A*–G	APS
Art	Girls	66	94	4.7
	Boys	55	91	4.6
Business Studies	Girls	51	93	4.7
	Boys	65	95	5.0
English Language	Girls	62	93	4.9
	Boys	46	89	4.3
French	Girls	49	90	4.2
	Boys	41	88	4.1
Geography	Girls	43	88	4.1
	Boys	53	90	4.2
Mathematics	Girls	47	91	4.2
	Boys	45	89	4.2
Religious Education	Girls	56	92	4.9
	Boys	61	94	5.1
Science	Girls	48	91	4.4
	Boys	45	88	4.3

Note:
You are reminded that any coursework submitted for your GCSE examination must be your own. If you copy from someone else then you may be disqualified from the examination.

MODULES 2 and 4

Use the data provided to write down a hypothesis to test.

Design and carry out a statistical experiment to test your hypothesis.

Investigate further.

Jade explores the hypothesis that:

Year 11 girls do better in their GCSE examinations than boys

To test the hypothesis she decided to concentrate on the core subjects and her findings are shown in the table:

A table to show the performance of Year 11 girls and boys in their GCSE examinations

		%A*–C	%A*–G	APS
English	Girls	62	93	4.9
	Boys	46	89	4.3
	All	54	91	4.6
Mathematics	Girls	47	91	4.2
	Boys	45	89	4.2
	All	46	90	4.2
Science	Girls	48	91	4.4
	Boys	45	88	4.3
	All	47	90	4.4

Now you try ...

- What do you notice about the percentages of A*–C grades?
- What do you notice about the percentages of A*–G grades?
- What do you notice about the average point scores?
- Does the information support the hypothesis?

The data has been sorted into different categories and represented as a table.

Jade could use comparative bar charts to represent the data as it will allow her to make comparisons more easily.

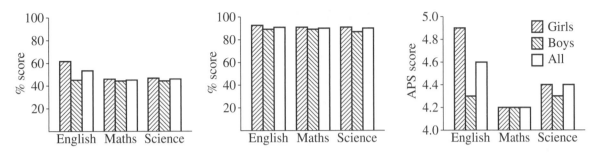

Summarising and interpreting data

Jade summarises her findings like this:

> From my graph, I can see that Year 11 girls do better in their
>
> GCSE examinations than boys in terms of A*–C grades,
>
> A*–G grades and average point scores.
>
> The performance of Year 11 girls is significantly better than boys
>
> in English although less so in mathematics.

Moderator comment:
You should refer to your original hypothesis when you summarise your results.

Moderator comment
In your conclusion you should also suggest limitations to your investigation and explain how these might be overcome.
You may wish to discuss:

- sample size
- sampling methods
- biased data
- other difficulties

Hint:
You need to appreciate that the data is more secure if the sample size is 500 rather than 50.

Extending the task

To gain better marks in your coursework you should extend the task in light of your findings.

In your extension you should:

- Give a clear hypothesis
- Collect further data if necessary

MODULES 2 and 4

- Present your findings using charts and diagrams as appropriate
- Summarise your findings referring to your hypothesis

Extending task 3: Gender differences in examinations

Jade extends the task by looking at the performance of individual students in combinations of different subjects.

> I am now going to extend my task by looking at the performance of individual students in English and mathematics. My hypothesis is that there will be no correlation between the two subjects.

She represents the data on a scattergraph:

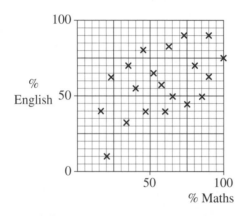

Note:
You should only draw a line of best fit on the diagram to show the correlation if you make some proper use of it (for example to calculate a students' likely English mark given their mathematics mark).

She summarises her findings:

> From my scattergraph, I can see that there is some correlation between the performance of individual students in English and mathematics.

Note:
The strength of the correlation could be measured using higher level statistical techniques such as Spearman's Rank Correlation.

She extends the task further;

> I shall now look at the performance of individual students in mathematics and science. My hypothesis is that there will be a correlation between the two subjects.

She presents the data on a scattergraph.

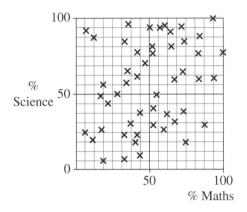

> *From my scattergraph, I can see that there is no correlation*
> *between the performance of individual students in mathematics*
> *and science.*

Extending task 2: The guessing game

Maurice extends 'The guessing game' like this:

> *I am now going to extend my task by looking to see whether*
> *people who are good at estimating lengths are also good at*
> *estimating weights. My hypothesis is that there will be a strong*
> *correlation between peoples' ability at estimating lengths and*
> *estimating weights.*

He draws a scattergraph:

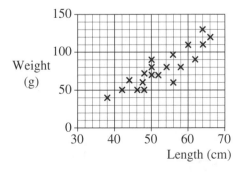

He summarises his findings:

> *From my scattergraph, I can see that there is a strong*
> *correlation between peoples' ability at estimating lengths and*
> *estimating weights.*

The strength of the correlation can be measured using higher level statistical techniques such as Spearman's Rank Collection.

I am now going to extend my investigation by using Spearman's Rank Correlation to calculate the rank correlation coefficient.

Person	Length	Weight	Rank Length	Rank Weight	Difference D	D²
Jane	15 cm	102 g	22	18	4	16
Suresh	16 cm	108 g	11	12	−1	1
					Total	2250

$$r = 1 \frac{6(\Sigma\ D^2)}{n(n^2 - 1)}$$

$$r = 1 \frac{6(2250)}{50(50^2 - 1)}$$

$$r = 1 \frac{13500}{50(2499)}$$

$$r = 1 \frac{13500}{124950}$$

$$r = 1\ - 0.108043 \ldots$$

$$r = 1\ 0.891956 \ldots$$

$$r = 1\ 0.89\ (2dp)$$

The value for the rank correlation coefficient is quite close to 1 so that there is a strong positive correlation between my results.

This tells me that there is a strong correlation between peoples' ability at estimating lengths and estimating weights and confirms my original hypothesis.

Moderator comment:
The development of the task to include higher level statistical analysis must be 'appropriate and accurate'.

50 people were in the survey so $n = 50$

Using a computer

It is quite acceptable that calculations and representations are generated by computer, as long as any such work is accompanied by some analysis and interpretation.

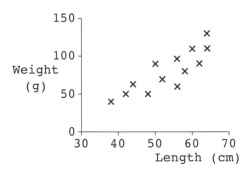

From my computer generated scattergraph, I can see that there is a strong correlation between peoples' ability at estimating lengths and estimating weights.

In this unit we have tried to give you some hints on approaching statistical coursework to gain your best possible mark.

These statistics are often useful in investigative tasks:

- Calculating averages (mean, median and mode)
- Finding the range
- Pie charts, bar charts, stem and leaf diagrams
- Constructing a cumulative frequency graph
- Finding the interquartile range
- Histograms
- Calculating the standard deviation
- Drawing a scattergraph and line of best fit
- Sampling techniques
- Discussing bias

Summary

These are the grade criteria your coursework will be marked by:

Foundation statistical task (grade E/F)

To achieve this level you must:

- set out reasonably clear aims and include a plan
- ensure that the sample size is of an appropriate size (about 25)

- collect data and make use of statistical techniques and calculations

    For example: pie charts, bar charts, stem and leaf diagrams, mean, median, mode and scattergraphs

- summarise and interpret some of your diagrams and calculations

Intermediate statistical task (grade C)

To achieve this level you must:

- set out clear aims and include a plan designed to meet those aims
- ensure that the sample size is of an appropriate size (about 50)
- give reasons for your choice of sample
- collect data and make use of statistical techniques and calculations

    For example: pie charts, bar charts, stem and leaf diagrams, mean, median, mode (of grouped data), scattergraphs and cumulative frequency

- summarise and correctly interpret your diagrams and calculations
- consider your strategies and how successful they were

Higher statistical task (grade A)

To achieve this level you must:

- set out clear aims for a more demanding problem
- include a plan which is specifically designed to meet those aims
- ensure that sample size is considered and limitations discussed
- collect relevant data and use statistical techniques and calculations

    For example: pie charts, bar charts, stem and leaf diagrams, mean, median, mode (of grouped data), scattergraphs, cumulative frequency, histograms and sampling techniques

- summarise and correctly interpret your diagrams and calculations
- use your results to respond to your original question
- consider your strategies, limitations and suggest possible improvements

ANSWERS MODULE 1

D1 Data handling 1

Exercise 1A

1. qualitative
2. quantitative, discrete
3. qualitative
4. qualitative
5. quantitative, discrete
6. quantitative, discrete
7. qualitative
8. quantitative, discrete
9. quantitative, discrete
10. quantitative, continuous
11. quantitative, discrete
12. quantitative, continuous

Exercise 1D

1. (a) 97, P, Escort 1.4 Encore, £3995; 95, N, Escort 1.4 Encore, £3485
   (b) 97, P, Red, Fiesta 1.25 Auto; 95, N, White, Escort 1.4 Encore
   (c) 00, W, Thistle, Fiesta 1.25 Ghia; 00, X, Silver, Fiesta 1.25 Ghia; 00, W, Pepper red, Focus Zetec
   (d) blue or green
   (e) 6
   (f) 97, R, Mondeo 1.8 Verona, 29 500 miles, £7495
2. (a) 8   (b) 1   (c) 4
3. (a) 5   (b) 3   (c) 1
4. (a) 2   (b) £195, Nerja   (c) 2
5. (a) M   (b) Anne-Marie and Judith; Julian, Clive and George   (c) 6   (d) 64 cm

Check out D1

1. (a) quantitative   (b) qualitative   (c) quantitative   (d) quantitative
2. (a) discrete   (c) discrete   (d) continuous
3. By checking the national population database.
4. Too expensive and time-consuming.
5. 20–50

Revision exercise D1

1. (a) 26   (b) 2   (c) 2.1
2. (a) 219   (c) He is only asking girls. He is only asking people who exercise.
   (d) (i) It is a leading question.   (ii) There is no 'No' option.
4. (a) They are uneven. The numbers are too low. 6 is included in two intervals.
   (b) Anna, she used a larger sample.
5. (a) Too personal.
   (b) In question 2 it is unclear which box to tick if you spend £20, £40 or £60 pounds.
        Also, there is no box for £80–£100. Question 3 is too vague.
6. (a) 9108 miles   (b) 9735 miles   (c) Vauxhall

D2 Data handling 2

Check in D2

1. (a) 28.8   (b) 12.5%
2. $1:2:3$

Exercise 2A

1. (a) 85   (b) 64   (c) 149
2. (a) 2   (b) 114   (c) 102   (d) 167
3. (a) Boys: 72, 63, 42; Girls 75, 48, 15   (b) (i) 72   (ii) 113
4. (a) 91   (b) 113
5. (a) 75   (b) 225   (c) 10   (d) 29   (e) 74   (f) 13

Exercise 2B

1. Frequencies are: 22, 20, 4, 4, 6, 0, 4
2. Frequencies are: 1, 8, 3, 5, 8, 7, 10, 4, 3, 1
3. Frequencies are: 4, 6, 2, 6, 2
4. Frequencies are: 4, 7, 7, 4, 6
5. Frequencies (W, M, B, G) are: 15, 10, 6, 5
6. Frequencies $(2-2\frac{1}{2}, 3-3\frac{1}{2}, 4-4\frac{1}{2}, 5-5\frac{1}{2}, 6-6\frac{1}{2}, 7-7\frac{1}{2}, 8-8\frac{1}{2}, 9-9\frac{1}{2}, 10-10\frac{1}{2}, 11-11\frac{1}{2})$ are: 2, 0, 4, 6, 13, 13, 6, 1, 4, 1

Exercise 2C

1. (a) 40   (b) 60
2. (a) 45   (b) 135
3. (a) £240   (b) 300

Exercise 2D

1. (a) 3   (b) 5   (c) 19   (d) 38
2. (a) Greece   (b) France   (c) 63   (d) 116   (e) Turkey

Exercise 2E

1. (a) blue 72°, yellow 132°, red 30°, green 42°, black 48°, brown 36°
2. (a) Ford 150°, Vauxhall 160°, Rover 50°
3. (a) sleeping 120°, eating 30°, working 135°, watching TV 30°, driving 45°
4. (a) dog 100°, cat $106\frac{2}{3}$°, goldfish $66\frac{2}{3}$°, hamster $33\frac{1}{3}$°, bird $26\frac{2}{3}$°, other $6\frac{2}{3}$°, none 20°
5. rent 84°, travel 24°, clothes 60°, food 108°, savings 48°, entertainment 36°

Exercise 2F

1. striped 108°, no tie 144°, plain 72°, spotted 36°   (b) 9°   (c) (i) 12   (ii) 16
2. (a) netball 100°, weight lifting 14°, dance 46°, hockey 90°, football 110°   (b) 23   (c) 150
3. (a) 4   (b) 120°   (c) 59
4. $x = 48°, y = 228°$
5. (a) $x = 108°, y = 51°$
   (b) camping 20, fishing 34, computing 72, historical visits 28, sporting activities 86

Exercise 2G

2. (a) 1 hour   (b) 4°F, 3 hours   (c) 6.5 hours   (d) about 100.5°F
4. (a) Sunday   (b) Thursday   (c) Monday and Friday
5. (a) 450, 1 pm   (b) 5   (c) The graph has peaks at meal times.   (d) about 335
6. (b) Saturday in the second week   (c) Sunday in the first week
7. (b) (i) 9 m   (ii) 29 m   (c) No digging took place, perhaps they were on a lunch break.
8. (c) She withdrew some money.
9. (b) The volume rose, there must have been a petrol delivery.
   (c) Between 5 pm and 6 pm, people may have been filling up after work.

Exercise 2H

3. Frequencies are 6, 3, 6, 18, 11, 11, 5

Check out D2

1. 19
7. (a) (i) semi-detached (ii) 45

Revision exercise D2

1. (a) 100   (b) 400
2. (a) (i) Britain   (ii) 18   (b) 12%
3. (a) Sector angles: 170°, 120°, 70°
   (b) (i) 480
       (iii) Most national daily newspapers are sold in the morning; the Echo is only sold in the afternoon, with sales peaking at the end of the day.
4. (a) 47   (b) 9   (c) 17
5. (a) Sector angles: 24°, 126°, 210°   (b) (i) $\frac{5}{36}$ (ii) 72
   (c) Gas, because it is the mode for the large town (there are so few houses in the small village that they have no effect).

D3 Data handling 3

Check in D3
1. (a) 322   (b) 136   (c) 99   (d) 46   (e) 2.81
2. 1, 8, 11, 12, 15, 19, 21

Exercise 3A
1. 30.6 minutes   2. 95 letters   3. 32 points   4. 266 cars
5. (a) 169.7 cm   (b) 168 cm
6. (a) £62.70   (b) £45.12
7. 10.64 seconds   8. 19

Exercise 3B
1. (a) 6   (b) 15
2. 1.80 m   3. 241–300 seconds   4. blue   5. 100 seconds

Exercise 3C
1. (a) 5   (b) 17   (c) 20   (d) 16   (e) 80.5   (f) 3.0
2. 4
4. (a) 7   (b) 5
5. 27

Exercise 3D
1. (a) £120   (b) £120   (c) £205   (d) mode or median
2. (a) mode = 6 letters, mean = 7.1 letters, median = 7 letters
   (b) mode = 8 letters, mean = 6.2 letters, median = 6.5 letters
3. median   4. median   5. mean

Exercise 3E
1. 3.3   2. 14.2   3. 161.8 cm   4. 4.65 years
5. 2.4 tonnes   6. 4 hits   7. 26.5 minutes

Exercise 3F
1. (a) Groups of three days.
   (b) Moving averages are: 156, 158.7, 147.7, 154.3, 155, 159, 160.7, 161.7, 165.3, 167.7
   (c) Attendances are increasing.
2. (a) five-point
   (b) Moving averages are: 1950, 2000, 2000, 2100, 2000, 1700, 1700, 1700, 1800, 1900, 2100
   (c) Sales fell, then rose.
3. (b) Moving averages are: 109.5, 103, 103.5, 104, 101.5, 112.5, 114, 111.5
   (d) Payments fell, then rose.
4. (b) Moving averages are: 16, 15.7, 15.5, 14.7, 15, 15, 15.5, 15.5
   (d) Profits are quite steady.
5. (b) Moving averages are: 339.3, 358.3, 374.3, 385.3, 399.3, 404, 399.3, 384.3, 376.7, 372.7
   (d) Good prospects. Agency has consistent number of vacancies which peak in the summer.
6. (b) Moving averages are: 84, 83, 81, 81, 80, 81, 80, 80, 79.5, 78.5, 79.3, 77.3, 78.2
   (d) Trend line remains fairly constant. Yes.
7. (b) Moving averages are: 43, 44, 47, 43, 44, 43, 47, 45, 47.8, 45.2, 49.6
   (d) Trend line show a slow but gradual increase in numbers attending.

Check out D3
1. 23.3
2. (a) 19   (b) 24.5
3. 9   4. Median (or possibly mode)
5. (a) 2.6 books   (b) 22.26 people
6. three-point, $61\frac{2}{3}$, 63, $60\frac{1}{3}$, $62\frac{2}{3}$, $63\frac{1}{3}$

Revision exercise D3

1. (a) (i) £3   (ii) £3.49
   (b) The 16-year-olds, because those who get pocket money receive more, but a lot of them get none at all.
2. (a) (i) $20 \leqslant t < 24$ (ii) 23 minutes   (b) 14 minutes
3. (a) £24.60   (c) The shoppers spent more, on average, on Saturday. The spread was also larger on Saturday.
4. Probably, as using midpoints gives an estimated total weight of 1240 kg.
5. (a) (i) 2   (ii) 2.28   (b) (i) 2.5   (ii) 2.63   (c) The median is too low.

D4 Data handling 4

Check in D4

1. 23

Exercise 4A

1. (a) 2   (b) 6
2. (a) £14.21   (b) £5.74
3. (a) 13.2   (b) 19
4. (a) 56.4   (b) 50
5. (a) £14.67   (b) £27

Exercise 4B

1. (a) Cumulative frequencies are: 4, 14, 28, 54, 76, 90, 97, 100   (b) 45 men
2. (a) Cumulative frequencies are: 8, 29, 70, 135, 206, 244, 250   (b) 30%
3. (a) Cumulative frequencies are: 6, 16, 34, 80, 146, 182, 196, 198, 200
   (b) Cumulative frequencies are: 2, 4, 8, 16, 32, 58, 94, 130, 172, 192, 200
4. (a) Cumulative frequencies are: 15, 25, 40, 75, 170, 350, 455, 485, 495, 500   (b) 58
5. (a) 100

Exercise 4C

1. (a) 179 cm   (b) 176 cm, 182 cm   (c) 6 cm
2. (a) 45 mph   (b) 40 mph, 49 mph   (c) 9 mph
3. (a) First set: median = 1330, interquartile range = 175; second set: median = 1620, interquartile range = 280.
4. (a) median = 55, interquartile range = 17   (b) 6%
5. (a) 12.36   (b) 93

Check out D4

1. 71
2. (a) 13   (b) 16   (c) 10   (d) 6
4. (a) 11, 26, 9   (b) positively skewed

Revision exercise D4

1. (a) 2 : 3   (b) 20%
   (c) On average, the boys shoe sizes are larger (boys mode is 5, girls mode is 4).
       The girls shoe sizes are more spread (girls range is 4, boys range is 3).
2. (a) (i) 14 minutes (ii) 5 minutes
   (b) The buses are later, on average, or the spread of lateness for the trains is higher.
3. (b) 8   (c) (i) 25 hours   (ii) 5 hours   (d) No, its interquartile range is higher.
4. (b) The spread of weights is much greater for the economy potatoes (80 g compared with 150 g).
5. (a) 242, 250, 242, 231, 216, 198, 180

D5 Data handling 5

Exercise 5B
1. High positive correlation
2. Low positive correlation
3. High positive correlation
4. High negative correlation
5. High positive correlation

Exercise 5C
1. (a) 20 cm   (b) 15 cm
2. (i) 56   (ii) 65
3. (a) £108 000   (b) 73 000
   (c) No, the data only goes up to £135 000, so the answer would be highly unreliable.
4. (c) 64
5. (a) Positive correlation   (c) 176 cm

Check out D5
2. (b) 27°C
3. (a) High positive correlation   (b) Zero correlation

Revision exercise D5
1. (a) 3400 g
   (b) The point is outside the range of data used to create the line of best fit.
2. (b) High positive correlation
   (c) 6 years
3. (c) (i) 84 km   (ii) 12.6 litres
   (d) (i) because it is within the range of the data used to create the line of best fit.

D6 Data handling 6

Check in D6
2. (a) $\frac{1}{2}$ (b) $\frac{1}{12}$ (c) $\frac{3}{20}$

Exercise 6A
1. (a) evens   (b) very unlikely   (c) evens   (d) unlikely   (e) impossible   (f) unlikely
3. $\frac{1}{4}$
4. $\frac{1}{2}$
5. $\frac{1}{4}$

Exercise 6B
2. 8, 23, 38, 31
3. $\frac{3}{5}$
4. No, the relative frequency would be about 0.25 if it was a fair pack.
5. Mary: she is unlikely to have had as many as four sevens, and if she had that would have given a relative frequency of 0.4.
6. (a) 0.38, 0.41, 0.403, 0.395   (b) 0.4

Exercise 6C
5. (a) $\frac{3}{28}$ (b) $\frac{1}{7}$ (c) $\frac{2}{7}$ (d) $\frac{13}{28}$ (e) $\frac{3}{4}$
6. (a) $\frac{7}{15}$ (b) $\frac{1}{3}$ (c) $\frac{19}{30}$ (d) $\frac{3}{8}$
7. (a) $\frac{1}{4}$ (b) $\frac{11}{20}$ (c) $\frac{3}{4}$ (d) 1   (e) 0
8. (a) $\frac{1}{4}$ (b) $\frac{3}{4}$ (c) $\frac{17}{20}$
9. $\frac{7}{18}$
10. (a) $\frac{1}{5}$ (b) $\frac{1}{5}$ (c) $\frac{3}{4}$ (d) $\frac{2}{5}$

Exercise 6D

1. (a) Mon, Tue, Wed, Thu, Fri, Sat, Sun   (b) 2
2. AB, AC, AD, AE, BC, BD, BE, CD, DE
3. ACF, ADF, AEF, ACG, ADG, AEG, BCF, BDF, BEF, BCG, BDG, BEG
4. (a) FGHI, FGIH, FHGI, FHIG, FIGH, FIHG, GFHI, GFIH, GHFI, GHIF, GIFH, GIHF, HFIG, HFGI, HIFG, HIGF, HGFI, HGIF, IFHG, IFGH, IGFH, IGHF, IHFG, IHGF
   (b) 9
5. (b) 5
6. HHH, HHT, HTH, THH, HTT, THT, TTH, TTT
7. 1–1, 1–2, 1–3, 1–4, 2–1, 2–2, 2–3, 2–4, 3–1, 3–2, 3–3, 3–4, 4–1, 4–2, 4–3, 4–4   (b) 4
8. (a) 16   (b) 6   **9.** (b) 10   **11.** (b) 12

Exercise 6E

1. (a) yes   (b) yes   (c) no   (d) yes   (e) yes   (f) no
2. (a) $\frac{1}{5}$ (b) $\frac{4}{5}$ (c) $\frac{2}{5}$ (d) $\frac{3}{5}$
3. 0.4
4. (a) $\frac{1}{11}$ (b) $\frac{6}{11}$ (c) $\frac{5}{11}$ (d) $\frac{2}{11}$ (e) $\frac{3}{11}$ (f) $\frac{5}{11}$
5. (a) $\frac{1}{75}$ (b) 0.995
6. $\frac{91}{100}$ **7.** 0.506   **8.** 75%
9. (a) $\frac{1}{17}$ (b) $\frac{49}{51}$ (c) $\frac{4}{17}$
10. (a) 0.1   (b) 0.6

Exercise 6F

1. $\frac{1}{36}$
2. (a) $\frac{1}{78}$ (b) $\frac{1}{4}$ (c) $\frac{3}{26}$
3. (a) $\frac{1}{100}$ (b) $\frac{9}{100}$ (c) $\frac{49}{100}$ (d) $\frac{9}{100}$
4. $\frac{4}{25}$
5. (a) $\frac{2}{35}$ (b) $\frac{2}{21}$ (c) $\frac{8}{35}$
6. $\frac{1}{128}$
7. (a) $\frac{4}{25}$ (b) $\frac{27}{125}$ (c) $\frac{36}{625}$
8. (a) $\frac{1}{9}$ (b) $\frac{2}{9}$ (c) $\frac{1}{6}$
9. (a) $\frac{1}{32}$ (b) $\frac{3}{32}$ (c) $\frac{1}{2}$ (d) $\frac{9}{16}$

Exercise 6G

1. (b) $\frac{25}{64}$ (c) $\frac{9}{64}$ (d) $\frac{39}{64}$
2. (b) (i) $\frac{17}{75}$ (ii) $\frac{101}{200}$
3. (a) 0.042 875   (b) 0.274 625   (c) 0.443 625
4. (a) 0.12   (b) 0.56
5. $\frac{1}{36}$
6. (a) $\frac{1}{12}$ (b) $\frac{5}{36}$ (c) $\frac{1}{2}$
7. (a) $\frac{1}{64}$ (b) $\frac{9}{64}$ (c) $\frac{1}{8}$
8. (a) 17%   (b) 9%   (c) 41%

Exercise 6H

1. 1185
2. (a) 25   (b) 75   (c) 100
3. (a) (i) $\frac{2}{21}$ (ii) $\frac{2}{7}$ (iii) $\frac{1}{3}$ (b) (i) 64   (ii) 150
4. 5000
5. (a) 0.62   (b) 684
6. (a) 1–1, 1–2, 1–3, 2–1, 2–2, 2–3, 3–1, 3–2, 3–3   (b) 3   (c) 200
7. (a) $\frac{4}{15}$ (b) 8
8. (a) $\frac{1}{14}$ (b) (i) 280   (ii) 180   (c) 42

Check out D6

2. $\frac{37}{50}$

3. (a) $\frac{1}{13}$ (b) $\frac{1}{2}$

4. $\frac{2}{3}$

6. 0.288

7. 161

8. (a) $\frac{1}{36}$ (b) $\frac{5}{18}$ (c) $\frac{25}{36}$

9. $\frac{7}{30}$

Revision exercise D6

1. (a) 1–2, 1–3, 1–4, 2–2, 2–3, 2–4, 3–2, 3–3, 3–4   (b) $\frac{2}{9}$

2. (a) 0.72   (b) 0.26

3. (a) $\frac{7}{9}$ (b) $\frac{4}{5}$ (c) 0.24   (d) No, the proportions are very similar.

4. (a) $\frac{5}{19}$ (b) 0.75

5. (a) 90   (b) 0.42

6. (a) $\frac{1}{15}$ (b) $\frac{2}{5}$ (c) $\frac{2}{15}$

7. (b) 200

8. (a) (i) 1–2, 1–4, 1–6, 2–2, 2–4, 2–6, 3–2, 3–4, 3–6   (ii) $\frac{2}{3}$ (iii) $\frac{1}{3}$

     (b) (i) $\frac{1}{6}$ (ii) $\frac{2}{3}$

9. (a) (ii) $\frac{1}{4}$ (b) $\frac{5}{36}$

Module 1 Practice calculator test

1. (a) 248°   (b) Sectors: 248°, 72°, 24°, 16°

2. (a) The rows are: 2, 1, 1; 1, 2, 0; 1, 0, 2   (b) $\frac{2}{9}$

3. (a) 46   **4.** 16, 17   **5.** $\frac{27}{64}$

Module 1 Practice non-calculator test

1. (a) 0.3   (b) 0.8

2. (a) 6   (b) 10   (c) 7

3. (a) (i) *C*   (ii) *B*   (iii) *D*

     (b) The more time pupils spent revising, the better their tests results were.

5. (a) 45   (b) 16   (c) 46

ANSWERS MODULE 3

N1 Number 1

Exercise 1A

1. (a) Three hundred and forty   (b) Five hundred and eighty

     (c) Two thousand, one hundred and thirty   (d) Six thousand, eight hundred and two

     (e) Twenty-one thousand and five

2. (a) 2024   (b) 317   (c) 9307   (d) 8830   (e) 1 020 056

3. (a) 200   (b) 80   (c) 3000

4. (a) Nine thousand, four hundred and twelve   (b) Four thousand, two hundred and ten

     (c) Two thousand, seven hundred and sixty-four   (d) Nine thousand, three hundred and twenty-seven

     (e) Two thousand, one hundred

5. (a) 2 060 000   (b) 300 000   (c) 90 743   (d) 26 005

Exercise 1B

1. (a) $^-$12, 14 (b) $^-$12, $^-$4, 2, 14, 24 (c) 2, 5, 11 (d) 2, 5 (e) 24
2. 7, 11, 25, 31 (b) 7, 11, 31 (c) 16 (d) 4, 16 (e) 4, 16, 25
3. (a) 14 (b) 5, 41 (c) 14, 21, 35 (d) 14, 21 (e) 9
4. (a) 10, 16, 24, 42 (b) 5, 7 (c) 24, 42 (d) 16, 24 (e) 16
5. (a) 11, 13, 15, 35 (b) 11, 13 (c) 11, 22, 44 (d) 11, 22 (e) none
6. (a) $^-$5, $^-$2 (b) $^-$5, 21 (c) none (d) 6, 12, 21

Exercise 1C

1. (a) 81 (b) 8 (c) 36 (d) $\frac{1}{4}$
2. (a) 9 (b) 15 (c) 12 (d) 13
3. (a) 2 (b) 3 (c) 5 (d) $\frac{1}{2}$
4. (a) 0.25 (b) 0.1 (c) 7 (d) 5 (e) 4 (f) 1.5
5. (a) 29 (b) 144 (c) $^-$5
6. (a) $2\sqrt{5}$ (b) $4\sqrt{3}$ (c) $6\sqrt{2}$ (d) $4\sqrt{10}$

Exercise 1D

1. (a) $2^3 \times 3$ (b) $2 \times 3 \times 7$ (c) $2^5 \times 3$ (d) $2^4 \times 7$ (e) $2^3 \times 3^2$
2. (a) 6 (b) 2 (c) 11 (d) 12 (e) 14 (f) 4
3. (a) 175 (b) 48 (c) 60 (d) 480 (e) 450 (f) 280
4. 4 min 40 s after noon
5. 24

Exercise 1E

1. (a) 7 and 23 (b) 36 and 11 (c) 7 and 15 (d) 46 and 23
2. (a) 24 and 76 (b) 76 and 36 (c) 36 and 18
3. (a) 12 and 48 (b) 48 and 36 (c) 19 and 21 (d) 48 and 12 (e) 14 and 21
4. (a) 24 and 36 (b) 36 and 12 (c) 12 and 24 (d) 24 and 8 or 36 and 12
5. (a) 18 and 270 (b) 18 and 45 (c) 9 and 18

Exercise 1F

1. (a) 1556 (b) 3613 (c) 15 138 (d) 1861 (e) 4085
2. (a) 553 (b) 421 (c) 655 (d) 5619 (e) 1378
3. (a) 324 (b) 1888 (c) 6244 (d) 26 075 (e) 31 191
   (f) 25 488 (g) 26 049 (h) 30 504 (i) 25 839
4. (a) 16 (b) 12 (c) 21 (d) 26 (e) 15 (f) 29
   (g) 13 (h) 13 (i) 26 (j) 29 (k) 19 (l) 35
5. (a) (i) 250 (ii) 367 (iii) 591
   (b) (i) 135 (ii) 149 (iii) 593
   (c) (i) 353 (ii) 558 (iii) 1044

Exercise 1G

1. 19 2. 36 3. 32 4. 32 5. 45
6. 2 7. 3 8. 62 9. 32 10. $^-$20

Exercise 1H

1. 65 2. 95.6 3. 100.65 4. 76.03
5. 73.4 6. 140.849 7. 17.4 8. 22.3
9. 10.73 10. 212.38 11. 456.74 12. 13.65

Exercise 1I

1. 140.4 2. 505.8 3. 2006.2 4. 6.6
5. 4.2 6. 26.9 7. 60 000 8. 180 000
9. 90 000 10. 8000 11. 0.0015 12. 0.012
13. 0.0001 14. 5000 15. 25 16. 150

Exercise 1J

1. (a) 10   (b) 32   (c) 20   (d) 500
2. (a) 7000   (b) 700   (c) 0.28
3. £90   4. £80   5. 12p   6. £280   7. 10 000 FF

Exercise 1K

1. 37.48   2. 4.85   3. 27.39   4. 113.5   5. 27.4   6. 29.0
7. 37.50   8. 30.70   9. 39.9   10. 37.5   11. 28.7   12. 380
13. 3000   14. 20.4   15. 0.000 75   16. 0.0089   17. 0.009   18. 0.0340

Exercise 1L

1. 5   2. 5 bunches, £30   3. 29p   4. 3p   5. 18p   6. 13

Exercise 1M

1. (a) 1   (b) 4   (c) $^-3$ (d) 3   (e) $^-17$
2. £38.04 credit   3. £46 overdrawn   4. $^-783$ feet   5. 2739 below sea level   6. $^-9°$

Exercise 1N

1. (a) $^-24$ (b) $^-40$ (c) 21   (d) 24
2. (a) $^-55$ (b) 48   (c) 15   (d) $^-28$
3. (a) 96   (b) 105   (c) $^-40$ (d) 30
4. (a) $^-24$ (b) $^-15$ (c) $^-56$ (d) $^-12$
5. (a) 4   (b) $^-27$ (c) $^-60$ (d) $^-26$

Check out N1

1. (a) 5, 11, 17   (b) 25   (c) 8, 22   (d) 8   (e) 11, 22
2. (a) 121   (b) 64   (c) 4096   (d) 6   (e) 4
3. (a) 6   (b) 120
4. (a) (i) 4633   (ii) 1956   (b) (i) 28 314   (ii) 28
5. 18
6. (a) 46.32   (b) 24.546
7. 20 000   8. 1.28
9. (a) $^-3°C$ (b) $^-£18.43$

Revision exercise N1

1. (a) (i) 38   (ii) $\frac{1}{4}$ (b) 2.65   (c) 343
2. 5.6
3. (a) 273.8   (b) 49.1   (c) (i) 225   (ii) 15
4. (a) 31.3   (b) 30
5. (a) $2^3 \times 3^2$ (b) 54
6. (a) 250   (b) (i) $p = 2, q = 3$ (ii) 2×3^2 (iii) 72
7. (a) 36   (b) 1   (c) 4.2

N2 Number 2

Check in N2

1. 6, 252
2. (a) 14   (b) 3   (c) 3

Exercise 2A

1. (a) $\frac{5}{8}$ (b) five eighths
2. (a) $\frac{3}{4}$ (b) three quarters
3. $\frac{3}{5}$
4. (a) $\frac{2}{3}$ (b) two thirds
5. (a) $\frac{1}{4}$ (b) one quarter

Exercise 2B

3. (a) $\frac{3}{5} = \frac{6}{10} = \frac{9}{15} = \frac{15}{25}$ (b) $\frac{3}{7} = \frac{6}{14} = \frac{12}{28} = \frac{15}{35}$ (c) $\frac{35}{42}$

    (d) $\frac{8}{12}$ (e) $\frac{28}{63}$ (f) $\frac{45}{50}$ (g) $\frac{16}{40}$ (h) $\frac{42}{48}$

4. (a) $\frac{1}{4}$ (b) $\frac{3}{7}$ (c) $\frac{5}{8}$ (d) $\frac{3}{4}$ (e) $\frac{5}{6}$

5. (a) $\frac{1}{4}$ (b) $\frac{3}{4}$

6. (a) $\frac{2}{3}$ (b) $\frac{4}{9}$

Exercise 2C

1. (a) $\frac{13}{10}$ (b) $\frac{9}{2}$ (c) $\frac{13}{5}$ (d) $\frac{41}{9}$

    (e) $\frac{31}{4}$ (f) $\frac{71}{15}$ (g) $\frac{31}{8}$ (h) $\frac{38}{7}$

2. (a) $3\frac{1}{2}$ (b) $4\frac{3}{4}$ (c) $5\frac{4}{5}$ (d) $3\frac{9}{10}$

    (e) $3\frac{5}{6}$ (f) $4\frac{3}{4}$ (g) $3\frac{8}{11}$ (h) $7\frac{2}{7}$

4. (a) $\frac{18}{10}$ (b) $\frac{27}{12}$ (c) $\frac{68}{20}$

5. (a) $2\frac{1}{2}$ (b) $1\frac{1}{2}$ (c) $3\frac{3}{4}$ (d) $3\frac{1}{2}$

Exercise 2D

1. (a) 9   (b) 40   (c) 24 cm

    (d) 75   (e) 456 cars   (f) 91 people

2. 72   **3.** £76   **4.** 120   **5.** 100

Exercise 2E

1. (a) $\frac{5}{7}$ (b) $\frac{3}{4}$ (c) $1\frac{1}{5}$ (d) $1\frac{3}{8}$ (e) $\frac{3}{4}$ (f) 1

2. (a) $4\frac{3}{8}$ (b) $5\frac{5}{8}$ (c) $5\frac{1}{16}$ (d) $5\frac{1}{8}$ (e) $6\frac{1}{6}$ (f) $3\frac{11}{30}$

3. $\frac{33}{50}$ kg   **4.** $\frac{29}{40}$

6. (a) $\frac{1}{6}$ (b) $\frac{5}{8}$ (c) $\frac{3}{7}$ (d) $\frac{1}{4}$ (e) $\frac{1}{3}$ (f) $\frac{1}{2}$

7. (a) $1\frac{1}{5}$ (b) $2\frac{1}{9}$ (c) $1\frac{4}{15}$ (d) $3\frac{4}{9}$ (e) $1\frac{13}{24}$ (f) $2\frac{34}{35}$

8. $1\frac{33}{40}$ kg   **9.** $1\frac{5}{8}$ m

Exercise 2F

1. (a) $\frac{3}{8}$ (b) $\frac{5}{14}$ (c) $\frac{4}{15}$ (d) $\frac{1}{6}$

    (e) $\frac{2}{7}$ (f) $\frac{11}{20}$ (g) $\frac{7}{10}$ (h) $\frac{33}{64}$

2. (a) $\frac{9}{16}$ (b) $\frac{9}{14}$ (c) $13\frac{1}{2}$ (d) $13\frac{1}{2}$

    (e) $3\frac{3}{4}$ (f) $4\frac{1}{5}$ (g) $1\frac{13}{15}$

3. (a) $9\frac{1}{6}$ (b) $1\frac{4}{5}$ (c) $2\frac{4}{5}$ (d) $1\frac{2}{3}$ (e) $1\frac{1}{3}$

4. (a) 36 pints   (b) 180 people   (c) 120 toys   (d) 570 cars

5. $45\frac{1}{3}$ hours

7. (a) $\frac{2}{5}$ (b) $3\frac{3}{5}$ (c) $\frac{2}{3}$ (d) $\frac{2}{9}$

    (e) $\frac{9}{16}$ (f) $2\frac{1}{10}$ (g) $1\frac{4}{5}$ (h) $\frac{9}{14}$

8. (a) $\frac{8}{9}$ (b) $\frac{2}{3}$ (c) $\frac{2}{3}$ (d) $\frac{25}{39}$ (e) $1\frac{1}{4}$ (f) $3\frac{1}{11}$

9. 6   **10.** 60

Exercise 2G

1. (a) $\frac{3}{10}$ (b) $\frac{2}{5}$ (c) $\frac{7}{10}$ (d) $\frac{9}{10}$

2. (a) 0.25   (b) 0.4   (c) 0.75   (d) 0.2

3. (a) $\frac{12}{25}$ (b) $\frac{7}{25}$ (c) $\frac{16}{25}$ (d) $\frac{23}{25}$

4. (a) $0.\dot{1}4285 7\dot{1}$ (b) 0.03   (c) $0.8\dot{3}$ (d) $0.0\dot{6}$

5. (a) $\frac{3}{8}$ (b) $\frac{1}{16}$ (c) $\frac{12}{25}$ (d) $\frac{77}{80}$

Exercise 2H

1. (a) $\frac{7}{2}$ (b) $\frac{21}{4}$ (c) $\frac{36}{5}$ (d) $\frac{13}{3}$
2. (a) $2\frac{1}{2}$ (b) $1\frac{2}{5}$ (c) $1\frac{5}{6}$ (d) $3\frac{3}{7}$
3. (a) $2\frac{1}{4}$, 2.25   (b) $2\frac{1}{5}$, 2.22   (c) $5\frac{1}{2}$, 5.5   (d) $9\frac{1}{2}$, 9.5
4. (a) $3\frac{1}{2}$ (b) $7\frac{2}{5}$ (c) $11\frac{1}{5}$ (d) $9\frac{1}{4}$
5. (a) $2\frac{3}{5}$ (b) $3\frac{3}{10}$ (c) $4\frac{3}{4}$ (d) $7\frac{2}{7}$

Exercise 2I

1. (a) £12.50   (b) £6.40   (c) £27.30   (d) £9   (e) £10.50
   (f) £47.60   (g) £4.80   (h) £2.94   (i) £20.40
2. 60
3. 64
4. 17 496
5. £94

Exercise 2J

1. (a) (i) $\frac{1}{5}$ (ii) 0.2   (b) (i) $\frac{3}{10}$ (ii) 0.3   (c) (i) $\frac{11}{20}$ (ii) 0.55
   (d) (i) $\frac{7}{20}$ (ii) 0.35   (e) (i) $\frac{11}{50}$ (ii) 0.22
2. (a) (i) 30%   (ii) $\frac{3}{10}$ (b) (i) 70%   (ii) $\frac{7}{10}$ (c) (i) 15%   (ii) $\frac{3}{20}$
   (d) (i) 35%   (ii) $\frac{7}{20}$ (e) (i) 58%   (ii) $\frac{29}{50}$
3. (a) (i) 75%   (ii) 0.75   (b) (i) 40%   (ii) 0.4
   (c) (i) 10%   (ii) 0.1   (d) (i) 15%   (ii) 0.15

Check out N2

1. $\frac{15}{25}$
2. (a) $4\frac{5}{8}$ (b) $\frac{11}{5}$
3. (a) £16.20   (b) £13.20   (c) £4.55
4. (a) $1\frac{3}{20}$ (b) $\frac{11}{35}$ (c) $3\frac{1}{3}$ (d) $\frac{7}{16}$ (e) $\frac{3}{5}$ (f) $1\frac{3}{8}$
5. (a) (i) $\frac{2}{5}$ (ii) 0.4   (b) (i) $\frac{3}{10}$ (ii) 30%

Revision exercise N2

1. (a) £50.40   (b) £56   (c) $\frac{7}{15}$
2. (a) (i) 80p   (ii) 42p   (iii) 60p   (b) 56.5 g
3. (a) £39.95   (b) £39.17
4. (a) 22.4%   (b) 1 : 7

N3 Number 3

Check in N3

1. (a) (i) 2340   (ii) 2026.9   (b) (i) 28.91   (ii) 0.347
2. (a) 47p   (b) 17p

Exercise 3A

1. (a) 7830   (b) 38 400   (c) 2 950 000   (d) 34 700
2. (a) 39.4   (b) 2.748   (c) 0.412   (d) 0.29
3. (a) 7420   (b) 25 700   (c) 413.4   (d) 8750.1
4. (a) 0.342   (b) 0.0718   (c) 0.028   (d) 0.000 034
5. (a) 740.02   (b) 241.3   (c) 0.0024   (d) 0.034

Exercise 3B

1. 230 cm
2. 0.314 m
3. (a) 148.7 m
   (b) 1.487 m
4. 2.47 cm
5. 3920 m
6. (a) 0.254 m
   (b) 0.000 254 km
7. (a) 48 900 cm
   (b) 0.489 km

Exercise 3C

1. 0.278 kg
2. 0.394 g
3. (a) 0.0074 kg
   (b) 7400 mg
4. (a) 2900 kg
   (b) 2 900 000 g
5. (a) 0.453 kg
   (b) 453 000 mg

Exercise 3D

1. (a) 1.748 kg
   (b) 3450 m
   (c) 2850 g
   (d) 0.4125 litres
   (e) 8948.7 cm
   (f) 0.9248 km
2. 0.75 litres
3. 355.3 m
4. 66 g
5. (a) 1.06 m
   (b) 1060 mm

Exercise 3E

1. (a) 45 inches
   (b) 32 pints
   (c) 7 feet 10 inches
   (d) 158 lb
   (e) 144 oz
   (f) 92 inches
   (g) 10.5 gallons
   (h) 5808 feet
2. 16 pints
3. (a) $11\frac{1}{4}$ feet by $9\frac{5}{6}$ feet
   (b) 135 inches by 118 inches
4. $1\frac{1}{6}$ feet by $\frac{7}{8}$ foot
5. 360 feet by 210 feet

Exercise 3F

1. (a) 17.8 cm
   (b) 68.6 cm
   (c) 295 cm
   (d) 1.9 kg
   (e) 0.34 kg
   (f) 26.8 kg
   (g) 12.6 litres
   (h) 34.2 litres
2. (a) 12.6 inches
   (b) 189 inches
   (c) 10.6 miles
   (d) 5.2 miles
   (e) 0.472 lb
   (f) 9.24 lb
   (g) 15.6 gallons
   (h) 20.9 gallons
3. 654 miles
4. 3.55 kg
5. 31.2 lb

Exercise 3G

1. (a) 0315
   (b) 0520
   (c) 1520
   (d) 1740
   (e) 1430
   (f) 0115
   (g) 0750
   (h) 1745
2. (a) 8.20 am
   (b) 9.45 am
   (c) 4.40 pm
   (d) 6.20 pm
   (e) 12.15 am
   (f) 11.10 pm
3. 5 hours 45 minutes
4. 4 hours 45 minutes
5. 7 hours
6. 8 hours 20 minutes
7. 8 hours 15 minutes
8. 2 hours 33 minutes
9. (a) 23 minutes
   (b) 3 hours 44 minutes
10. 2.05 pm

Exercise 3H

1. 36 mph
2. 30 mph
3. 2625 miles
4. 322 km
5. 3 hours 25 minutes
6. (a) 9 hours 11 minutes
   (b) 8 hours 6 minutes
7. 16.5 mph
8. 2.77
9. 18.75
10. £5.26
11. 1.13
12. 2.86 cm^3

Check out N3

1. (a) 3.75 m
   (b) 201 cl
2. (a) 40 in
   (b) 31 lb
3. (a) 11 lb
   (b) 16 km
   (c) 90 cm
4. (a) 3 hours 30 minutes
   (b) 5 hours 55 minutes
5. (a) 28 mph
   (b) 32 mph
   (c) 4 hours 18 minutes

Revision exercise N3

1. (a) 2.5 kg   (b) 3
2. (a) 166 cm   (b) 14%
3. (a) 32   (b) £1.95   (c) 495 g
4. (a) 1705   (b) 1 hour 44 minutes
5. (a) 40 mph   (b) 1204
6. (a) 62.4 kg   (b) 10%   (c) (i) 53.5 kg   (ii) 119 lb
7. (a) 1.5×10^6 (b) 1.2×10^8 (c) 200 g
8. 0924
9. (a) 2.25×10^7 (b) 0.0095 cm

N4 Number 4

Check in N4

1. (a) £28.80   (b) £14   (b) £7.60   (d) £16.65
2. 32p

Exercise 4A

1. £45.65   **2.** £54.60   **3.** £90.88   **4.** £91.64   **5.** £49.95
6. £36.40   **7.** £33.75   **8.** £36   **9.** 24 h 30 min
10. (a)   29 hours 15 minutes   (b) 7p

Exercise 4B

1. £37.50   **2.** £28   **3.** £33.83   **4.** £41.54
5. £284.41   **6.** £314.76   **7.** 4 hours   **8.** 3 hours 20 minutes

Exercise 4C

1. (a) £755   (b) £75.50
2. £129.30   **3.** £113.30   **4.** £91.30   **5.** £8.31   **6.** £392.96   **7.** £1327.65
8. (a) £7789   (b) £1547.07
9. (a) £10 805   (b) £2240.75
10. (a) £21 277   (b) £4649.31

Exercise 4D

1. (a) £4   (b) £84
2. £147   **3.** £77.19   **4.** £97.19
5. (a) £131.08   (b) £880.08
6. (a) £22.40   (b) £150.40
7. £4.96   **8.** £19.18   **9.** £452.02
10. £56.95   **11.** £7893.62   **12.** £6.27

Exercise 4E

1. (a) £4.50   (b) 36%
2. 60%   **3.** 66.7%
4. (a) 85%   (b) 15%
5. (a) £13.80   (b) £7590
6. (a) 46p   (b) £115   (c) 91.7%
7. (a) £1.39   (b) £823.80

Exercise 4F

1. £72   **2.** £370.24   **3.** 2.96%   **4.** £534.88   **5.** 2.26%
6. £375   **7.** £46.20   **8.** £128.13   **9.** £509.58   **10.** £306.04
11. £307.56   **12.** £45.91   **13.** £2774.84   **14.** £1460.45   **15.** £874.63
16. £35 100.53   **17.** £2306.23   **18.** £4242.14   **19.** £8697.02

Exercise 4G

1. (a) £245   (b) £35
2. (a) £171.95   (b) £22
3. (a) £3850   (b) £800
4. (a) £217.75   (b) £18.75
5. (a) £545.70   (b) £46.70
6. (a) £348   (b) £48.01
7. (a) £274.80   (b) £14.81
8. (a) £594   (b) £14

Exercise 4H

1. 2.4-litre pack   2. 100 sheets   3. 5 tapes   4. 10 litres   5. 0.75-litre bottle
6. 1.25 litres   7. 450 g   8. 36 biscuits   9. 450 g   10. 36 tiles

Exercise 4I

1. £10   2. £18.33   3. £1.53   4. £20.54   5. £85.24   6. £1.85
7. £5.30   8. £10.32   9. £15.35   10. £3.90   11. £18.83
12. (a) $61.09   (b) £41.56

Check out N4

1. £163.24   2. £25.50   3. £1255.30
4. (a) £6.62   (b) £385.99
5. 58%
6. (a) £108   (b) £1814.12
7. 1 kg pack
8. (a) £33.52   (b) 148.5 krone

Revision exercise N4

1. (a) 37p   (b) 145 g stick
2. £34.69
3. (a) £6.54   (b) 3%
4. £40.72
5. £2289.80
6. (a) (i) £7.22   (ii) £181.94   (b) £52.49
7. The small bottle.
8. (a) £828   (b) 26%
9. (a) £8532   (b) 18%

Module 3 Practice calculator test

1. (a) 140   (b) 49
2. £3.24
3. (a) 2.2   (b) 2.015, $\sqrt{4.56}$, 2.15, 1.48^2, $2\frac{1}{5}$
4. (a) £4000   (b) 321%
5. £69.80
6. 2.39
7. At least one of the numbers is divisible by 2 and exactly one of the numbers is divisible by 3, so their product is divisible by 2 and 3 and so must be divisible by 6.
8. £214.96
9. £39.60

Module 3 Practice non-calculator test

1. (a) (i) 1.6 kg   (ii) £1.12   (iii) 20   (b) 45 g
2. (a) $4\frac{4}{5}$ (b) 13   (c) (i) 0.0009   (ii) 1   (d) 0.2
3. 3
4. £56
5. 8 hours 24 minutes
6. 2.4×10^{15}

ANSWERS   MODULE 5

AS1 Algebra 1

Check in AS1
1. (a) 3^7 (b) 3^2
2. (a) $^-12$ (b) $^-10$ (c) 30

Exercise 1A
1. (a) $p - 5$ (b) $6p$
2. (a) $4s$ (b) $4s - 5$ (c) $s - 5$
3. (a) $25n$ pence
4. $\dfrac{b}{4}$
5. (a) 27 (b) 135 (c) $9g$
6. (a) $c + 4$ (b) $c - 2$ (c) $c + x$
7. $6b$ **8.** $5x + 3y$ **9.** $n - m$ centimetres
10. $5w$ grams   **11.** $\dfrac{r}{9}$
12. £$(3x + 5y)$
13. (a) £st (b) £$(25 - st)$

Exercise 1B
1. $6a$ **2.** $6b$ **3.** $3c$ **4.** ^-d
5. $e - 3$ **6.** $t + 5s$ **7.** $2 - a$ **8.** $b + 9c$
9. $2 - 3x - 2c$ **10.** $4a + 2b - 2c$ **11.** $3c + d$ **11.** $2c - 2$
13. $7x - 3y - 1$ **14.** $9c - 2a - 2b$ **15.** $1 - b$ **16.** $y - x - 3z$

Exercise 1C
1. $3a$ **2.** $20b$ **3.** $8ab$ **4.** $60st$ **5.** $120gpr$
6. $2qy$ **7.** $\dfrac{ab}{c}$ **8.** $\dfrac{3ac}{b}$ **9.** ^-12xy **10.** $\dfrac{^-4pr}{q}$
11. ^-216rst **12.** ^-60abc **13.** $^-2x^3$ **14.** ^-4s

Exercise 1D
1. a^7 **2.** b^2 **3.** w^{12} **4.** d^4 **5.** t
6. a^9 **7.** x^{14} **8.** x^9 **9.** $16x^4$
10. $64x^6$ **11.** 1 **12.** x^{-2} **13.** $9a^8$
14. $\frac{4}{5}a^4$ **15.** $\frac{2}{3}d^2$ **16.** a^5b^6 **17.** $96b^5c^4$
18. $\dfrac{2x}{y}$ **19.** 1 **20.** $6d$ **21.** $\dfrac{3x^3y^2}{2z^4}$ **22.** $\dfrac{49y^4}{2wx^7}$

Exercise 1E
1. $4x + 4y$ **2.** $6x + 12y$ **3.** $10x - 5y$ **4.** $5a - 5b + 5c$ **5.** $p^2 + pq$
6. $12x - 8$ **7.** $3y^2 - 2y$ **8.** $4y^2 - 24y$ **9.** $6x^4 - 4x^2$ **10.** $10r - 2$
11. $10x - 5y$ **12.** $10m - 7n$ **13.** $2t^3 + t^2$ **14.** $x + 3y$ **15.** $a + 5b$
16. $ab - 3a$ **17.** $20c^2 - 23c + 3$ **18.** $2x - x^2$ **19.** $3x^2 - x^4 - x$ **20.** $10x^4 + 5x^3$

Exercise 1F
1. (a) $3(a + b)$ (b) $2(5a - 6b)$ (c) $4(3x + 4y)$ (d) $b(a - c)$
     (e) $d(d - 1)$ (f) $2m(m + 2)$ (g) $3c^2(c + 1)$ (h) $9x(4 - 3x)$

2. (a) $4(5x + 2y)$ (b) $3(9a - 11b)$ (c) $7(5p + 7q)$ (d) $6(5x - 4y)$
    (e) $2(6a + 4b - 5c)$ (f) $8(2x - y + 3z)$ (g) $4(2 - 3x)$ (h) $3x(3y + 4)$
    (i) $3a(2a - 3b)$ (j) $x(x - 3)$ (k) $3p(p - 3q + 9)$ (l) $p(1 - p)$
    (m) $8(6m + n - 3x)$ (n) $5(5x^2 - 6y^2)$ (o) $7ab(a + 4b)$ (p) $2x(x - 2)$
    (q) $\pi r(2 + h)$ (r) $x^2(x + 1)$

Exercise 1G

1. 4	**2.** 17	**3.** 8	**4.** 11.4	**5.** 6.5
6. 12	**7.** 7.5	**8.** 14	**9.** 6	**10.** 13.5
11. 1	**12.** $^-4$	**13.** 3	**14.** 8	**15.** 4
16. 38	**17.** 3	**18.** 3.5	**19.** 9	**20.** 12
21. 7.5	**22.** 1.5	**23.** 5	**24.** 8	**25.** 21
26. 12				

Exercise 1H

1. 0	**2.** 5.5	**3.** 1	**4.** 2	**5.** 5
6. 3	**7.** 3	**8.** 1.5	**9.** $^-4$	**10.** 0.8
11. 2.25	**12.** $^-1.5$	**13.** 1.5	**14.** $^-8$	**15.** 2
16. 1.5	**17.** $^-12$	**18.** 25	**19.** 15	**20.** 6.625
21. $\frac{2}{3}$	**22.** 3.2	**23.** $\frac{5}{3}$	**24.** $^-4.75$	

Exercise 1I

1. 10	**2.** 36	**3.** 13	**4.** 14.5	**5.** 9.5
6. 16	**7.** 11.3	**8.** 7	**9.** 58, 59, 60	**10.** 205
11. 6.5 cm	**12.** 8.7 cm	**13.** 4.5 cm	**14.** 7.5 cm	**15.** 39 years old
16. 10 years old				

Exercise 1J

1. $s = g + b$ **2.** $A = x^2$ **3.** $A = bh$ **4.** $s = \dfrac{d}{t}$ **5.** $A = lw$

6. $P = 2w + 2l$ **7.** $p = x + y + z$ **8.** $w = xh$ **9.** $L = B - \dfrac{xs}{100}$

Exercise 1K

1. 141   **2.** 126
3. (i) 5   (ii) $^-3$ (iii) 11
4. 72.8
5. (i) 54   (ii) 14   (iii) 30
6. (i) 36   (ii) 36
7. (i) $\frac{1}{64}$ (ii) $\frac{1}{400}$
8. (i) 20   (ii) $^-5$
9. 45   **10.** 60
12. (a) 59°F   (b) 108°F
13. (a) 10.37   (b) 185
14. (a) 3.94   (b) 3.95
15. 2.24
16. (a) 85.5   (b) 126

Check out AS1

1. $x + 5$
2. (a) $5a$ (b) $6a - 4b$ (c) $a - b$ (d) $3a - 2b - 4c$
3. (a) $2a + 2b$ (b) $12a + 11b$
4. (a) $60a^9b^4$ (b) $3a^3b^2$
5. (a) $21p^{13}$ (b) $2p^4$
6. (a) $10x - 15$ (b) $^-16x - 28y + 20$ (c) $6x^2 + 12x^3 - 18x^4$
7. (a) $4(y - 2)$ (b) $3a(b - 2c)$ (c) $3x(x + 2y)$ (d) $4x(x - 2)$

8. (a) 2   (b) 5   (c) $1\frac{2}{7}$
9. $x = 14$
10. (a) 2   (b) 196π

Revision exercise AS1

1. (a) $4x$ (b) $4m - 1$ (c) $x = 6$ (d) $x = 3$ (e) $x = 1.5$
2. (a) $5x + 1$ (b) (i) $x = 3$ (ii) 5
3. (a) $500x$ kg   (b) 2.4 kg
4. (a) $2a$ (b) 14   (c) $x = 6$
5. (a) $x = 5$ (b) $x = 2$
6. (a) $(6x + 2)$ cm   (b) 7 cm
7. (a) (i) $6a^7$ (ii) $4a^4$ (b) $3x(x - 3)$
8. (a) $x + 1$ (b) 3
9. (a) $x = 3$ (b) $x = 2$
10. (a) $12a^7$ (b) $3a^3$
11. (a) $(2x + 21)$ kg   (b) $x = 30$
12. (a) $(24x + 12)$ kg   (b) $x = 5$
13. (a) $2x - 1$ (b) $2a(2 - b)$ (c) $x = 5$
14. (a) $9x - 22$ (b) $x = 7.5$
15. (a) 2.8×10^{-1}
16. (a) 2.44018×10^5 (b) 0.05%
17. (a) 6.3×10^5
18. (a) 4×10^4 (b) 1.6×10^7

AS2 Algebra 2

Check in AS2

1. (a) $^-2$ (b) $^-11$ (c) $^-12$
2. 5

Exercise 2A

1. A(1, 2), B(3, $^-1$), C($^-2$, $^-1$), D($^-1$, 2), E($^-4$, 0)

Exercise 2B

1. (a) $y = x + 2$ (b) 1, 2, 3, 4, 5, 6

2. (a) $y = 3x$; $^-3$, 0, 3, 6, 9, 12   (b) $y = \dfrac{x}{2}$; $^-0.5$, 0, 0.5, 1, 1.5, 2   (c) $y = 8 - x$; 9, 8, 7, 6, 5, 4

3. (a) (i) $y = x + 5$ (ii) $y = 2x + 1$ (iii) $y = 3x - 1$
    (b) (i) $y = 4, 5, 6, 7, 8, 9, 10$ (ii) $y = ^-1, 1, 3, 5, 7, 9, 11$ (iii) $^-4, ^-1, 2, 5, 8, 11, 14$

Exercise 2C

1. They are all horizontal straight lines.   **2.** They are all vertical straight lines.
3. (b) They are all parallel.   (c) The point where they cross the y-axis.
4. (b) They are all parallel.   (c) The point where they cross the y-axis.
5. (a) They all cut the y-axis at (0, 2).   (b) The steepness of the lines.
6. (a) They all cut the y-axis at (0, $^-1$).   (b) The steepness of the lines.

Exercise 2D

1. (a) 3   (b) $\frac{3}{4}$ (c) $^-1\frac{1}{2}$ (d) 1   (e) $\frac{-1}{4}$
2. (a) (i) 3   (ii) $\frac{1}{4}$ (iii) 1   (iv) $\frac{-3}{4}$
    (v) $\frac{2}{3}$ (vi) $\frac{4}{5}$ (vii) $\frac{1}{2}$ (viii) $^-1\frac{1}{2}$

Exercise 2E

1. 4   **2.** $^-1$ **3.** 0   **4.** 6
5. 4.5   **6.** 0   **7.** 2.5   **8.** 8

Exercise 2F

1. (a) $y = 2x + 2$ (b) $3y = x - 3$ (c) $3y + x = 3$
   (d) $y + 2x = {}^-2$ (e) $3y = 7x + 12$ (f) $8y + x = 37$
2. (a) (iii)   (b) (vi)   (c) (iv)
   (d) (ii)   (e) (i)   (f) (v)

Exercise 2G

1. (a) $x = 0$ (b) $x = 0$ (c) $x = 1.5$ (d) $x = 0$
   (e) $x = 2$ (f) $x = 1$ (g) $x = {}^-1$
2. (a) $y = 24, 15, 8, 3, 0, {}^-1, 0, 3, 8, 15$ (c) (i) $x = 4$ or 6 (ii) $x = 2.4, 7.7$
3. (a) $y = 19, 6, {}^-3, {}^-8, {}^-9, {}^-6, 1, 12, 27$ (c) (i) $x = {}^-0.4, 3.9$ (ii) $x = 0.5, 3$
4. (a) $x = 2, 3$ (b) $x = {}^-4, 0.5$ (c) $x = 1, {}^-2.5$
5. (a) 0.75 km   (b) 7.5 km
6. (b) (i) 72 m   (ii) 81 m   (iii) 1.5 s   (iv) 6 s
7. (b) (i) 50 m^2 (ii) 5 m   (iii) 3.4 m or 6.6 m

Check out AS2

3. $\frac{1}{3}, 2$
4. (b) (i) $x = 1$ or 2 (ii) $x = {}^-0.3$ or 3.3

Revision exercise AS2

1. (b) $x = {}^-1$
2. (a) ${}^-30, {}^-2, 10$ (c) $x = 1.5$
3. (a) $a = \frac{3}{4}, b = 3$
5. (b) $7, 2, {}^-2$ (c) $x = 0.6$ or 3.4
6. (b) $A(0, {}^-1), B(2, 0)$ (b) $\frac{1}{2}$
   (c) The lines are parallel.   (d) $x + y = 2$
7. (a) ${}^-4, 4, 1$ (c) $x = {}^-2.2$ or 2.2
8. (a) $5, {}^-1, 1$ (b) $x = {}^-0.6$ or 1.6

AS3 Algebra 3

Check in AS3

1. (a) $2x + 6$ (b) $2x^2 + 3x$ (c) ${}^-15x + 10y - 35$
2. (a) ${}^-3$ (b) $2\frac{1}{2}$ (c) $\frac{5}{8}$

Exercise 3A

1. (a) $11, 13$ (b) $14, 16$ (c) $27, 31$ (d) $1, {}^-1$
   (e) $85, 79$ (f) ${}^-11, {}^-14$ (g) $0, {}^-5$ (h) $33, 41$
   (i) ${}^-16, {}^-22$ (j) ${}^-5, {}^-12$ (k) $32, 64$ (l) $59, 75$
   (m) $36, 49$ (n) $21, 28$ (o) $35, 48$ (p) ${}^-\frac{1}{12}, {}^-\frac{1}{6}$
2. (a) $5, 7$ (b) $27, 243$ (c) $1000, 100\,000$ (d) $\frac{1}{16}, \frac{1}{64}$
   (e) $9, 21$ (f) $8, 16$
3. 1(a), (b), (c), (d), (f);   2(a), (d), (e)

Exercise 3B

1. (a) (i) $21, 25$ (ii) $4n - 3$ (iii) 89
   (b) (i) $19, 21$ (ii) $2n + 7$ (iii) 53
   (c) (i) $29, 34$ (ii) $5n - 1$ (iii) 114
   (d) (i) $41, 48$ (ii) $7n - 1$ (iii) 160
   (e) (i) $4\frac{1}{2}, 5$ (ii) $\frac{1}{2}n + 1\frac{1}{2}$ (iii) 13

(f) (i) 10, 8   (ii) $22 - 2n$ (iii) $^-24$
(g) (i) $^-5, ^-9$ (ii) $19 - 4n$ (iii) $^-73$
(h) (i) $^-18, ^-21$ (ii) ^-3n (iii) $^-69$
(i) (i) $^-3, ^-7$ (ii) $21 - 4n$ (iii) $^-71$
(j) (i) 2.25, 2   (ii) $3.75 - 0.25n$ (iii) $^-2$
2. (a) 5   (b) 1, 6, 11, 16, 21
3. (a) $^-\frac{3}{4}$ (b) $6\frac{1}{4}, 5\frac{1}{2}, 4\frac{3}{4}, 4, 3\frac{1}{4}$

Exercise 3C

1. 2, 4, 8, 16   2. 5, 2, $^-1, ^-4$ 3. $^-2, ^-1, 0, 1$ 4. 9, 7.5, 6.75, 6.375
5. 3, 4, 6, 10   6. 4, $^-5, ^-14, 23$ 7. 24, 24, 24, 24   8. 5, 7, 5, 7
9. $\frac{1}{2}, ^-1\frac{1}{2}, ^-3\frac{1}{2}, ^-5\frac{1}{2}$ 10. 2, 3, 5, 8   11. 1, 3, 6, 10   12. $^-\frac{1}{4}, 0, \frac{1}{2}, 1\frac{1}{2}$

Exercise 3D

1. (c) $m = 4n + 1$ (d) 101
2. (c) $m = 3t + 2$ (d) 62
3. (c) $m = 5r + 2$ (d) 77
4. (a) 9, 11   (c) $s = 2p - 1$ (d) 51
5. (c) (i) $c = 4p - 3$ (ii) $l = 4p - 4$ (iii) $c = l + 1$ (d) 72 lines, 73 crosses
6. (c) (i) $c = t + 2$ (ii) $l = 2t + 1$ (iii) $l = 2c - 3$ (d) 26 crosses, 49 lines
   (e) 19 crosses, 35 lines

Exercise 3E

1. (a) 2, 3, 4   (b) $^-1, 0, 1, 2, 3$ (c) 3, 4, 5, 6
   (d) 0, 1, 2, 3   (e) 3, 4   (f) 2, 3, 4, 5, 6, 7

Exercise 3F

1. $x > 4$ 2. $x \le 8$ 3. $x \ge 5$ 4. $x \ge 12$
5. $x < ^-\frac{3}{5}$ 6. $x < 58\frac{1}{3}$ 7. $x < 15$ 8. $x > 3\frac{2}{7}$
9. $x < 1\frac{1}{17}$ 10. $x < ^-3$

Exercise 3H

1. $x = 3, y = 1$ 2. $x = 4, y = ^-1$ 3. $x = 2, y = ^-2$ 4. $x = 1, y = 5$
5. $x = 4, y = 1$ 6. $x = 5, y = ^-2$ 7. $x = 4, y = ^-2$ 8. $x = 3, y = ^-5$
9. $x = 1, y = 5$ 10. $x = 2, y = 3$ 11. $x = \frac{2}{3}, y = \frac{2}{3}$ 12. $x = \frac{3}{4}, y = \frac{1}{4}$
13. $x = 3, y = 2$ 14. $x = 3, y = 1$ 15. $x = 1, y = 3$ 16. $x = ^-3, y = 4$
17. $x = ^-1, y = ^-3$ 18. $x = 4, y = 3$

Exercise 3I

1. $2x^2 + 7x$ 2. $3y^2 - 5y$ 3. $x^2 + 5x + 6$ 4. $x^2 + 12x + 35$
5. $x^2 - 2x - 15$ 6. $x^2 + x - 12$ 7. $6x^2 + 17x + 7$ 8. $10x^2 + 19x + 6$
9. $6x^2 + 7x - 20$ 10. $3x^2 - 40x + 77$ 11. $6x^2 - x - 40$ 12. $2a^2 + 6b^2 + 7ab$
13. $3x^2 - 2y^2 - 5xy$ 14. $9x^2 - 1$ 15. $4x^2 - 25$ 16. $4x^2 - 9y^2$

Exercise 3J

1. $(x + 1)(x + 3)$ 2. $(x + 1)(x + 7)$ 3. $(x - 1)(x - 4)$ 4. $(x - 11)(x + 1)$
5. $(x + 1)(x - 4)$ 6. $(x + 5)(x - 7)$ 7. $(x + 1)(x - 9)$ 8. $(x + 6)(x - 2)$
9. $(x + 3)(x - 8)$ 10. $(x + 8)(x - 3)$ 11. $(y + 2)(y - 5)$ 12. $(y + 3)(y - 4)$
13. $(x + 4)(x - 6)$ 14. $(x + 3)(x - 6)$

Exercise 3K

1. $x = {}^-5$ or $^-2$
6. $x = {}^-1$ or 3
2. $x = 2$ or 5
7. $x = 1$ or 2
3. $x = {}^-1$ or 6
8. $x = {}^-6$ or 1
4. $x = {}^-1$ or 8
9. $x = {}^-8$ or 1
5. $x = {}^-4$ or 2
10. $x = {}^-4$ or 3

Exercise 3L

1. $r = \dfrac{(v - 7)}{3}$

2. $R = \dfrac{(8 - r)}{3}$

3. (a) $u = v - at$

(b) $t = \dfrac{(v - u)}{a}$

4. (a) $I = \dfrac{V}{R}$

(b) $R = \dfrac{V}{I}$

5. (a) $u = \dfrac{(2s - at^2)}{2t}$

(b) $a = \dfrac{2(s - ut)}{t^2}$

6. (a) $T = \dfrac{100I}{PR}$

(b) $R = \dfrac{100I}{PT}$

7. (a) $P = A\left(1 + \dfrac{R}{100}\right)^{-n}$

(b) $R = 100\left(\sqrt[n]{\left(\dfrac{A}{P}\right)} - 1\right)$

8. (a) $l = \dfrac{\lambda x^2}{2E}$

(b) $x = \sqrt{\left(\dfrac{2El}{\lambda}\right)}$

9. $v = \dfrac{(I + mu)}{m}$

10. $l = \dfrac{gT^2}{4\pi^2}$

Exercise 3M

1. $x = 2.5$
6. $x = {}^-2.6,\ ^-0.1$ or 2.7
2. $x = 3.0$
7. $x = 2.1$
3. $x = 1.1$
8. $x = {}^-2.5,\ ^-0.8$ or 3.3
4. $x = {}^-2.8,\ ^-0.1$ or 2.9
9. $x = {}^-4.7,\ ^-1.4$ or 1.1
5. $x = 2.1$
10. $x = 2.4$

Check out AS3

1. 19, 22
2. (a) $3n + 4$ (b) 16, 14, 12, 10
3. 2, 3, 5, 9
4. (a) $x > 7$ (b) $x \geqslant {}^-2$ (c) $^-4 \leqslant x \leqslant 4$
6. $x = 4,\ y = 1$ 7. $x = 5,\ y = {}^-1$
8. (a) $2x^2 - 7x$ (b) $x^2 + 2x - 15$
9. (a) $(x + 1)(x - 7)$ (b) $x(x + 11)$ (c) $(x + 1)(x + 3)$
10. (a) $x = {}^-10$ or 1 (b) $x = 0$ or 7 (c) $x = 1$ or 5
11. (a) $x = 4y + 4$ (b) $r = \sqrt[3]{\left(\dfrac{3V}{4\pi}\right)}$ 12. $x = 1.9$

Revision exercise AS3

1. (a) $2n + 3$ (b) $n^2 + 2$
2. (a) 19 (b) (i) $x + 4$ (ii) $x - 4$
3. (a) (i) 8 (ii) 6 (b) $^-1,\ ^-5$
4. (a) $^-5$ (b) $7 - 2n$
5. (a) $x - 6$ (b) $x = 2$ (c) $x = 3.6$
6. (a) $4n + 1$ (b) $n(n + 1)$
7. (a) $3n + 2$ (b) $n^2 - 1$
8. (a) $x = 0$ or 8 (b) $6 \leqslant x < 10$
9. (a) (i) either (ii) even
   (b) They must both be odd or both be even. (c) $p = 7,\ q = 4$
10. (a) $2x(x + 2)$ (b) $x = {}^-5$ or 2 (c) $1 < x < 2$
11. (a) $(a + 2)(a - 4)$ (b) $y = 0$ or $^-4$
12. (a) $a(a + 3)$ (b) 2, 3

AS4 Shape 1

Check in AS4

1. 73
2. (a) 90   (b) 24   (c) 30

Exercise 4A

1. 140°   **2.** 53°   **3.** 125°, 55°, 125°   **4.** 62°   **5.** 101°
6. 66°, 87°, 27°, 66°   **7.** 142°, 38°, 142°   **8.** 36°, 72°, 72°   **9.** 25°, 50°, 75°   **10.** acute
11. acute   **12.** obtuse   **13.** reflex   **14.** right angle   **15.** obtuse
16. acute   **17.** reflex

Exercise 4B

1. 108°, 72°, 72°, 72°   **2.** 73°, 107°, 73°, 107°, 107°
3. 123°, 123°, 57°, 123°, 57°, 123°   **4.** 111°, 111°, 111°, 69°, 69°, 111°, 69°, 69°
5. 47°, 133°, 133°   **6.** 37°, 143°, 127°, 127°, 127°, 53°
7. 24°, 156°, 24°, 156°, 128°, 128°, 52°

Exercise 4C

1. (a) 2   (b) 1   (c) 2   (d) 0   (e) 2   (f) 5
    (g) 4   (h) 4   (i) 4   (j) 2   (k) 2   (l) 1

Exercise 4D

1. (a) 2   (b) 1   (c) 2   (d) 1   (e) 2   (f) 5
    (g) 4   (h) 4   (i) 4   (j) 2   (k) 2   (l) 1
2. (a) 1   (b) 5   (c) 1   (d) 6

Exercise 4E

1. ∞   **2.** 1   **3.** 4   **4.** ∞   **5.** ∞

Exercise 4F

7. (a) a square-based pyramid   (b) a cuboid

Exercise 4G

1. 36°   **2.** 35°   **3.** 53°   **4.** 80°, 80°   **5.** 30°, 75°
6. 68°, 44°   **7.** 61°, 61°   **8.** 20°, 60°   **9.** 129°   **10.** 27.5°, 27.5°   **11.** 20°

Exercise 4H

1. 45°   **2.** 52°, 128°, 128°   **3.** 23°, 23°, 134°   **4.** 111°
5. 105°, 88°   **6.** 122°   **7.** 63°, 108°   **8.** 126°, 54°, 95°, 95°
9. 49°, 131°, 69°   **10.** 184°   **11.** 99°, 122°

Exercise 4I

1. (a) 10   (b) 12   (c) 18   (d) 36
2. (a) 36°   (b) 24°   (c) 12°
3. (a) 135°   (b) 157.5°
4. (a) 65°, 83°, 97°   (b) 106°, 128°, 128°

Exercise 4J

1. 49°   **2.** 57°   **3.** 58°, 64°   **4.** 37°   **5.** all 48°
6. 90°, 28°   **7.** 12°, 26°, 90°   **8.** 95°, 65°   **10.** 52°, 52°

Exercise 4K

1. 65°
2. 59°
3. both 66°
4. 123°, 237°
5. 44°
6. 61°, 61°
7. 16°

Exercise 4L

4. 8.2 cm

Exercise 4M

1. (a) 135°   (b) 90°   (c) 135°   (d) 112.5°   (e) 67.5°
2. (a) 045°   (b) 225°   (c) 315°   (d) 022.5°   (e) 292.5°
3. 250°   4. 295°   5. 115°   6. 195°

Exercise 4N

1. 49°   2. 77°   3. 5.6 cm   4. 6.5 cm   5. 8.8 cm   6. 12.2 cm

Exercise 4O

1. (d) 4.6 cm

Check out AS4

1. (a) An angle between 0° and 90°.   (b) They intersect at right angles.   (c) They add up to 180°.
3. Order of rotational symmetry = 2
6. (a) Four equal sides, four equal angles.   (b) 2 lines of symmetry, order of rotational symmetry 2.
7. (a) 18°   (b) 162°
8. (b) Angles in the same segment are equal.
9. It is a diameter.
10. 105°
11. 97°
12. (b) The locus of *T* is the bisector of angle *A*.

Revision exercise AS4

1. (a) $\frac{1}{3}$
2. (a) 50°, 40°   (b) (i) kite   (ii) 100°, 118°
3. (a) 240°
4. (a) 30°   (b) 23°
5. (a) 135°   (b) (i) 30°   (ii) $n = \dfrac{360}{180 - p}$
6. (a) 130°   (b) 36.5 km

AS5 Shape 2

Check in AS5

2. (a) 28   (b) 56

Exercise 5A

1. *A* and *E*, *B* and *F*, *C* and *D*
2. One could be an enlargement of the other.
3. (a) Congruent; AAS   (b) Congruent; RHS   (c) Congruent; SSS
   (d) Congruent; AAS   (e) Not congruent   (f) Congruent; SAS
4. *ABC*, *ADC*; SSS

Exercise 5B

1. *D*
2. yes
3. (a) 5 cm, 9.6 cm, 120°   (b) 102°, 5.25 cm, 9.33 cm

Exercise 5C

1. (a) 22.5, 8   (b) 15, 8   (c) 22.5, 40   (d) 6.05, 27.7, 17.4
2. (a) 9.44, 4.72   (b) 1.76, 50.6   (c) 4.97, 6.77
3. (a) 8   (b) 9   (c) 3
4. (a) 3.6   (b) 7.5
5. No, corresponding sides are not in the same ratio.
6. (a) *PQR* and *QSR*   (b) (i) 12   (ii) 12
7. 10
8. (b) 20.8 cm

Exercise 5D

1. 3900 m   2. 158 m
3. (a) 1.275 km   (b) 31.6 cm
4. 45.3 cm   5. 8.41 cm
6. (a) 73 cm   (b) 56 cm   (c) 41.3 cm   (d) 11.2 cm   (e) 78 cm

Check out AS5

1. Same size and shape   2. SSS, SAS, AAS, RHS   3. All of them.
4. (a) and (b)   5. 5.7 cm, 12.3 cm   6. 120 m

Revision exercise AS5

1. (a) *DFA*   (b) 30°
2. (a) 1   (b) 56°   (c) (i) 93°   (ii) 4.4 cm
3. (a) 130°, 20°   (b) 8 cm
4. (a) 70°   (b) 10 cm
5. (a) 105°   (b) 3.6 cm
6. (a) *QRS* or *TUP*   (b) (i) 30°   (ii) 21.6 cm

AS6 Shape 3

Exercise 6A

1. (a) (5, 6)   (b) (7, 12)   (c) (2, 2)   (d) (3, 0)
   (e) (1, ⁻2)   (f) (⁻5, ⁻9)   (g) (⁻4, ⁻12)
2. (a) $\begin{pmatrix}8\\3\end{pmatrix}$ (b) $\begin{pmatrix}1\\4\end{pmatrix}$ (c) $\begin{pmatrix}-5\\1\end{pmatrix}$ (d) $\begin{pmatrix}-8\\-13\end{pmatrix}$ (e) $\begin{pmatrix}-3\\-1\end{pmatrix}$
3. (2, ⁻2), (7, 11)   4. (0, ⁻1), (⁻5, ⁻10)

Exercise 6B

3. (a) *y*-axis   (b) *y* = *x*   (c) *y* = ⁻*x*

Exercise 6C

3. (a) 90° clockwise about (0, 0)   (b) 72° clockwise about (6, ⁻3)   (c) 90° clockwise about (4, 0)

Exercise 6D

3. (a) An enlargement with scale factor $\frac{1}{2}$ (b) An enlargement with scale factor 3

Exercise 6E

1. (a) A reflection in *y* = ⁻*x*
   (b) A rotation through 180° about (0, 0)
   (c) A rotation through 180° about (0, 0)

3. A translation of $\begin{pmatrix}6\\2\end{pmatrix}$

Exercise 6F

1. A translation of $\begin{pmatrix} -5 \\ -3 \end{pmatrix}$

2. A translation of $\begin{pmatrix} -2 \\ 4 \end{pmatrix}$

3. A reflection in the y-axis
4. A reflection in $y = x$
5. A reflection in $2y + x = 7$
6. A rotation about O through 90° clockwise
7. A rotation about O through 120° clockwise
8. A rotation about O through 150° clockwise

9. A reflection in the x-axis followed by a translation of $\begin{pmatrix} -5 \\ -3 \end{pmatrix}$

10. A rotation through 90° clockwise about (1, 2) followed by a translation of $\begin{pmatrix} -3 \\ 2 \end{pmatrix}$

Exercise 6G

2. 36 cm²
3. (a) A square   (b) 4 cm²

Check out AS6

1. (7, 1)

Revision exercise AS6

1. (a) Rotation through 180° about (0, 0)   (b) Reflection in the line $y = x$
2. (a) Rotation through 180° about (3, 0)   (c) Reflection in the line $x = 3$
3. (c) Rotation through 180° about (0, 4)
4. (a) Squares and hexagons tessellate, pentagons and octagons do not.   (b) (i) *ABF*   (ii) 135°
5. (a) P   (b) R
7. (a) Reflection in the line $x = 3$ (b) Rotation through 180° about (3, 0)

AS7 Shape 4

Check in AS7

1. The lengths in *PQR* are 1.5 times the lengths in *ABC*.
2. (a) 30.6   (b) 73.6

Exercise 7A

1. (a) 30 cm   (b) 36 cm   (c) 44 cm   (d) 54.4 cm
    (e) 45.4 cm   (f) 61.6 cm   (g) 52.4 cm
2. (a) 120 cm

Exercise 7B

1. (a) 28 cm²   (b) 27 cm²   (c) 60 cm²
2. (a) 9 cm   (b) 8.5 cm   (c) 7.75 cm   (d) 5.05 cm
3. (a) 24 cm²   (b) 39 cm²   (c) 80.01 cm²
4. (a) 49 cm²   (b) 0.04 cm²   (c) 4.41 cm²
5. (a) 6 cm   (b) 15 cm   (c) 5.85 cm
6. (a) 37.2 cm²   (b) 70 cm²   (c) 336 cm²
7. (a) 12 cm²   (b) 20 cm²   (c) 37 cm²   (d) 0.045 cm²
8. (a) 6 in²   (b) 30 cm²   (c) 42 cm²   (d) 24.1 cm²   (e) 12.7 cm²
9. (a) 48 cm²   (b) 18 cm²   (c) 92.5 cm²
10. (a) 8 cm   (b) 6.4 cm   (c) 13.3 cm   (d) 5.93 cm
11. (a) 74 cm²   (b) 117 cm²   (c) 22.3 cm²

Exercise 7C

1. (a) 25.8 cm   (b) 39.9 cm   (c) 20.1 cm   (d) 42.7 cm
2. 72.3 mm
3. (a) 4.52 cm   (b) 2.74 cm   (c) 1.38 cm   (d) 3.87 cm
4. (a) 52.8 cm^2 (b) 127 cm^2 (c) 32.2 cm^2 (d) 145 cm^2
5. (a) 6 cm   (b) 13 cm   (c) 2.95 cm   (d) 2.41 in
6. 6.53 cm^2

Exercise 7D

1. 80.1 cm^2 2. 68.0 cm^2 3. 39.8 cm^2 4. 14.8 cm^2
5. 45.9 cm^2 6. 63.2 cm^2 7. 63.3 cm^2 8. 138 cm^2

Exercise 7E

1. (a) 96 cm^3 (b) 124 cm^3 (c) 840 cm^3 (d) 138 cm^3 (e) 910 in^3
2. 5 cm
3. (a) 64 cm^3 (b) 216 cm^3 (c) 572 cm^3 (d) 754 cm^3
4. (a) 5 cm   (b) 3.34 cm   (c) 2.58 cm
5. (a) 10.8 cm^3 (b) 0.6 m
6. (a) 216 cm^3 7. 330 cm^3 8. 276 cm^3 9. 48.4 cm^3 10. 18 m^3

Exercise 7F

1. (a) 236 cm^2 (b) 286 cm^2 (c) 208 cm^2 (d) 146 cm^2 (e) 216 cm^2
2. 28.8 cm^2 3. 20.5
4. (a) 91.9 cm^2 (b) 110 000 cm^3
5. (a) (i) 188 cm^2 (ii) 314 cm^2 (iii) 452 cm^2 (iv) 1.88 cm^2
   (b) (i) 283 cm^3 (ii) 785 cm^3 (iii) 1630 cm^3 (iv) 4.60 cm^3
6. 377 cm^2 7. 2 cm   8. 133 cm

Exercise 7G

1. length   2. none   3. volume   4. volume   5. none
6. none   7. area   8. none   9. area   10. none

Exercise 7H

1. 40.5 cm^2 2. 111 cm^2 3. 54 cm^2 4. 81.6 cm^2 5. 2   6. 13
7. 243 cm^2 8. 10.9 cm^2 9. 2.76   10. 0.209   11. 0.324

Exercise 7I

1. 1600 ml   2. 6750 ml   3. 3840 cm^3 4. 4.44 cm^3 5. 225 cm^3
6. 2 litres   7. 62 kg   8. 2.58   9. 0.427

Check AS7

1. (a) 26 cm   (b) (i) 20 cm^2 (ii) 36.9 cm^2
2. (a) 49 cm^2 (b) 11 cm
3. (a) 144π cm^2 (b) 4.9 cm
4. (a) 141 cm^2
5. (a) 6000 cm^3
6. (a) 184 cm^2 (b) 210π cm^2
7. (a) $\pi r^3 + r^2h$ (b) $4r^2 + rh$
8. (a) 1483 cm^2 (b) 2.5
9. (a) 728 cm^3 (b) 0.75

Revision exercise AS7

1. (a)   P and R   (b)   54 cm^2 (c)   300
2. (a) $2\pi a(a + b)$ and $\frac{1}{2}(a + b)c$ (b) $\pi a^2 b$
3. (a) $2(v + 2w + x + y + z)$ (b) $\frac{1}{2}z(x + y)w$
4. (a)   440 cm   (b)   0.77 m^3
5. 14.4 cm
6. (a)   18 cm   (b)   15 625 cm^3
7. (a)   220 cm   (b)   30 800 cm^3
8. (a)   4000 cm^2 (b)   10 000 cm^3
9. (a)   66.4°   (b)   10.1 m^3
10. 27 cm^2
11. 1890 cm^3

AS8 Shape 5

Check in AS8

1. 323°

Exercise 8A

1. (i)   9.22 cm   (ii)   11.5 cm   (iii)   10.9 cm   (iv)   20.7 cm
2. (i)   6.57 cm   (ii)   14 cm   (iii)   5.43 cm   (iv)   120 mm
3. 14.4 mm   4.   10.6 cm
5. (i)   10.4 cm, 7.63 cm   (ii)   8.76 cm, 14 cm
6. 4.6 cm   7.   7.6 cm   8.   10.3 cm
9. (i)   19.7 cm   (ii)   9.72 cm
10. (a)   9.37 m, 6.63 m   (b)   10 m

Exercise 8B

1. 0.53, the same
2. (a)   0.47, the same   (b)   0.88, the same

Exercise 8C

1. 2.11 cm   2.   7.89 cm   3.   57.9°   4.   34.9°
5. 40.9°   6.   25.7°   7.   10.7 cm   8.   7.74 cm
9. (a)   6.8 cm   (b)   10.8 cm
10. 34.9°

Exercise 8D

1. 6.77 cm   2.   6.94 cm   3.   7.17 cm   4.   26.9°   5.   50.1°
6. 53.4°   7.   8.89 cm   8.   7.8 cm   9.   10.3 cm
10. (a)   5.35 cm   (b)   2.51 cm   (c)   4.72 cm

Exercise 8E

1. 7.67 m   2.   23.6°
3. (a)   12.9°   (b)   25.9°
4. (a)   1900 ft   (b)   43 400 ft

Check out AS8

2. 10.9 cm, 8 cm   3.   tangent   4.   AB = 25.8 cm   5.   272 ft

Revision exercise AS8

1. (a)   61.9°   (b)   6.03 m
2. (a)   6.39 cm   (b)   8.67 cm
3. (a)   12 cm   (b)   10.5 cm
4. (a) $\frac{3}{5}$ (b)   (i) $\frac{4}{5}$ (ii)   9 cm
5. (a)   9.38 m   (b)   65.9
6. (a)   6.75 m   (b)   17.3°
7. (a)   6.4 m   (b)   68.3°

AS9 Algebra 4

Check in AS9
1. 20 mph

Exercise 9A
1. (a) £147   (b) $6\frac{1}{2}$ years
2. (a) 25%   (b) 3   (c) 900 miles   (d) 124.5 litres
3. (a) 26 cm   (b) 4.7 years   (c) 4.4 years
4. (a) 3.25 cm   (b) (i) 90 cm²   (ii) 123 cm²   (iii) 75 cm²   (c) 2.2 cm, 4.7 cm

Exercise 9B
1. (a) (i) 7.6 cm   (ii) 15.7 cm   (b) 10.5 days
2. (a) (i) 13°C   (ii) 1.8°C   (b) (i) 4 min   (ii) 23 min
3. (a) 49 m   (b) 3.5 s   (c) 45 m   (d) 1.6 s and 5.4 s
4. (a) 10.4 cm   (b) 89 ml
5. (a) 7 m   (b) 2.8 s   (c) 2.3 s

Exercise 9C
1. (a) (i) 1 mph   (ii) 2 km/h
   (b) (i) 67 km/h   (ii) 59 mph   (iii) 9 mph   (iv) 118 km/h   (v) 35 mph
2. (a) 7 kg   (b) 92 lb   (c) 26 kg   (d) 42 lb   (e) 13 kg   (f) 79 lb
3. (a) (i) 34%   (ii) 89%   (b) 23   (c) 26
4. (a) £35   (b) £87.50   (c) 4 h 20 min
5. (a) (i) 39 litres   (ii) 5 gallons   (iii) 9 litres   (iv) 19 gallons   (v) 65 litres   (vi) 12.5 gallons
   (b) 0.4 gallons   (c) 77 litres

Exercise 9D
1. (a) (i) 800 m   (ii) 10 min   (b) 48 km/h   (c) 5 min
   (d) (i) 1200 m   (ii) 400 m   (e) (i) 15 min   (ii) 4.8 km/h
2. (b) 9 km/h
3. (b) (i) 21 km/h   (ii) 24 km/h
4. (a) (i) 67 mph   (ii) 32 mph   (iii) 40 mph   (b) 34 mph   (c) 40 mph
   (d) 78 miles from P at about 10:50 pm   (e) About 70 miles
5. (b) (i) 1107   (ii) 17.5 km
6. (a) (i) After $4\frac{1}{2}$ hours   (ii) 36 mph

Check out AS9
1. (a) 68°F   (b) 11°C
2. (a) 0 mph   (b) 1 hour

Revision exercise AS9
1. (a) $y = 0.1x + 480$ (b) £1020
2. (a) 16.2 km/h   (b) (ii) 0831
3. (a) $y = 0.4x + 18$ (b) £58
4. (a) 12 cm   (b) 2   (c) 10 kg
5. (a) (i) 1000 m   (ii) 1502   (iii) 15 km/h
6. (b) £12.50   (c) 576 francs

ANSWERS MODULE 5

Module 5 *Practice calculator test*

1. (a) 2 cm   (b) 3.5 km   (c) 055°
3. 95p
4. (a) 33, 45
    (b) (i) 65, 129   (ii) The difference between terms is doubling
    (c) $2n + 1$
5. (a) 53   (b) $n + 1, n + 10$ (c) $3n + 11$ (d) 46
6. (a) 6.5π cm   (b) 9.61π cm^2
7. (a) 5.7 cm   (b) 42.4°
8. (a) 7 cm   (b) 4.76 cm
9. (b) Enlargement, centre O, scale factor $\frac{1}{3}$
10. (a) 207 cm   (b) 241   (c) 0832
11. (a) $3(a + 2b)$ (b) 2.3   (c) $x = 3, y = {}^-1$
12. (b) $x = {}^-2.2$ or 1.5
13. 17.6 m

Module 5 *Practice non-calculator test*

1. (a) 40°   (b) 120°
2. (a) (i) $8p$ (ii) t^4 (b) $a + 9b$ (c) $x = 10$
4. A
5. (a) 4 cm   (b) 30 cm^2 (c) 122°
6. (a) 25   (b) (i) 11   (ii) 70   (iii) $\frac{4}{3}$ (c) 2, 3, 4, 5, 6
7. (a) $x = \frac{1}{5}$ (b) (i) $12 - x$ (ii) t^{11} (iii) $\dfrac{1}{p^3}$ (iv) $x^3 - 2x$
8. (a) $5n$ (b) $n = 3k$
9. (b) $y = x$
10. (a) 45°   (b) 135°   (c) $180° - 110° = 70°$, which is not a factor of 360°.
11. (a) $y = {}^-\frac{1}{3}x + 4$ (b) $p = s(t - q)$ (c) $(x - 2)(x - 3), x = 2$ or 3
12. $\pi r(a^2 + b^2)$ and $\left(\dfrac{\pi r^2}{3}\right)(h + 2r)$
13. (a) trapezium   (b) rhombus   (c) rectangle
14. (a) $(0, 1)$ (b) $\begin{pmatrix} 3 \\ -6 \end{pmatrix}$

INDEX